# HORDES

# METAMORPHOSIS

# CREDITS

**Creators of the Iron Kingdoms**
Brian Snoddy
Matt Wilson

**Creative Director**
Matt Wilson

**Project Director**
Bryan Cutler

**Game Design**
Matt Wilson

**Lead Developer**
Jason Soles

**Art Direction**
Kris Aubin

**Development**
Michael Faciane
Rob Stoddard
Erik Yaple

**Writing**
Douglas Seacat

**Painting Guide Writing**
Matt DiPietro
Ron Kruzie

**Continuity**
Jason Soles

**Rules Editing**
Kevin Clark
Bryan Cutler
Brian Putnam
Jason Soles
Rob Stoddard

**Editorial Manager**
Darla Kennerud

**Editing**
Christopher Bodan
Darla Kennerud

**Cover Illustration**
Matt Wilson

**Illustrations**
Carlos Cabrera
Matt Dixon
Emrah Elmasli
Marek Okon
Karl Richardson
Andrea Uderzo
Chris Walton
Eva Widermann
Kieran Yanner

**Concept Illustration**
Roberto Cirillo
Jason Hendricks
Chris Walton
Matt Wilson

**Graphic Design & Layout**
Kris Aubin
Kim Goddard
Josh Manderville

**HORDES Logo**
Brian Despain
Matt Wilson

**Product Line Coordinator**
Rob Stoddard

**Miniatures Direction**
Ron Kruzie

**Sculpting**
Sean Bullough
Gregory Clavilier
Jeff Grace
Todd Harris
Jason Hendricks
Vladd Jünger
Werner Klocke
Aragorn Marks
Nicolas Nguyen
Edgar Ramos
Jose Roig
Steve Saunders
Ben Siens
David Summers
Kev White
Jeff Wilhelm

**Miniatures Painting**
Matt DiPietro

**Terrain**
Rob Hawkins

**Photography**
Steve Angeles
Rob Hawkins
Ben Misenar

**President**
Sherry Yeary

**Executive Assistant**
Chare Kerzman

**Marketing Director**
Andrew Lupp

**Marketing Coordinator**
Bobby Stickel

**Retail Support**
William Shick

**Customer Service**
Adam Johnson
Adam Poirier

**Convention Coordinator**
Dave Dauterive

**Events Coordinator**
Kevin Clark

**Volunteer Coordinator**
Dan Brandt

**NQM EIC**
Eric Cagle

**Licensing and Contract Manager**
Brent Waldher

**Hobby Manager**
Rob Hawkins

**Production Director**
Mark Christensen

**Technical Director**
Kelly Yeager

**Production Manager**
Doug Colton

**Production**
Trey Alley
Greg Anecito
Max Barsana
Simon Berman
Alex Chobot
Jack Coleman
Joel Falkenhagen
Joe Lee
Mike McIntosh
Jacob Stanley
Ben Tracy
Clint Whiteside

**System Administrator/ Webmaster**
Daryl Roberts

**Infernals**
Jeremy Galeone
Peter Gaublomme
Brian Putnam
Gilles Reynaud
John Simon
Donald Sullivan

**Playtest Coordinator**
David Carl

**Internal Playtesting**
Kris Aubin
Christopher Bodan
Dan Brandt
Erik Breidenstein
Dave Dauterive
Joel Falkenhagen
Christopher Frye
Rob Hawkins
Miluo Hsu
Del Ivanov
Adam Johnson
Adam Poirier
Douglas Seacat
Brent Waldher
Chris Walton

**External Playtesting**
Alex Badion
Andrew Brandt
Carl Brannon
Edward Bourelle
Jessica Carl
Jim Cartwright
Eric Ernewein
Seth Ferris
Logan Fisher
Christian Fontaine
Brian Grist
Andrew Inzenga
Peter Jenisch
Mike Kelmelis
Nick Kendall
Brad Lannon
Jeff Long
Geoffrey Long
Rob Miles
Derek Osborne
Jay Powel
Adam Rosenblum
Thelord Schuart
Dan Seeley
Timothy Simpson
David W. Sininger
Mark Thomas
Dan Webber

**Proofreading**
Dave Dauterive
Michael Faciane
Darla Kennerud
William Shick
Rob Stoddard
Sonya Vatomsky

METAMORPHOSIS

# TABLE OF CONTENTS

## Visit www.privateerpress.com

Privateer Press, Inc. • 13434 NE 16th St. Suite 120 • Bellevue, WA 98005
Tel (425) 643-5900 • Fax (425) 643-5902

**For online customer service, email frontdesk@privateerpress.com**

First printing: December 2008. Printed in China.

HORDES: Metamorphosis . . . . . . . . . . . . ISBN: 978-1-933362-38-0    PIP 1017
HORDES: Metamorphosis Special Edition Hardcover . . . ISBN: 978-1-933362-39-7    PIP 1018

# FOREWORD

If you're reading this, you've probably also read the forewords in our previous HORDES books, and if you were paying attention you caught the name of this one a year and a half ago. I wanted to plant our flag on that name back then because we had already known for a few years what we would call the third book in the HORDES line. That should give you an idea of how far we're looking ahead with this stuff.

By the time you have a product in your hands, we are well into the development of whatever is coming next. The pace is almost frantic as we work to stay ahead of our release dates without missing a beat. This can't be accomplished without careful planning and a fully formed vision of where we're headed in the future.

After spending years thinking about the same characters day in and day out, we actually start to think like them. Every day is an exercise in stepping in and out of the skin of an emotionally tortured trollkin chieftain or power-hungry skorne warlord. Whether scripting the story, conceptualizing the visual look, or developing new rules for how a model will operate on the tabletop, in a sense we have to become that thing, creature, or character for a moment. Not that we have to become bloodthirsty, psychotic dragon-blighted conquerors, but to do this stuff right as authors, artists, and game designers, we have to be able to feel the emotional vibe that resonates with each of our creations. Hopefully our effort makes the characters feel more real for you too.

When we're sitting around a table thinking about where our story is headed, we're asking questions about what these characters would do if they actually existed. In truth—and I don't think I'm alone here—I know more about some of our fictional creations than I do about some people I've known since childhood. No matter what events surround us in the real world, our minds are never far from the Iron Kingdoms and all that occurs there.

In the pages before you lie the twists and turns of an epic saga that is years in the making. We have personally spent time with each of these characters, examining their ambitions, observing their exploits, and exploring the most intimate workings of their inner psyches. Like you, we have often been surprised at what we have found skulking around the corner.

The origins of this story began over eight years ago, and I'd be lying if I said that we knew then where we'd be today. Despite our far-reaching design to weave a story as precisely intricate as any Swiss watchmaker's creation, the act of discovery has on many occasions overpowered our best-laid plans. However, a good plan doesn't require you to account for every detail, just every possibility. In these pages we have realized possibilities that, though unimagined at the outset, have indeed lurked beneath the surface all along.

These daily, unpredictable revelations make our work here exciting and keep us enthusiastic about the next projects to come. We are spectators in a world of our own creation, and we have a front-row seat to every mind-blowing development. I can only hope that you will feel the same exhilaration of discovery as you journey through the pages of *Metamorphosis*.

## THINGS CHANGE. IT'S PART OF NATURE. IT'S PART OF GROWTH. YOU CAN'T STOP IT.

The weak fear change. They shiver in solitude, destined to starve beneath their tear-soaked blankets of cowardice.

The strong embrace change. They hunt it down and bask in the riveting pain that heralds their transformation to a new, more powerful existence.

The strong not only survive, they dominate, propagate, and feed off the weak. The strong are strong by choice. That means food is food by choice.

### DON'T BE FOOD.

You stand now at the precipice of change, and you must ask yourself, "Is my spirit frail? My flesh, infirm? Or do I possess the raw, unbridled aggression necessary to triumph over the soul-crushing challenges that stand before me?"

### WE BOTH KNOW THE ANSWER.

Change is inevitable, but adaptation is a choice only the strong can make. You have chosen a path more formidable, more intense, and more demanding than ever before. The baby fat has melted from your body to be replaced with flesh-tearing muscle. Your once tepid nature has grown into voracious, all-consuming bloodlust. You have become a savage monster clawing your way to the top of the food chain and marking your territory with the musk of mass destruction.

**WELCOME TO YOUR METAMORPHOSIS.**

**EMBRACE THE TRANSFORMATION, AND**

## PLAY LIKE YOU'VE GOT A PAIR.

# FACING THE ABYSS

## BURIAL BY DOLMEN

Once the warlocks of Everblight's legion crossed the Hawksmire River they began to consider the real possibility of escape. Their flight since leaving the Castle of the Keys had been a long sequence of running battles and diversions. The obvious pains they took to evade combat confused their adversaries, but this time the blighted army was not looking for victory. Reaching safety to buy time was their only priority.

None of them had known what to expect when Thagrosh swallowed Pyromalfic's athanc. The Nyss had celebrated victory only a short time before Everblight had withdrawn his mind from them to focus on the battle of wills against the vanquished dragon's core. After that Thagrosh alone was privy to Everblight's inner struggle.

Both physical and mental suffering consumed the ogrun. Shortly after devouring the athanc he became confused and distracted, not even seeming to hear their voices as he stumbled along. During an early battle to break through Circle Orboros defenses, Thagrosh suddenly collapsed in powerful convulsions. Blighted spines tore through the skin of his back as he howled in pain. They surrounded him protectively and kept the enemy at bay, but his state took them by surprise and shook the morale of other Nyss who witnessed it.

With Rhyas and Saeryn carving a bloody path through those who would oppose them, it fell to Vayl and Lylyth to speak to the blighted rank and file. Thagrosh's transformation was too vital to allow even a shred of doubt to slow their progress. "Everblight will soon become mightier than ever before," Vayl assured them, "but we must reach safety to buy time. This is our duty and honor."

Vayl believed these words with her whole being, since she had witnessed the blighted waves of energy rolling from Thagrosh during his spasms. She had never seen such power as was pouring from the conjoining athancs. The strength was chaotic now, mixed as it was in the struggle between the dragons, but she could see the possibilities it would hold when whole. If only they lived to see it.

Vayl and Saeryn soon learned they could use their sorcery to draw away the deadly radiance of the blighted energy permeating Thagrosh's flesh. They siphoned and unleashed it to wither nearby trees, blacken stone, and boil lively streams into muck. Whenever the spasms overtook him they came to his side and plunged their hands into the flow to send it away, fighting to keep from disintegrating in the process themselves. His tissues were in a constant state of death and rebirth.

Everblight rarely emerged from his inner maelstrom to give them a plan of action. "Toward Ios," he said once, and then bothered no more with mental directives shaped into words. Instead he sent a flood of images and memories too overwhelming for mortal minds to comprehend. It required days to sort through those sensations and grasp the dragon's plan.

One imperative was clear: they must preserve as many Nyss as possible and avoid further casualties at all costs. This was difficult given how many spawn they had expended at the Castle of the Keys to defeat Pyromalfic. Stripped of sacrificial beasts and with little time to generate more, their army felt anemic. Absylonia was to be their primary salvation; even now she traveled to join them from the north where she had been spawning reinforcements.

They relied heavily on the archers and striders to strike from afar to evade a direct clash with any significant foe. The Circle was the most tireless and deliberate of their adversaries, but several times they had to change their course to avoid unwanted entanglements with the local trollkin or skorne forces also patrolling the region.

A low line of rocky hills lay just north of them as they made their way from the river through the lightly forested area that filled out to become the Glimmerwood farther to the west. The time had come to divide their forces, on Everblight's explicit directive. Rhyas faced her sister with a troubled expression. "I do not think it wise to separate."

Saeryn sighed, and her irritation was felt across the link they all shared. She saw no point in discussion. Everblight's instructions were clear, even if His mind currently faced inward. "Vayl and I must go with Thagrosh," she replied flatly. "The Legion cannot survive the tunnels we will take. The passage under Ios to the mountains beyond could take weeks or months through the cold darkness."

Rhyas scowled. "I'm not suggesting they follow. But let me come with you. Lylyth can guide the army without me."

Saeryn stepped closer and spoke with barely restrained anger. "What you *prefer* does not matter. It is decided. Someone must fight those who are chasing us. It is vital they do not know where we go. Let them chase you elsewhere." When Rhyas continued to stare at her with a sullen look, she added, "Lylyth needs you more than I do."

Lylyth stood nearby radiating impatience with bow in hand. "We have no time for this. We must prepare."

Rhyas still seemed dissatisfied but nodded at last. She locked eyes with her twin and vowed, "I will see you on the other side, in the mountains."

"In the mountains," Saeryn agreed. She let her sister clasp her hand briefly. "Now go." She turned and walked back to Thagrosh and Vayl. The other warlock awaited her with an amused look at the sisterly exchange. Saeryn's emotional state across the athanc connection was smooth and impenetrable. She gave Vayl a cold and insincere smile.

With Vayl on one side and Saeryn on the other, they guided Thagrosh toward the hills where a simple cave would initiate their descent into the bowels of Caen.

The way the enemy evaded all attempts at engagement was becoming tiresome. Baldur the Stonecleaver pushed on relentlessly at the head of the pursuing Circle forces. Despite their best efforts the Legion had proven inexhaustible and swift in retreat. He had almost stopped them at the Bones of Orboros at the Hawksmire River bend, but they had managed to shatter the transportation stones at that site and rush onward. At last he was closing the gap. He did not have time to relent despite certain misgivings.

Baldur had fanned out an array of wolds along his forward path, relying in particular on the woldwyrds for their steady speed. The moment the enemy twisted west or east he could close the vice, but his center was soft and his line spread thin. If he attempted to tighten it the enemy would have the opportunity to evade in either direction. One thing was certain, though. The Legion could not keep going north. Soon they would hit the border of Ios.

So far the Legion had demonstrated a blithe disregard for national boundaries, but even the omnipotents did not enter Ios uninvited. The Iosans repaid every breach with deadly force. They *must* break west or east to avoid Ios. The only other option was to turn and fight.

Such a battle had been his original goal, but Baldur was no longer sure he had sufficient forces to engage the enemy decisively. Of course the Legion did not know this, but it made for a dangerous game. Baldur's main advantage was that Thagrosh's force had clearly suffered heavy losses at the Castle of the Keys and was reluctant to endure more. Such timidity might vanish if he could corner them.

Morvahna directed the largest single collection of their strength, but she was dozens of miles behind him and lagging farther every hour. She refused to leave the slower elements of her contingent to allow the faster ones to range ahead. Meanwhile Baldur had collected every local resource he could muster, pulling old woldwardens and woldwatchers from sites they had watched for centuries. He had stripped the local territories bare of guardians. It was an impressive arsenal, but he had spread it in a longer line than he would have liked in order to herd the enemy better.

He turned to the nearest overseer among the druids assisting him. "What say you, Jarcetto? Are you a gambler? Do we keep the pressure up and see if they blunder into Ios?"

Overseer Jarcetto had never had much of a sense of humor. Beneath his cowled hood his expression was blank. "That is your decision, Potent, not mine."

Baldur sighed at the man's dour attitude and wished—not for the first time—that Kaya were with him instead. It had been a largely rhetorical question. "Despite that ogrun body he chooses to wear, this is a dragon we face. We must presume the snake knows the borders of Ios and will not want to provoke an enemy ahead as well as behind." He grimaced and continued, "Send word along the left flank. Let the line falter and fall behind. Make it appear we are losing wind. Give the enemy an opening to the west." He turned to a subordinate on his other side. "The line on the right needs to pivot north. Prepare to shift at my command. Have the reeves double back on the far right flank to hasten toward the enemy. Maintain pressure, but drift back if the enemy stops to engage. They outrange us in the open."

He looked westward. The Ring of Willows was that direction, intact within the Glimmerwood. If other Circle leaders could spare any men, the sacred site might be of use to reinforce Baldur's forces and intercept the enemy. All he could do now was try to drive his adversaries in that direction and hope his allies could take advantage of the opportunity.

"We're falling behind!" Kaya's posture suggested a stretched bowstring, and her mood was clearly having an impact on the nearest beasts of the column. Several warpwolves howled and were joined by the higher-pitched barks of a dozen argus. One of the nearby satyrs rammed a withered tree trunk and splintered it.

> ## "At these times it is imperative we remember the larger picture. You will learn this in time."

Alongside her, Morvahna marched with her great blade strapped to her back. "Be calm," she instructed, her tone suggesting strained patience. "We will arrive when we arrive, no sooner and no later."

"At least send our swiftest Tharn to him. The wolf riders and Bloodweavers could reach him well ahead of us."

Morvahna's voice was soft, contrasting the steel in her eyes. "At these times it is imperative we remember the larger picture. You will learn this in time. Baldur has matters under control. Do not underestimate the force he already has at his disposal."

"I think you may be the one underestimating—" Kaya began hotly.

The crackle and flash of a wayfarer appearing interrupted her. This one was Veltison, a young prodigy only recently past his mentorship. He staggered slightly before catching his balance. Many wayfarers had reached their limits in recent weeks, having overused their skills to travel long distances in the blink of an eye. In time the miles they crossed exacted a toll on their bodies and minds. Breathlessly he reported, "The Legion army breaks west, mistress!"

The news prompted a cunning smile from Morvahna. "Excellent. This will be our best chance." She turned to Kaya. "I presume you wish to lead an interception force?"

"Of course," Kaya replied with ready enthusiasm.

"Very well. Take your beasts and go northwest, following those hills." She indicated the direction with an abrupt wave of her hand. "Force them to stop to deal with you, but remember this is a diversion *only*. You will not have the strength to hold. Engage just long enough for Baldur to hit their flank. We will be there shortly." She paused, leveling a stare at the younger druid. "Strike and stall. You know the way."

Kaya nodded and ran in the indicated direction, her cloak billowing behind her. A pack of argus, three warpwolves, and two satyrs went with her. Wayfarer Veltison watched her go with a worried frown, stepping closer to Morvahna. "Can even she control so many?"

Morvahna gave a small smile and shrugged. "Why bother with control? It will suffice to let them loose on the enemy. It will divert their attention, for a time. Perhaps long enough."

Morvahna closed her eyes to visualize the landscape around her and the movements of their forces in her mind. Her awareness of the local geography was flawless, and she could easily deduce Baldur's intent. She spoke again to the wayfarer, "Baldur drives them to the Ring of Willows. Find Bradigus Thorle and instruct him to send reinforcements to that site, with all haste."

---

## He saw it was no arrow that leapt from her bow but rather a slender shaft of blighted energy stretched into a projectile.

---

Veltison blinked in surprise. "If that is Baldur's plan, why send Kaya . . . ?" His voice faltered as he seemed to realize whom he was questioning.

She replied as if indulging someone not blessed with abundant intelligence. "One cannot expect a plan to succeed without effort. Reinforcements take time. Kaya knows the risks." Her tone became clipped. "You have your orders, Wayfarer."

Lylyth waited amid the branches of the trees while the rest of the Legion sped west under Rhyas' command. This environment was hot and dry, the land arid and the ground yellow with desiccated growth. It was nothing like their home in the northern mountains, but the blighted Nyss had learned to adapt. They no longer felt the dry heat and had learned to blend in even here. A single raek was with her, lying almost flat to hide in the undergrowth at the tree's base. Also accompanying her were several hand-selected striders perched in other slender trees. They were as still as death itself.

As reward for their patience the enemy line approached and quickly passed them entirely oblivious to their existence. The various stone constructs moved through the nearby trees with quiet ease despite their bulk. Lylyth watched

the floating stone eyes with particular wariness, having recently been on the receiving end of their attention. She knew that invoking any magic would be like a beacon to those hunters.

Her helmet sealed Lylyth's eyes from normal light, but her ability to perceive through blight-enhanced senses had many advantages. Since the restoration of her athanc at the Castle of the Keys she had found new appreciation for the unique subtleties through which she interpreted the world. She could see thin lines of distortion rippling mirage-like from each of the stone constructs passing below. It was subtle, but each line traced back to a single source like spokes in a wheel. Could a single powerful druid be directing so many of these weapons?

Lylyth focused her mind to send a message to Rhyas, finding this normally simple task more difficult without the dragon's active awareness to facilitate. "I have my target. I may be able to disrupt the pursuit with a single strike."

Rhyas sent a sensation of acknowledgement and added, "A smaller force closes on me from the south. I will deal with them."

There was a familiar vengeful note in her mental voice that Lylyth recognized only too well. As much as she would have enjoyed encouraging Rhyas to sate her appetites, things had changed. "Remember, minimal casualties. We cannot afford to be pinned down." Under other circumstances Lylyth would have been the last to discourage delight in slaughter, but the dragon's instructions had been clear and Lylyth felt a deeply imprinted need to obey.

Lylyth felt Rhyas extend her awareness back. "You intend to fight that force with a single spawn?"

"Anything more would be detected. It will be enough, if I am quick." She sensed the recently spawned raek's hunger and sent a tendril of empathic reassurance to it. *Food soon.* It shivered and clicked its teeth.

The central body of the Circle force passed within fifty yards of her position. She soon spotted her quarry, recognizing the druid as one named Baldur amid shared memories drawn from Thagrosh. The ogrun had fought a single indecisive clash against this druid nearly a year ago. This memory gave her insight into several of the enemy's tricks, and she smiled with the awareness that she remained a mystery to him. A group of armored men in furs with heavy crossbows marched as escort, as did a smaller group of druids in dark robes.

More dangerous to her was an enormous stone and wood construct striding several yards to the man's left. Tremendous polished spheres of green-lit crystal were set in the oversized granite plates comprising its forearms. Lylyth's discerning senses told her this was a specially augmented weapon. Baldur had many other constructs in the general vicinity, but only this one was close enough to be of immediate concern.

She knew she had but one chance. In her veins the dragon's blood ignited with battle lust, and the sensation pushed all doubts aside. She let her mind release into the spirit of the hunt. She could feel the subtle creak of every piece of leather, the smallest shifts of wind, and the pressure of each individual footfall on the soil.

Lylyth and her striders sprang into motion simultaneously without a single spoken word. The Nyss herself ran like a shadow across the dry grass, sweeping unseen to the left as the group of striders went right. Their uniquely adapted legs sent them flying across the intervening soil in great leaps. Their bows lifted, and they fired into the backs of the Orboros reeves before those soldiers even realized they were marked for death. As soon as the druids became aware of the threat, the Deathstalkers among the striders let loose their arrows silently and unerringly. One barbed shaft pierced the warder's throat. The overseer took two quick shots to the chest; the first pierced a lung and the next penetrated his side as he tried to spin away. The arrow sank downward at a precise angle to sever one of the major arteries in his heart.

The surviving druids gathered their magic to hurl stones toward the attackers at deadly velocities, but their disorganized volley made little difference. There was the distinct thrum of crossbows firing as the reeves tried to track the blurs that were their targets. Those quarrels were also ineffective, sinking into the trunks of trees where striders had been moments before.

Baldur and the great towering wold turned simultaneously and in the same posture, as if the stone walker were a puppet with strings connected to its master. Each extended a single arm and hand, and the ground split in two places as sharp lengths of jagged stone exploded outward and the air filled with a roaring sound like an earthquake. Lylyth saw three of her striders torn to pieces, but she could spare them no thought. The raek became a streak of scaled flesh racing directly for the druid who was Lylyth's primary target. Its jaws were open in hungry anticipation, and the razor tip of its tail lashed behind it as it ran.

As she also ran, Lylyth smiled to see the speed with which the raek closed on its target. The elemental construct moved to intercept, and as she expected Baldur touched the bark of a nearby tree with his left hand and gestured with his right. He shimmered and was gone. Lylyth instantly felt the movement of the air to her left with her heightened senses and turned to see him stepping from the divided trunk of a nearby birch. She had chosen her path because it was perilously close to several nearby constructs that had already reversed course and were trying to rejoin their master. Stepping this way Baldur evaded the striders and came closer to his nearest animated weapons, just as Lylyth had predicted he would.

Even as the singular woldwarden brought both its massive fists crushing down to shatter the spine of the raek, Lylyth pulled back her bowstring and released. Baldur caught the movement as she began to fire and tried to shield himself behind the nearest tree. He saw it was no arrow that leapt from her bow but rather a slender shaft of blighted energy stretched into a projectile. It sprang unerringly from Whisper to strike his chest and send shimmering blackness writhing along his body and clinging to him like chains. The impact of this magic was not immediately obvious, but Lylyth could feel her anticipation rising.

Baldur had his enormous stone sword in hand as he turned to her with his face reddening in anger. Still running, she sensed several floating stone constructs hurrying at her from behind. Her right arm blurred as she notched and released one arrow after another at a ferocious pace. The first two arrows sank into his chest, but their shafts shattered and fell loose as he channeled the force of their impact into the wold fighting her raek.

The entropic forces Lylyth had unleashed on him made Baldur's reflexes sluggish and impaired his ability to dodge the arrows that would find the weak spots in his armor as if guided by an unseen hand. Two more sank into his body, one penetrating deep into his left shoulder and the other his right thigh. Lylyth felt tremendous satisfaction as she saw them take hold. She savored the pain in the ugly human's bearded face.

His allies were rapidly converging on her position. The floating orbs were almost in range to fire on her with their crystalline eyes. The giant wold had left the raek and was moving toward her as swiftly as its stone steps could take it. The wold stretched its hand and the earth erupted in jagged stones beneath her feet, but she leapt and twirled in the air, managing a flip that took her entirely clear.

As she landed she saw Baldur disappear again. For a moment she thought he had escaped her noose. Her eyes widened as the fool appeared directly next to her, stepping from the small slender stalk of a young tree to her left. He gave a triumphant shout and leveraged the weight of his stone sword in an impossibly swift slash toward her midsection.

Lylyth lurched to the side and twisted, feeling the flat stone tip of the blade redden her skin with abrasive friction as it barely breezed past her stomach. She tumbled backward in an impossible vault, pulling back the string of her bow as she did so and releasing while upside down. It was not an arrow she launched but another shaft of blighted power. It struck Baldur and sent snakelike tendrils rippling down his legs and into the earth to trap him in place. As she landed a beam of energy burned a hole through the armor on her left leg and seared her thigh. The woldwyrd blast was painful, but the actual injury was slight and Lylyth ignored it. She gave Baldur a feral grin and shook her head.

Her raek had killed two reeves in the abandoned clearing nearby but faltered as two quarrels in its chest finished it off. Lylyth collected its dying strength. Those bolts would be the last fired by the reeves as the remaining striders reaped their deadly harvest. The Deathstalkers followed the wold but their eyes focused on Baldur, needing no further instruction after spotting Lylyth's snared prey. They notched arrows even as Lylyth raised her bow and fired into the struggling body of the Stonecleaver. He strained against the blighted ropes, trying to escape but finding his magic failed him.

Baldur's eyes on Lylyth blazed in hate and defiance as arrow after arrow sank into his stone-hardened flesh. He made no sound, not a single shout or groan of pain, despite the barrage of injuries inflicted upon him. One by one the floating wyrds shattered to dust as he sent his wounds into their fragile frames, but then his resources were spent. Several more arrows struck before he finally toppled to his knees. He coughed in a single spray of red mist and sank to the ground as his blood seeped into the hungry earth. The stone sword tumbled from his fingers.

Behind him the enormous woldwarden gave a sound like the cracking of a great tree falling to timber. It walked toward the dying man with stilted steps as if in grief. Lylyth could sense other nearby constructs turning toward him as well. He had been their master, and they were bereft of his will to guide them.

She had hoped they would cease functioning at his death, but though they continued to move, they seemed disordered and almost pathetic in their apparent confusion. She had no doubt they were still dangerous individually, but she was fairly certain that without Baldur's instructions they would not pursue her army. Her objective accomplished, Lylyth gathered the remaining striders and fled. She heard a sound behind her like the grinding and toppling of stone and wood.

Morvahna the Autumnblade stormed imperiously into the wooded clearing to find Kaya kneeling on the dry ground before the half-stooped form of a woldwarden. "Why did you break off your attack?" Her voice was strident. "We had them! All you had to do was hold—"

Kaya's voice was subdued. "I felt it. I don't know how or why, but I felt it when he fell." It was as if she were speaking to herself.

At last Morvahna took a better look at the scene around them. Several pieces of stone nearby were the exploded remnants of woldwyrds. The woldwarden she had presumed incapacitated before Kaya was Megalith, and she could sense it was alert and intact. The damage it had sustained was fading as she watched. There was something highly unusual about its mental condition, and it deflected her mental touch in a way that would have vexed her had not numerous other elements of the situation demanded her attention.

She saw the pool of drying blood beneath Megalith's rooted feet and the thick robes caught up in the living root structure. It took her a moment to realize Megalith had planted itself atop a fallen druid and a few seconds more to notice the unmistakable stone sword laying several feet away. "Baldur?" she exclaimed. "It cannot be." She walked close. It remained impossible to force her mind into Megalith's complex consciousness. Morvahna had controlled the entity before, but now it refused to listen to her imperatives.

Morvahna sighed and shook her head as she walked to Kaya to put a hand on her shoulder. "I am sorry, my child. He will be sorely missed. This is a great blow."

"He's still alive. Can't you feel him?"

"What? Impossible." Morvahna stepped closer to Megalith. Touching a stone leg where runes pulsed gently with green light, she closed her eyes and reached past the construct. She could sense only the barest hint of life below those roots, the tiniest sliver of consciousness not connected to the lattice of wood comprising the construct's connective frame. Some unnatural force had gripped that last wisp of life and clutched it tight.

Kaya looked to the elder with tears streaking her upraised face. "Do something. Heal him!"

Morvahna sighed and spoke again in a gentler voice. "I'm sorry, Kaya. Your hopes were raised for no purpose. There is nothing I can do."

"But Megalith—"

"Megalith tried to save him, but there is not enough to salvage. It is just a simple creature of rock and wood. It does not know its efforts are futile. It grieves in its own way. That is all." She paused to probe at the faint life spark, but it slipped from her mental gaze like a mirage. "If I had arrived sooner, maybe, but not now."

Kaya's expression fell and she stood to her feet, staring at the fallen stone sword. Her fists suddenly clenched. "We could have prevented this."

"Do not blame yourself, child. He fought his battle even as you fought yours. This was unforeseen. There was nothing you could have done."

Kaya turned on her with a face full of rage and emotions so palpable that Morvahna took a step back in surprise. "I do not blame myself. I blame you. No one matters to you. You have made it clear we are all dispensable."

"You are overtaken by grief. You do not know of what you speak." Morvahna had pulled herself upright and her eyes simmered dangerously. "I will not hold this outburst against you."

Kaya refused to relent. "You could have sent Tharn ahead to help him. Wolf riders, bloodtrackers, Bloodweavers. Do you think the enemy would have ambushed him so easily if we had given him proper support? You refused. You kept them to yourself like a coward. I should have insisted, but I was afraid to defy you. I have had enough of this." Morvahna became increasingly aware that Kaya was not alone; nearby several beasts waited for the young overseer, and now they stared at Morvahna with dark eyes. They were tense and unmoving, and their minds were closed to her.

"Think carefully on what you say, child. This is no time for tantrums. The Legion escapes and we must pursue. We will all grieve Baldur, but this is not the time. We must hurry, before the trail becomes colder still."

"No." Kaya was unmoving. "I will stay here and watch over him. I will not give up hope so long as there is any trace of life. Nor will I leave him to die alone."

"The enemy is escaping!" Morvahna hissed. "Gather your forces and follow Everblight's army. We must stop them. It is not too late."

Kaya shook her head. "It *is* too late. This was a distraction. They accomplished what they set out to do." She looked to Megalith and her eyes became watery again. She had to look away. "Their leader was not with those I fought, nor were others we saw at the Castle of the Keys. I am certain of it.

I do not know where they went, but only a single warlock led the force I saw. She sought to lead me on a chase. When I felt Baldur fall . . ." She left the sentence unfinished.

"A diversion? With the entirety of their remaining army as bait?" Morvahna asked, but not entirely disbelieving. The direction of her thoughts was evident on her face as she considered what she knew of Everblight. "It is possible . . ."

"Following them will achieve nothing except more deaths," Kaya insisted. "I have had enough of this chase. I will watch over Baldur. If there are any of our order who can heal him, send them here."

"If I cannot restore him, no one can." Morvahna snarled. The suggestion that someone might succeed where she had failed galled her. "You promised to obey me. Baldur was witness to that."

---

> ## "I do not blame myself. I blame you. No one matters to you. You have made it clear we are all dispensable."

---

Kaya winced but shook her head, standing firm. "That service is ended. Do as you feel you must, but I am not leaving. When I am finished here, I may return to help you. Otherwise, I will fight them on my own. I will repay them for what they have done, but not today." She knelt beside Megalith, all her attention focused on the barely perceptible sensation of life.

She did not even hear Morvahna and the others leave. Nor did she notice as woldwatchers, wardens, and wyrds began arriving at the clearing. They formed a loose ring around the perimeter of the clearing, leaving Megalith at its center.

# MANNING THE FORTS

Archdomina Makeda turned to regard Lord Tyrant Hexeris as he entered her small chamber. It was more of an administrative office than a proper receiving room for someone of her stature. An assortment of rolled maps and stacked dispatches, a small portion of the paperwork a widespread army inevitably generated, littered the desk and floor. There was no sign of the slaves or clerks who customarily labored here. Master Tormentor Morghoul stood nearby, leaning against the wall and eyeing Hexeris from behind his mask.

Hexeris bowed with proper respect. "Archdomina Makeda, I serve at your pleasure. How can I aid you before your departure?"

The archdomina had earlier gathered her officers to declare her intention of marching the army east to overthrow the Conqueror. They had first received this announcement with shock and disbelief, but Makeda had anticipated this and chose her words well. She spoke with heartfelt emotion as she called for skorne leadership and unity in tones of growing fervor and urgency. Rarely had the soldiers seen their leader's mind and heart laid bare to them so completely. By the time she finished her speech she had their full support, and they met her closing words with a roar of approval. It had certainly helped that Morghoul stood resolutely by her side as she spoke. Makeda did not threaten or cajole her officers or ever once point to Morghoul, but his clear solidarity was a message nonetheless. Those who may have felt reluctant to turn from the Conqueror were even more reluctant to draw the attention of the master tormentor who had almost single-handedly arranged for the Second Unification in Halaak.

Makeda faced Hexeris coldly with her arms crossed. "I am surprised you even answered my summons. Given your recent efforts to undermine my orders, I thought perhaps you would flee and go into hiding."

The lord tyrant's smile was as chilling as ever, and his eyes met hers with his customary unsettling interest. He always seemed to look through a person's face to trace the lines of the skull beneath, eager to extract it for closer examination. His voice, though, was neutral. "You confuse me, Archdomina. I would never seek to undermine your orders. I admit and apologize for certain . . . confusions at the battle of the ruins. Things there did not proceed as intended. I take full responsibility."

---

## The fact that he was indisputably alive was a vexing riddle that contradicted everything the skorne believed they understood about life and death.

---

"I have spoken with Xerxis, so there is no need to deny it. You deliberately overrode my orders to redirect his forces toward that ill-conceived defense of a worthless pile of rubble. That was an unforgivable lapse in judgment—a crime worthy of execution."

Hexeris spread his hands, still evidencing no apparent concern. "I agree with your assessment, Archdomina. I offer no excuses, but I suggest you speak with Supreme Aptimus Zaal regarding our reasons. We made a discovery we thought could be significant to the army and felt it was our obligation to investigate. I earnestly believed Tyrant Xerxis and his soldiers were required to secure this discovery. I admit we acted before we fully understood the situation, but we meant no disloyalty. Our aim was to harness relics of power for the use of your army." This attempt at humility seemed practiced and insincere. When she did not immediately reply he asked, "Am I to be given over to Morghoul's ministrations?" His tone was curious rather than alarmed.

"To what purpose?" Makeda asked. "A master mortitheurge of your abilities could hardly be expected to break under torture. Ignoring your flesh's pain would be simple for you."

Morghoul interjected, "I can reach him, if you require it, Archdomina. I have been considering several techniques I am confident he cannot ignore." Hexeris faced the master tormentor as if fascinated by the prospect of his own excruciation.

"If I had the luxury, Lord Tyrant, I might indeed torture and execute you. I would give you to Morghoul, not expecting answers, but for a public display. To provide an example to the other tyrants. However, I do not have that luxury." Makeda paused to let that sink in. "I need you in another capacity. Quite against my personal preferences you will have the opportunity to redeem yourself. Whatever your follies and personal ambitions, I believe you genuinely seek the empowerment of our people. I will make use of you."

"Such an unexpected mercy is—"

"Silence!" Makeda cut him off. "This is not mercy, but a burden—and your last chance. As you are aware, I will soon be taking the bulk of the army east to face the Conqueror. Our enemies here will see that as a retreat in the wake of our recent defeat. We will not be giving up our western fortresses, however. Indeed, I expect for you to expand them in my absence."

"Let me take this opportunity, Archdomina, to congratulate you on your realization that the Conqueror is not the Reborn." Hexeris saw anger in her eyes at this; they both knew how long he had been arguing that very point. He continued, "As I said when I entered, I serve at your pleasure. You intend for me to oversee our defenses while you are gone? This is more honor than I expected."

"You will command our forces here. I will be leaving you with extremely limited reserves. We require almost the entirety of the army to besiege the Abyssal Fortress. The supreme aptimus and most of his order will also remain behind working to increase the number of guardians and Immortals at your disposal. You will need to rely heavily on them until we return with reinforcements."

Hexeris was not slow to grasp the situation. His eyes went distant a moment, as if hearing a voice from elsewhere. He spoke as if a sudden idea had occurred to him. "I will require access to Void Seer Mordikaar. His efforts will be essential if we are to hold with so few soldiers."

Makeda's eyes narrowed. Hexeris' pretending to have arrived at this idea just now did not fool her. She knew quite well how hard Hexeris had lobbied for Mordikaar to join the Army of the Western Reaches; Hexeris had gone out of his way to persuade the seer to leave his seclusion in Malphas. She had certain reservations about that particular occultist, even though she had to admit his power was genuine and useful. She was not in a position to refuse adding any weapons to her arsenal, however, and certainly both Hexeris and Mordikaar qualified. One reassurance regarding the pair was the fact that the supreme aptimus seemed to have a strong loathing for Mordikaar. She was certain his presence would provide a balancing influence.

She glanced at Morghoul to see his opinion but returned her scrutiny to Hexeris when none was offered. "Very well. We have no use for Mordikaar on our journey. He is yours.

Be cautious. You yourself admitted we do not understand the nature of his condition nor of his servants."

Hexeris bowed more deeply this time. "Our research will be conducted with all the proper precautions, I assure you."

Makeda continued, "You will not sit idle while we risk our lives to ensure the empire's future. I require you to gather a substantial stock of slaves by the time we return. They must be put to work expanding our holdings in this land by extending our fortifications. Agricultural efforts and the construction of habitation must accompany this expansion. Capture as many as possible—whatever their race—without inviting a retaliation you cannot handle."

"It will be done," Hexeris assured her. "Let your ancestors guide you in the tasks ahead as mine have guided me in mine." This was a traditional skorne invocation for luck, and Makeda was too distracted by her plans to consider that Hexeris was not one for pious homilies. As he took his leave she turned back to her maps and army reports to evaluate how badly they had suffered in recent battles. Morghoul's gaze lingered more suspiciously in the lord tyrant's direction.

Observing Void Seer Mordikaar at work was akin to watching an incomprehensibly intricate ceremony or dance. He moved in sweeping motions across the open and strangely cold chamber beneath the central fortress. This was a laboratory sealed specifically for his use, and only a few individuals had access. Hexeris watched from an upper deck intended for that purpose, not wishing to interrupt the seer at a crucial stage of his preparations.

The chamber was not entirely dissimilar from Hexeris' own working spaces. Shelves containing books, scrolls, and jars of organic tissue preserved in various fluids lined its walls. Mordikaar owned a particularly rich collection of old lore brought west from Halaak and rarer scrolls and inscriptions from ancient Malphas, including a number of volumes Hexeris was eager to copy. The bulk of the central floor was open, containing countless sigils inscribed in long looping lines of silver. Mordikaar had dusted these patterns, words, and lines with the ashes of the cremated dead. Those ashes stirred beneath his steps as he walked.

The empty floor allowed for the void seer to move freely when engaged in rites with the spirits clustering around him, made visible to those with the sight by the sweeping arcs of light emitted from his peculiar lanterns. The room was thick with cloying and dizzying incense, and the swirling vapors responded to the beams of light passed through them as the void seer moved. At times it seemed the room was crowded with countless silently howling phantoms. At other times a single stronger specter would move in conjunction with his steps while it leered, screamed, and clawed at the air with unnatural fingers eager to rend living flesh. The lanterns kept it at bay, each beam of radiance burning its insubstantial essence.

Hexeris thought he could almost see the shimmering portal to the Void in a flickering slick of dark ice behind the void

seer. It was as if shadowy clawed hands pushed at the opening in an attempt to force their way into this reality. As soon as he tried to focus on that yawning impossible chasm it would vanish, only to appear again in the corner of his eye like a persistent mirage.

Mordikaar used the piercing light of his lanterns to maneuver the most substantial of the spirits surrounding him into the center of the chamber where the floor patterns converged in a spiral. He finished his chanting intonation and bent his will to shackle the entity with spiritual chains. Its form solidified and its movements became more docile though it still radiated menace. In this state the void spirit would react to commands and could be entrusted to some degree in battle, at least while controlled by those properly trained. It still radiated a hunger to kill, but now its cold and hateful eyes could discern skorne allies from those it could annihilate with abandon. The use of such spirits was highly controversial and radical to say the least.

Hexeris at last stepped down the stairs into the central chamber, approaching Mordikaar. The void seer turned to face him as he attached his lanterns to hooks extending from a frame on his back. "Greetings, Lord Tyrant Hexeris. I assure you I have not exceeded Zaal's quota. This spirit is slated to replace one recently destroyed by the *duzusk* at the watch post near the northern breeding pens."

Hexeris inclined his head. "I bring glad tidings. You no longer need to concern yourself with quotas."

"Oh?" Mordikaar showed only guarded optimism. Hexeris knew he had been frustrated to arrive west only to discover the freedoms promised to him quickly denied. "Has Supreme Aptimus Zaal reversed himself on that policy?" Mordikaar spoke with the gentle inflections and sophisticated dialect of the Malphas scholars. This bothered some of the warrior caste, but Hexeris had no such prejudices.

Hexeris nodded sympathetically. "I know these limits have made progress difficult. Fortunately, things have changed. I have had the occasion to read your notes and see possibilities. Furthermore, Zaal's conservatism on this matter is no longer relevant. I will be in command during Makeda's absence. The demands set before me by the archdomina require us to accelerate your work." He opened his hands magnanimously.

Mordikaar's eyes gleamed, although habitual wariness tempered his enthusiasm. Even other mortitheurges within the western army had not welcomed him warmly. All knew quite well that the void seer should by all rights be dead. The fact that he was indisputably alive was a vexing riddle that contradicted everything the skorne believed they understood about life and death. Such incongruities made them extremely uncomfortable, and seeing him only reminded them of it. "I do not seek to antagonize the supreme aptimus needlessly, but I am eager to do my part to aid Archdomina Makeda. I know the army marches east and that a difficult struggle awaits them."

"Zaal will come around in time," Hexeris insisted. "He is locked within the constraints of his own research and studies, and his order has difficulty realizing the spirit world has its own hierarchies and castes. He is too focused on his exalted and on observing their maddened

transition to *kovaas*. He speaks only to the aristocracy of the spirit world. Your void spirits are just as vital. Even as our society rests on the foundation of its slaves, we must make proper use of their spiritual counterparts." He paused before bringing the conversation back to the matter immediately at hand. "With the army gone, our defenses are weak. I need to draw on your power to fill the gap. Quotas have been a needless and detrimental restriction. Indeed, I have plans which should enable us to advance your research."

"Oh? You have hinted at this before. I am eager to know your mind." Mordikaar's eyes contained a fierce hunger.

"I have been conducting research on certain parallels between the energies you have observed and very strong residual forces left behind at the ruins where the dragon fought and died. Have you heard of the energy westerners call 'blight'?" The void seer nodded, and Hexeris continued. "Yes, it is fascinating. I have reason to suspect your connection to the Void operates on similar principles. I would like to establish a laboratory at the battle site to see if that energy allows a greater influx of void spirits to enter our reality and be enslaved."

"Supreme Aptimus Zaal specifically forbade me approaching that site," Mordikaar reminded him.

"Of course. That was when we sought to *close* that inexplicable portal of yours. But as I say, things have

changed. Sealing your connection to the Void is the last thing I desire now. Indeed, I hope to pry it open! In a controlled environment and taking the proper precautions, naturally. I think there is much to gain. It should increase your stature tremendously, particularly if your efforts serve to free us from our reliance on the exalted and the honored companions rescued from battle. There are only so many sacral stones. Your access to the Void opens the possibility for a limitless supply of eager soldiers."

The void seer frowned at Hexeris' enthusiasm. "I am not sure I would go that far, Lord Tyrant. I appreciate your patronage, of course. But there are inherent problems with relying on void spirits to that extent. This is a temporary measure. My eventual goal is to allow us to evade the Void and live past death without relying on sacral stones. We must consider the use of void spirits as only a temporary measure, not a solution. The horrors of that environment drive its denizens insane. There are limits to the uses to which such spirits can be put."

Hexeris smiled reassuringly. "Of course, of course. I did not mean otherwise, my friend. Yes, we will pursue all these avenues—and without the stifling limits imposed on you here. Come with me and let us discuss your requirements for a new laboratory. I have conscripted a group of hardy slaves expressly for its construction. They can be put to work immediately."

# SALVATION'S PRICE

"Reinforcements from the west!" Madrak shouted. "Deal with them and prepare to turn about. Rally to me!" He hurled Rathrok through a gap between the nearest champions laying their axes into the Khadoran Iron Fangs. Rathrok clove cleanly through two ranks of the enemy and then returned to his hand with a keening noise.

The pikemen had made an impressive charge, but now that the fray was upon them they were finding the trollkin tenacious. Madrak's warriors were scattered and disordered as the fight became a more chaotic brawl, and the chieftain could see another tightly ordered formation of Khadoran pikemen swiftly approaching from behind. He muttered, "How are Khadorans so far south? Damn it all." He summoned his impaler Jor closer, for the full-blood troll had taken several deep gashes in the initial attack and Madrak worried about losing him. Fortunately the troll's injuries were regenerating rapidly. The axer Bron took up a protective stance in front of Jor, grinning eagerly as he looked toward the approaching wall of pikemen.

Borka pushed his way forward amid the champion line and let loose a bellow as he joined the fight directly. He shattered the shield and arm of one Iron Fang before swinging his mace so hard into the helmet of the man next to him it nearly tore off his head. "Ah! This is glorious, Madrak!" he shouted. "Better than expected! Wherever we go, you find an enemy worth killing! A stroll in the woods turns into a clash with the entire Khadoran Army!" He continued laughing as he toppled one pikeman after another, freeing up the champions to come around and heed Madrak's warning. It took more shouting and cajoling to muster the nearby kriel warriors into some semblance of order.

Madrak grimaced at Borka's words, but he had no energy to dispute them. Only the need to present a brave face to his warriors prevented him from succumbing to despair. The very thing that prompted delight in Borka had been weighing on his mind. Their journey south from the Scarsfell had been one misfortune after another, with the most unlikely clashes. Despite their efforts to return quietly to the south they had seemed to stumble upon every armed patrol, bandit camp, mercenary mob, druid sacred site, and Cryxian outpost between Ohk and the Dragon's Tongue. Madrak had lost count of the enemy corpses they had left behind them.

Even with their horrible luck at evading notice, he had to admit their force had weathered these clashes better than seemed possible and actually grown in size. Random pockets of kith and kriels had joined them, but whether seeking Madrak or Borka it was sometimes difficult to tell. Most of the newer volunteers were ill-tempered, loud, and brash trollkin who thirsted for violence. Increasingly Madrak looked around at the faces surrounding him and felt like a stranger among his own people.

At least he had some solace in several newfound friends, including an old grizzled hero named Naltor the Black Axe who fought beside him today. Originally from the Kovosk Hills, Naltor had a grim sense of humor and a cheerful pragmatism that was a welcome distraction from Madrak's bleak thoughts. Borka had also welcomed Naltor as a ready drinking companion, and the two of them enjoyed swapping tall tales regarding the number of offspring they had sired across the Khadoran wilds.

Despite his age Naltor was a peerless combatant, and Madrak was happy to have him on hand, particularly at times like this. The new Khadoran force bearing down on them was larger than expected, and again Madrak wondered how this was possible. Weren't they nearly to Point Bourne?

Naltor was the first to charge, knocking pikes and shields aside with his great axe and taking the forward Iron Fangs by surprise with his boldness. The nearest champions followed with a shout as Madrak and Borka rushed alongside. Madrak sent spell and axe past the forward line just as Borka hurled a spiked grenade to explode behind the enemy before the battle joined.

They were clearly outnumbered. Madrak took Rathrok in hand and leapt forward with Naltor and another veteran named Hakon. He sent Bron the axer toward the Khadoran flank, and the great troll swept cuts against those trying to encircle them. Jor was able to strike above the heads of the nearest champions with the length of his spear to pierce the enemy. Two of Borka's winter trolls were far in the left flank exhaling great plumes of freezing air to destroy those closing from that direction.

> "Ah! This is glorious, Madrak! Better than expected! Wherever we go, you find an enemy worth killing!"

Madrak's vision swam for a moment and he blinked against a sickening dizzy feeling. "Not now," he muttered, frustrated. For a moment the scene before him changed into something similar to what his true senses told him but with many telling differences. The Khadorans wore slightly different uniforms, and their shields bore different designs. The banners they held aloft displayed the emblems of some long-dead king. Instead of his kin, Cygnarans fought beside him to die screaming beneath the pikes. The sounds echoed strangely as blood drifted almost lazily through the air. He heard the crackle of thunder as rain began pouring down.

At last Madrak shook the vision away, knowing he had seen a battle that had taken place here perhaps a century ago. He gritted his teeth and scowled at the axe he held as its runes gleamed. These visions had been happening more frequently of late. He did not understand why they afflicted him, but they were an unwelcome distraction and filled him with the anger of men and trollkin long slain. Strangely the rain persisted from vision to reality, but he could no longer remember if it had started before. The flux of battle was confusing enough without his own senses deceiving him.

He came back to himself too late to try to evade an incoming pike jabbing downward toward him through a gap in the lines. A feeling of numbing warmth spread through Madrak's fingers on Rathrok's haft. Inexplicably, Naltor faltered next to him. The hero's right leg collapsed as his ankle twisted and he fell forward in front of Madrak, straight into the path of the incoming pike. Its point pierced Naltor's eye and emerged bloodily from the back of his skull and helmet with a spray of gore, killing him instantly. Madrak could only stare in open-eyed disbelief even as other pikes were thrust toward him.

A wedge had opened in their line. He raised Rathrok to knock aside the surging pikes. His vision blurred again and he saw savage axe-wielding Tharn attacking, one from each side. He battered one aside with Rathrok's edge only to realize they were illusions. A pike meant for him missed its target as someone barreled into Madrak's side and sent him tumbling. He looked up to see Hakon regarding a shaft emerging from his chest with surprise. The trollkin slumped off his feet as the Khadoran wielding the deadly pike worked to yank the weapon loose. Madrak screamed in anger and swung Rathrok up to carve straight through the man's helmet, shearing off the side of his face.

"Pull back, fools! Get back, into the trees!" ordered a vaguely familiar female voice. Madrak's irritation at someone telling his warriors what to do vanished as he saw reinforcements wearing familiar quitari patterns joining them. The Khadoran lines faltered and pulled back to regroup, buying a moment's pause.

Madrak felt his strength drain away and fell to one knee next to the still form of Naltor. "How did this happen?" He knew he could have endured that hit or deflected it to Bron to regenerate. Naltor's death had been needless. So too with Hakon, lying nearby. A sickening certainty gripped him that these deaths were not accidental. This was not the first time warriors fighting near him had been stricken. Madrak had taken few injuries in recent battles while seeing those closest to him killed in increasingly unlikely mishaps.

At first he had dismissed these incidents as the inevitable cost of war. Combined with the increased frequency of visions, though, he could no longer ignore them. The elders had been right: it was Rathrok. Each day he became more convinced. After the last battle he had even tried to hurl the axe into a pond, but it always returned to his hand. Madrak had begun to ponder how he might destroy the thing, if that was even possible.

"Come, Madrak! This is no time for prayers!" It was Borka, pulling him back to his feet. "We've bought time, but she has the right of it." His face showed none of Madrak's grief, which was not a particular surprise. Borka lost friends and companions regularly, and it left no lasting stain on his soul. The enormous trollkin looked down to Naltor and shook his head as he clapped Madrak's shoulder. "We will drink to him tonight, never fear. We will give him a proper sendoff."

Madrak let Borka pull him away. He recognized the newcomer who had arrived with the other trollkin, a stout female wearing a bright red scarf tied about her head. As he watched she recited Dhunian prayers while pointing a curved dagger toward a line of lingering pikemen who looked to be mustering an attack. The Khadorans shook their heads and backed away, looking confused and bewildered. The nearest trollkin warriors quickly gathered their injured friends to pull them to safety.

"Calandra?" Madrak spoke the shaman's name. The last time he had seen her she had insisted on staying behind among several stubborn kith in the Glimmerwood. He was surprised but pleased to find her here in his hour of need.

She turned to smile at him, setting large hands to her thick waist. "Thank me later, Ironhide. Now, get your people back. What were you thinking? Marching straight toward a newly built Khadoran fort! There are easier ways to commit suicide."

Madrak blinked in confusion. "What? We're almost at the Dragon's Tongue River!"

"How long have you been gone?" She saw his incomprehension and shook her head. "Khador owns the Thornwood now! Come, this is no time to talk." She unleashed an ear-splitting whistle and her trollkin began to withdraw. They took what injured and dead they could carry and followed her lead away from the battle. She gave Madrak another smile as they pulled back, as if oblivious both to the carnage around her and the chieftain's own dark mood. "Welcome home. Looks like you've been out of touch. Guess I have some stories to tell."

# NEW RULES

## EPIC WARLOCKS

Epic warlocks are variations of warlock models with fresh abilities, strengths, and weaknesses. Epic warlocks are not more powerful versions of the original warlocks but instead reflect character growth and changes set about in major story arcs. Epic warlocks do not replace the original warlocks; rather, they offer players the opportunity to play whichever version they prefer. These characters have adapted to the demands of war by adopting new tactics, weapons, and spells as necessary.

Because all versions of a warlock represent the same character, a horde or team may include only one version of a warlock. Just as a player cannot field two Alten Ashley, Monster Hunter models in the same horde, he cannot field both Master Tormentor Morghoul and Lord Assassin Morghoul at the same time.

To reflect the nature of epic warlocks and their interaction with their hordes as well as to preserve game balance, an epic warlock cannot be included in games with an army point limit smaller than 750 points. Only one more epic warlock can be added to the army for each additional increment of 750 points.

## EPIC WARLOCK WARBEAST BONDS

Some epic warlocks have the Warbeast Bond ability representing an exceptionally powerful connection between the warlock and a warbeast. This ability allows the epic warlock to start a game bonded to a warbeast. These bonds follow the rules given in Warbeast Bonds (see *HORDES: Evolution*, pp. 18–19) except as noted here. Do not roll on the bond effect tables for these bonds. Their effects are described in the epic warlock's special rules.

The epic warlock's controller must designate which warbeast is bonded to the warlock before each battle in which he is used. The warlock does not need to bond with the same warbeast from battle to battle. These bonds are in addition to any other bonds the warlock has formed during play. A warbeast can be bonded only once, however. If an epic warlock's Warbeast Bond ability is applied to a warbeast that is already bonded to a warlock, including himself, the previous bond is broken and its effects are lost. After the battle, do not make a bonding check for a warbeast affected by the Warbeast Bond ability: it is already bonded to the warlock.

## DRAGOONS

Dragoons are cavalry models that begin the game mounted but may become dismounted during play. For some dragoons the ability to be dismounted is optional. Adding this ability to the dragoon increases its point cost and total damage capacity.

While mounted, a dragoon is subject to all cavalry rules (see *HORDES: Evolution*, pp. 16–17). Once the dragoon has become dismounted, it is no longer a cavalry model and loses all cavalry abilities. Additionally, the dragoon loses all mounted dragoon abilities and may no longer use its mount and that mount's abilities. Some dragoons have stats with two different base values. Use the first value while the dragoon is mounted and the second once the dragoon has become dismounted.

When a mounted dragoon suffers damage, apply the damage to its mounted dragoon damage boxes. When all of these damage boxes have been marked, the dragoon is destroyed if it does not have the ability to become dismounted. If the dragoon does have this ability, it becomes dismounted instead of being destroyed. Damage points in excess of the mounted dragoon's wounds are lost. If this occurs during the dragoon's activation, its activation ends immediately. Remove the mounted dragoon model from the table and replace it with the dismounted dragoon model. Effects, spells, and animi on the mounted dragoon are applied to the dismounted dragoon. Apply any further damage suffered by the dragoon to its dismounted dragoon damage boxes. The model is destroyed when all its dismounted dragoon damage boxes have been marked.

## UNIQUE WARBEASTS

Unique warbeasts are character warbeasts representing the pinnacle of evolution. Due to their unusual or unpredictable nature, unique warbeasts cannot bond (see *HORDES: Evolution*, pp. 18–19).

## MODEL REFERENCES

Unless specified otherwise, when a model's rules reference another model by name, the model referenced is assumed to be a friendly model. For example, Laris has the Mystic Bond rule that allows Kaya the Moonhunter to draw her spells' ranges from Laris instead of herself. Only the Kaya model controlled by Laris' controller can draw her spells' ranges from Laris. An enemy Kaya model cannot draw her spells' ranges from Laris.

## AFFINITIES

Affinities are special abilities granted to some unique warbeasts when they are included in a horde with a specific warlock. The warbeast gains the affinity if it is included with any version of the warlock listed in the name of the affinity. A unique warbeast with an affinity may bond to the warlock listed in the name of the affinity.

## COHORTS

Some models grant abilities to other models of a certain type in the same army. Models that gain abilities from a Cohort rule retain them even after the model that granted these abilities is destroyed or removed from play.

# ATROCITY REPAID IN KIND

The rendezvous took place at a small abandoned farmstead just outside the patrol perimeter of Crael Valley. It was a half-collapsed building abandoned early in the trollkin seizure of the region and later damaged by mercenaries during one of the initial attempts by the Cygnarans to reclaim the area. Its location was too exposed to be useful, well outside the defensible valley. The small fields it served had long become overgrown and gone to seed.

Half a dozen trollkin elders waited in the largest intact room, having arrived separately after nightfall. The building was situated so that those within had some privacy while their guards could clearly see any approaching the structure.

"I dislike skulking about like thieves," Elder Martash muttered. He was a withered and slump-shouldered elder, so venerable his chin was thick with toughened skin growths.

"We take a risk coming here," the more slender Elder Kellista agreed. She added, "I believe the messenger was honest, as far as it goes."

The stout Elder Narvor grimaced. "Let them try treachery." He was a heavyset trollkin who boasted a commanding presence even as much of his former muscle had gone to fat. "I was a champion, in my youth—"

A signal knock on the outside wall silenced them. They heard a horse's approaching hooves followed by the creaking of saddle leather as someone dismounted. The muffled murmur of the guard questioning the rider was followed by a human stepping into the room, lit by the orange light of his torch. He was unarmed.

He looked like any other mud-spattered traveler, with simple breeches and a tunic. His hooded cloak was ragged at the fringes and patched throughout. The trollkin elders had seen enough humans to recognize this one was past his prime, his hair streaked with gray and the skin of his rugged face pallid and thin. His eyes were unwavering and his voice was firm. "Greetings, honored elders." He spoke in their dialect.

"We speak your tongue," Elder Martash snapped. "Do not try to impress us. Speak plainly."

The Cygnaran smiled thinly. "Yes, I will endeavor to do so. I wanted to express my appreciation for granting my unusual request."

Elder Narvor asked, "How do we know you are who you claim to be?"

The human opened a satchel at his waist and raised a thick folded parchment gleaming with gold seals and florid script. "These carry the sigils of Duke Mayhew Dergeral, Lord Mayor of Ceryl, proclaiming I speak in his stead." He offered a slight bow. "Major Liam Boylan at your service."

"Those papers could mean anything," retorted Martash. "We are far from Ceryl."

A trollkin standing apart in the shadows stepped forward. This was Elder Namorg of the Gnarls, delegated speaker for his people. "I have seen this man before. His claim is genuine."

"We are past the time for establishing identities," Major Boylan insisted. "The matter at hand is nothing less than ensuring the survival of your community. This is your last and best hope to avoid annihilation. I sincerely hope you seize it."

"Bold words," Elder Narvor sneered. "All attempts to uproot us have failed."

The agent's eyes were moist with feigned empathy as he spoke. "You have fought bravely against Duke Ebonhart, for which I offer congratulations. But he fought with his household guard and whatever mercenaries he could afford, nothing more. He never had the support of his entire garrison, let alone an entire division or army." He shook his head as if in worry and his brow furrowed. "Cygnar's 4th Army intends to deal with you. They are well trained and equipped—and over thirty thousand strong. Even Cygnar's least army is too much for you."

Martash scowled. "Why would the 4th Army concern itself with us? What threat are we to Ceryl?"

"The 4th Army no longer sits idle at the Ordic border. It is on the move and eager to prove itself. The war has not gone well for Cygnar, as you know. The 4th Army marches east to support the garrisons in this region. What better way to curry favor than to solve the trollkin menace? To return these farms to Cygnarans? The 4th is prepared to tackle tasks other armies prefer to ignore."

Major Boylan let that thought sink in before speaking again. "King Leto ordered restraint, and that stayed the hand of certain parties. Until now. The attack on the Cygnaran rail line, particularly that atrocity with the army hospital car . . ." He shook his head. "That is not something even the king can ignore. The king's boyhood friendship with your war chief no longer matters."

"We were not behind those attacks," Elder Kellista insisted. "You know who is responsible for that."

"Yes. So we come to the core of the matter. We are not interested in slaughtering your people. Any glory earned in such a battle would be tainted by the screams of the young and the innocent. No, it would be better for all if we resolved this matter with a single arrest. The 4th Army can still claim credit for settling the uprisings, but by more humane means."

"In exchange for peace, we must give you Doomshaper." Elder Narvor spoke the words with frank directness. The others looked away in uncomfortable silence.

"You need not play a part directly. All we need is a time and a place. We will handle the details."

"If we do this, Crael Valley will be left in peace?" Elder Kellista asked.

"Not just Crael Valley. The 4th Army has been evaluating the costs of putting down the Gnarls uprisings as well. They have the strength to threaten both regions should they see the need." He looked to Elder Namorg, still standing apart from the rest as representative of the Gnarls kriels.

The elders looked among themselves again and nodded one by one. The eldest, Martash, sighed and spoke last. "Very well. Let us be done with this."

On a steeply winding trail deep within the southern Dragonspine Mountains, Hoarluk Doomshaper paused in reflection. Ahead, in a sequestered natural cavern, rested an ancient runed pillar sacred to Dhunia. He had long kept a tradition of visiting this site when he was nearby, but its proximity to the settlement in Crael Valley had made it possible for him to go more regularly. He looked forward to resuming his ongoing discussion with the shrine's keeper, an old trollkin he had known for decades.

> There was no time to consider the murder. From the deeper darkness of the cave perimeter came flashes of gunfire, and Hoarluk staggered as more bullets tore his flesh.

As was his habit, he had left his escort behind to make the hike to the cave alone. Exercise and solitude focused his thoughts. The difficult pilgrimage took a toll, but he welcomed the opportunity to remind his flesh he was still its master. After spending so long in the wilds living and fighting alongside the dire trolls, though, this trek no longer fazed him. He felt new strength and vitality surging through his veins.

It was as though that last and most arduous rite conducted in the Wyrmwall three months earlier had shed decades from his body. One moment from that ritual stood out clearly in his mind: standing before Mulg the Ancient and severing his own right hand. He shuddered. It had been one of the most difficult tasks he had ever undertaken; he had bitten through his lip to avoid screaming. He had trusted in the refinement of his blood and had been rewarded with the miracle of his hand regenerating before his eyes. Hoarluk clenched his fist and looked in wonder at the new fingers. The unprecedented speed of their growth was proof that his blood was now pure. He had forged an inseparable bond to the full trolls. He felt their absence keenly now.

A sudden smell brought Hoarluk out of his thoughts and to heightened alertness. A rank odor like sweat mixed with decaying flesh drifted from the cave ahead, where the air should have been pure. Hoarluk scowled and gripped Gnarlroot, feeling a premonition of dread just before the explosive report of a rifle echoed in the air.

It was as though an unseen hammer slammed him against the rock outcropping near the cave's mouth. He could feel blood pouring from his chest onto the stone behind him. His breathing turned to fire as more blood frothed from his lips, and he realized the bullet had torn through a lung. He saw only a brief glint in the sloping cliff's face opposite the cave mouth, too far for him to repay the sniper with a proper curse. With hate kindling in his breast, he stumbled toward the relative shelter of the cave.

Almost immediately his breathing began to ease as his wound repaired itself, but Hoarluk barely registered it. The great runed pillar of Dhunia rose ahead of him in the chamber's only pool of light. At its base slumped a body—the shaman he had debated these many years. The smell suggested he was several days dead.

There was no time to consider the murder. From the deeper darkness of the cave perimeter came flashes of gunfire, and Hoarluk staggered as more bullets tore his flesh. One hit high on his leg, one buried itself in his stomach, and a third struck his shoulder. He fell to his knees, but even as pain filled him he could feel his flesh mending.

Human voices spoke into the clamor as Hoarluk began to rise, leaning on his staff. "Careful! Don't kill him! We need him alive."

"He can take it," insisted a rougher voice from the other side. "Keep firing."

"Damn you all!" Hoarluk shouted, pointing Gnarlroot toward the nearest of the men. He could barely see the gleam of bronze that suggested a Trencher helmet. He watched with satisfaction as the man fell writhing to the floor, muscles locked in a painful rictus that would cause him some torment before death brought relief. Ignoring the fresh injury to his leg, Hoarluk charged forward to crash his staff against the head of the next man. Both helmet and skull burst like overripe fruit, and the body toppled. More bullets tore into him. Why had he come here with no troll brothers at his side? It would not happen again, if he survived this.

"Watch your fire!" the earlier voice yelled. There were more than trenchers here, and men in heavier armor advanced on him. Hoarluk fell onto his back and watched as a hulking knight in silver plate stepped up to him and raised a massive Caspian battle blade. "Surrender or die!"

Hoarluk coughed blood as he raised a single finger to point at the knight. "Suffer . . ." As he spoke he sent power surging to seize the man, whose tendons erupted with fire. Howling in pain and fury, the knight brought the weighty blade down. Hoarluk lifted Gnarlroot to intercept and heard the sharp crack of his staff shattering before the blade bit his chest.

"They believe they acted as you wished, hard as that may be for you to accept. They probably thought you would be happy at this arrangement." Kargess said the words so plainly it enraged Madrak all the more.

TROLLBLOODS

She had come to him at his temporary battle camp, a place he had adopted to regroup between battles that was close enough to Crael Valley to allow the warriors to see their kin. Madrak himself had been avoiding entering the main hold where his kin had settled, a form of self-imposed exile that had strained relations with his mate even as she respected his pain. She had ignored his warnings to stay away in order to bring him this news. Horthol accompanied her, his face reflecting a similar pain at Madrak's orders to stay away from his chieftain and blood brother.

"They thought I would *approve*?" Madrak shouted the question in disbelief.

Kargess had hoped the small feast she had arranged for the warriors would ease the news. As the kriel women who had helped lay out the food flinched at Madrak's rage, she considered that perhaps she should have waited until the meal was finished before broaching the subject. Borka was the only of the nearby warriors still eating, pointedly pretending to ignore the raised voices.

Madrak smashed his fist through the nearest of the improvised tables, sending platters of meat flying. Borka grunted a protest and scrambled to salvage what food he could. Madrak whirled on his mate with his eyes ablaze, but she faced him calmly. "They betray their blood and expect me to thank them? Who are they, Kargess? Tell me so I may show them justice." From the next table Horthol looked between them but clearly did not feel it was his place to intervene.

Kargess replied, "I do not know who they are. I have only suspicions, no proof. They have been tight-lipped and protect one another. I do not believe the entire council conspired, but those who did were not alone. Gnarls elders surely attended. Doomshaper has many enemies."

"Tell me who spoke to you, then. I will find out the rest myself." His fists clenched.

"Do you think I'm going to set you to throttle anyone brave enough to approach me? No, I don't think so. I will not let you stomp around in a rage and stir everyone to panic. They are scared of you enough as it is." She folded her arms and matched his glare.

The last sentence had an impact. Madrak's fists unclenched and his voice was lower when he spoke again. "Do you understand it was Doomshaper who saved me when I was betrayed?" He began to pace. "Without Doomshaper I would be dead. This is how we repay his courage? His sacrifice for the gathered kriels?"

Horthol spoke up. "There are many who say he tried to usurp your authority when you were gone north." He paused, shaking his head gravely. "You did not hear his speeches. He put us all in danger."

Kargess nodded. "This is true. Doomshaper has done much to undermine your cause. He stirs up the youth. He pushes them to violence and imperils all we have worked to gain. He took the dragon's tail, attacking Cygnaran trains."

"So you agree with them? You would hand him to our enemies so quickly?"

Kargess set her hands to her hips in indignation. "Do not insult me by lumping me with those fools! They acted from fear. Fear for us. What they did was wrong, but they hoped to buy safety."

"Buy safety with the coin of betrayal? Damn their reasons! Give me names. Do not stand in the way of my vengeance."

"I will not stand in your way." Turning, she marched out. The trollkin women followed, casting fearful glances back at Madrak. Borka stared after them with a mournful expression. Horthol looked between them and Madrak, clearly torn. Ironhide waved for him to leave, to return to his duties guarding Crael Valley.

Madrak stared after them for a while before turning to face Borka. The larger trollkin lifted his thick chin. "If it would make you feel better, you can punch me in the face. Go ahead. Don't hold back. Pretend I am your mate."

This slightly broke Ironhide's foul mood. He shook his head and sighed. "I can't seem to control my temper. I no longer belong here. The visions still plague me. I look at our peaceful settlement and see flames rising, bodies everywhere. Then I hear screams. I know these things are not real, but I cannot ignore them." His fists clenched. After a moment he lifted his head, and the light of resolve was in his eyes. "Come. There is work to do."

The thick wrapping of burlap on Doomshaper's cage kept him in darkness, making it difficult to gauge the passage of time. Only the thirst in his throat and the regular stops told him three days passed before they dared approach him. When they did, he was ready. He took the water they thrust at him and drank it greedily, then seized the hand passing him bread. A single surge of power and that man died screaming and twitching on the ground. The cage's covering fell aside long enough for him to inflict further agonies on two soldiers before they surrounded his cage, jabbing poles through the bars with all their strength. He laughed at the naked fear he saw on their ugly monkey faces. He was still laughing even as his bones shattered.

The group made slow progress, and the beatings continued regularly. Even so, he did everything in his power to make the trip unforgettable. When they broke his fingers to stop his curses, he cackled at their horror as his hands healed in front of them. At night, he described at length the plagues that would consume their families, sparing no detail of their suffering and his own anticipation. Periodically someone would lose patience and beat him to silence, but he recovered rapidly. He also weathered sleep deprivation better than they could.

He often heard them praying to their gods, calling him an unholy creature. The terror in their voices strengthened him. Days later he heard them pulling lots to determine who would feed him again. For a time it seemed likely there would be mutiny. They did not want to keep him alive. Only the strong voice of their commanding officer insisted they would see their mission through—but they decided food was an unnecessary luxury for their captive.

Seeing their haggard faces when they arrived at their destination brought Hoarluk some small satisfaction. It took a moment to recognize the stout stone fort where he had been brought, very near the Gnarls. He was too weak from hunger to invoke curses, but he broke one of his captor's arms as they dragged him to an underground dungeon lined with cold stones. It was dark and damp, and its solid door afforded no view. His world became absolute darkness except for a brief gleam of light from the feeding slot when they pushed something unpleasant inside. He was famished and always ate what they offered, however rancid.

Hoarluk knew they could never break him. They were weak. But he also knew that his life neared its end. A public execution was only a matter of time. In the meanwhile he pondered his capture. It was no great leap in logic to see betrayal. But by whom? Had Ironhide been involved? His own escorts? His anger simmered but lacked specific targets other than the men resting comfortably above his prison.

In the darkness he began to cast his spirit outward. He could feel those of his blood connected through the living tide surging through their veins. He put forth a call with every thought. Eventually in the dark of his mind he sensed a piece of a mountain stand and begin to walk. Above, his guards heard a hard and bitter sound that left them unsettled and afraid. Doomshaper was laughing.

Madrak Ironhide called an emergency war council, ignoring those whom the kriels had declared the elders of their people. His refusal of their wisdom was deliberate, and he knew it would send a message. Madrak had few friends now among the residents of Crael Valley. They had heard rumors of grim battles, and they said madness latched onto Chief Ironhide. He invited only those he could trust to ignore this gossip.

## "Right now, I bring only fear. Until I deal with this, I am a burden on those I vowed to protect."

Grim Angus brought rough maps of what he had seen scouting abroad. "The elders had cause to be afraid. The 4th Army is not an empty bluff. They are gradually deploying men farther east to reinforce garrisons." He traced the movements with a finger. "The initial regiments are north of us, attached to Stonebridge. Several other battalions marched to Point Bourne. More soldiers are coming every day along the Gnarlwood Trail."

"Saves us the travel," Borka laughed. He was the only one who took the news with good cheer.

"Any sign of preparing to make a move on us here?" Grissel Bloodsong asked, leaning forward to scrutinize the maps. The fell caller had led many Ternon Crag and Hawksmire River refugees to the region in recent weeks and had demonstrated a strong protectiveness of them.

"No," Grim admitted, "but it would be easy to initiate such operations. The 4th Army is notorious for 'training missions' in the Gnarls." His lip curled at the term. "The forces at Stonebridge could easily attack Crael Valley without warning. The soldiers at Point Bourne can get here or to the Gnarls just as quickly; it is more or less the same distance."

"What of Hoarluk? Did you find him?" Madrak asked.

"My pygs picked up a cold trail but are reasonably confident he is here." Grim pointed to the eastern edge of the Gnarls. "There is an old stone keep at the north end of the Gnarlwood Trail manned by the 4th Army. Their commander enjoys leading his soldiers against the nearest Gnarls kriels. A good place to make an example of Doomshaper, if that is their aim."

Madrak pulled Grissel aside to speak to her in low tones while the others discussed the situation. "Borka and I will find Doomshaper. If we free him, expect retaliations here. You will be in charge in my absence."

"Rescue operations are a specialty of mine," Grissel offered.

"I need you here." His smile showed pain. "You inspire our people. Right now, I bring only fear. Until I deal with this, I am a burden on those I vowed to protect. I have spoken with Horthol. He and his Long Riders will obey you. I will also send word to Calandra to see if she can help." He ignored the face Grissel made at that name.

She asked, "What will you do after you find Doomshaper? Will you return?"

"Not immediately. Borka and I will go to help the trollkin of the Gnarls. We will give the 4th Army reasons to be elsewhere. If they attack here, remember this place is not our home. Do not die to preserve it. Seek us in the Gnarls if you must fall back." Grissel nodded. He clasped forearms with her, one warrior to another. "See to Kargess. Keep her safe."

Madrak said no more to the rest but simply took his leave. Borka soon hefted his great mace jauntily onto his shoulder and followed. He bellowed to a ragged assortment of northern berserkers and hardened warriors, each eager for blood, who fell in behind him. Watching them, Grissel sensed Madrak walked a dark path.

Mulg the Ancient slept heavily after devouring several wild boars, but the call reached into the inky depths of dream to shatter his calm. He arose with a startled roar, shaking the earth as he pushed himself erect. The stones on his back brushed against a nearby tree, shattering it in an eruption of splinters and bark as he whirled to find the source of his alarm. The mountain had gone quiet, without even a bird stirring. Above him stars glittered like tiny eyes. Mulg scowled into the darkness. A keening reached straight into his mind and grated like metal on stone.

TROLLBLOODS

He howled and smashed the earth with a fist, leaving a massive imprint of gnarled knuckles. Something pulled at him, calling him west. He could almost hear the voice of the little brother, of Krol. Krol was calling from far away. A sudden pain made Mulg sway. He felt something twisting in his stomach, like a fist squeezing his intestines. He groaned and put a hand to his belly, remembering when Krol had cut off his own little hand. Was it there inside? He didn't think he had eaten it. He shook his head and tried to remember what the little brother had told him, but the clever small ones spoke too fast and used too many words. 'One flesh,' he remembered. They were one flesh. Krol needed him. His brother was in pain.

A fresh hunger filled him despite his recent feast. Mulg snatched up the runed club resting against a trunk and walked in the direction of the pull, feeling anger and urgency and hunger together. He would hunt as he went to find Krol, and he would eat whatever was in the way. He would eat them all, maybe saving a few bites for the little brother if he could. The runes of his club gleamed green in affirmation and Mulg showed his massive teeth, feeling an itch from the stone on his back as it too filled with power. Excitement stirred in him. It was time for battle, for killing and the feast that would surely follow.

He bellowed to the star-filled sky, and every creature on the mountain cowered in abject fear.

Hoarluk lost track of time between day and night. He measured his reality by the periodic interval of food passed into his cell. During one fitful sleep he dreamed of his beating heart. He was inside its muscled chamber, watching the flow of his blood. He heard each spasm of the muscle like the beating of a war drum. *Boom!* It was deafening. He did not think his heart was large enough to make this explosive sound. *Boom!* He jerked suddenly awake and realized the sound did not come from his dream. Cannons?

His entire cell shook as if from an earthquake. Hoarluk felt a stirring of excitement and touched the nearest wall, feeling its stones with calloused fingertips. There was something else, something intimately familiar to him but gone so long that he could not immediately recognize it. Trolls! He could feel them at the fringes of his awareness. Dire trolls, some number of them, and something greater . . . an ancient of singular power. Even insulated in his sealed dungeon he heard distant screams.

Hoarluk sent his mind to look through the eyes of an earthborn as it shattered a low defensive wall and leapt to meet the defenders on the battlements. He saw a mauler nearly torn apart by the impact of a cannonball fall back to bleed in a murky ditch. He impelled it to mend its wounds. It rose to battle again, lurching into the Cygnaran soldiers manning the cannon and seizing several to hurl into its mouth. There at the center was Mulg the Ancient, whose great club smashed down repeatedly on an old Ironclad at the main gate. The next arc of the weapon swept men aside

like ants. Doomshaper delighted in the trolls' battle frenzy, drawing on their rage.

The ceiling of his underground cell suddenly shuddered with a single great blow, sending stone tumbling down. A great piece shattered his shoulder and momentarily buried him, but Doomshaper did not care. He could feel his bones already knitting. He borrowed strength from the nearest mauler and easily tossed the stone aside. He stood up to see Mulg peering down. In moments the ancient pulled him up to stand among those who had answered his call.

The trolls chased desperate soldiers and smashed them to bloody paste. They absorbed gunfire like the stinging of mosquitoes. Doomshaper put aside all rational thought and merged his mind with theirs, pushing them on to tear the enemy apart with enthusiasm. The fortress tumbled to ruin around them amid the screams of the dying.

Madrak Ironhide, Borka Kegslayer, and the many trolls and trollkin following them soon arrived at the ruins of what had been the Cygnaran fort. The keep itself was almost toppled, and even the ground looked torn apart by some tremendous force. The smell of death was present but not as strong as one might expect from the obvious signs of slaughter. There were few recognizable corpses, only shattered bones and blood-soaked clothes. The pygs immediately set to scavenging for leftover blasting powder and anything else useful.

Borka had leapt ahead of the rest, enjoying the signs of destruction. He called to Madrak from the center of the keep's shattered outer wall, "Look here! Doomshaper did not need our help."

Several paths of destruction converged on a single gaping hole in the ground. It was the demolished ceiling of some form of dungeon, a reeking pit that attested to the suffering inflicted on whoever had languished there. Madrak gazed toward the broken trees at the edge of the forest and the clear tracks of dire trolls. "No, Borka," he said grimly. "I think he needs us now more than ever."

TROLLBLOODS

# MADRAK IRONHIDE, WORLD ENDER
## TROLLBLOOD TROLLKIN EPIC WARLOCK CHARACTER

*That axe is fated to sunder Caen and drown us all in an ocean of blood.*

—Scarsfell Shaman Krasmar Jaggedscar

| SPELL | COST | RNG | AOE | POW | UP | OFF |
|-------|------|-----|-----|-----|----|----|
| KILLING GROUND | 2 | SELF | CTRL | | - | |

Friendly Trollblood models currently in Ironhide's control area may charge and slam across rough terrain and obstacles without penalty. Affected warbeasts may charge or slam enemy models without being forced. Killing Ground lasts for one turn.

| SPELL | COST | RNG | AOE | POW | UP | OFF |
|-------|------|-----|-----|-----|----|----|
| STONE FALL | 3 | 8 | 4 | 13 | | X |

On a critical hit, models in the AOE suffer Concussion. A model suffering Concussion forfeits its next activation and cannot allocate focus for one round.

| SPELL | COST | RNG | AOE | POW | UP | OFF |
|-------|------|-----|-----|-----|----|----|
| WARPATH | 2 | SELF | CTRL | | - | X |

While in Ironhide's control area, when a friendly Trollblood model destroys one or more enemy models with a melee or ranged attack during its activation, immediately after the attack has been resolved, one friendly Trollblood warbeast in Ironhide's control area may move up to 3". A model may only move once per turn as a result of Warpath.

When Madrak Ironhide first took up the ancient axe Rathrok in defense of the united kriels, he knew he had chosen a grim path. He accepted the cursed weapon rather than standing idly by as enemies destroyed his people. Now he fears the worst misgivings of the superstitious elders may be rooted in truth. He has not given up hope, but tragedy surrounds him like a constant wind.

For a time, concerns over the fate of his dislocated people occupied all of Madrak's attention, and their eventual disposition remains a burden on his shoulders. In recent months, however, it has been eclipsed by difficulties of a more personal and ominous nature. As Madrak fought and killed with Rathrok, something deep within that weapon awoke. Mastering his own fate may now be more difficult than he ever imagined.

Foul weather seems to follow Madrak, as rainstorms become torrents. The great chief suffers visions of things he knows not to be real. Walking past a summer meadow, he sees instead an ancient battlefield strewn with corpses and the tattered banners of forgotten nations and tribes. Everywhere the marks of war appear to him, and his blood surges with a peculiar longing for strife.

In the heat of combat Madrak's growing power has brought him victory after victory, and yet between those bloody disputes he finds no peace or calm. He can take delight neither in the arms of his mate nor in the sight of young trollkin. Everywhere he looks he sees the signs of future and past conflict, and he feels the tug of some ancient primordial call. The warriors gathering around him are different than they were in months past: darker of mien, fiercer in temperament, and more eager to kill and throw their lives away for his cause. Old friends who once trusted him with their lives look at him with fear and uncertainty.

Since these strange events began, Madrak has tried to rid himself of the axe. He knows now he cannot simply put it aside. Countless times he has left it locked away behind him, only for it to arrive in his hand when battle comes. He has taken the axe to the best smiths of his people and asked them to destroy it, but they cannot even mar its leather bindings. It will not let him go. He senses it has tasks to perform and even death may not free him from its grasp.

His followers still shout his name and praise his strength and wisdom, but others spread warnings. Many kriels are afraid of the storms lingering where Madrak passes. It is Madrak—not his axe—they now call the "World Ender."

## SPECIAL RULES

### Feat: Desperate Hour

*Madrak Ironhide has led his people through innumerable seemingly hopeless battles and persisted even in the face of impossible odds. As Madrak rallies his warriors, Rathrok's power lets them tap into reserves they did not even know they had. When all hope seems lost, Madrak and his followers use this strength to expend themselves in one last desperate attack, giving their all to decimate the enemy.*

Friendly Trollblood models currently in Ironhide's control area may immediately make one normal melee attack against each enemy model in melee range or one normal ranged attack, regardless of a weapon's ROF. Affected models cannot make combined attacks when resolving attacks gained from this feat.

### Ironhide

**Elite Cadre** - Kriel Warriors included in an army with Ironhide gain +1 MAT, RAT, and CMD and Kriel Warrior Hand Weapons gain Knock Back. Enemy models hit by a melee weapon with Knock Back may be pushed 1" directly away from the attacking model immediately after resolving the damage roll. The attacking model may then move up to 1".

**Rathrok's Awakening** - Ironhide gains a blood token each time he destroys a living enemy model with a melee or ranged attack. Ironhide can have up to three blood tokens at any time. During his activation, Ironhide may spend a blood token to move up to 1", make an additional attack, boost an attack roll, or boost a damage roll.

**Tough** - When Ironhide suffers sufficient damage to be destroyed, his controller rolls a d6. On a 5 or 6, Ironhide is knocked down instead of being destroyed. If Ironhide is not destroyed, he is reduced to one wound.

### Thrown Axe

**Critical Fatality** - On a critical hit, the warlock hit cannot transfer damage suffered from the attack.

**Ricochet** - After directly hitting a target with a Thrown Axe attack, Ironhide may immediately make one additional Thrown Axe ranged attack targeting another model in Ironhide's LOS and within 4" of the original target. The point of origin of this additional attack is the model hit by the original attack, but Madrak is still the attacker. Attacks gained from this ability cannot generate further additional attacks from this ability.

**Thrown** - Add Ironhide's current STR to the POW of his Thrown Axe attacks.

**Wraith Bane** - This attack may damage models only affected by magic attacks. Ironhide may charge incorporeal models.

### Rathrok

**Critical Fatality** - On a critical hit, the warlock hit cannot transfer damage suffered from the attack.

**Grim Salvation** - When Ironhide is damaged by an enemy melee or ranged attack, instead of suffering the damage and effects triggered by taking damage from the attack, remove one friendly Trollkin warrior model within 1" of Ironhide from play.

**Wraith Bane** - This attack may damage models only affected by magic attacks. Ironhide may charge incorporeal models.

| MADRAK | | | | | CMD 9 |
|--------|--|--|--|--|-------|
| SPD | STR | MAT | RAT | DEF | ARM |
| 6 | 8 | 8 | 6 | 14 | 17 |

| THROWN AXE | | | |
|-----|-----|-----|-----|
| RNG | ROF | AOE | POW |
| 8 | 1 | — | 7 |

| RATHROK | | |
|---------|--|--|
| SPECIAL | POW | P+S |
| Multi | 7 | 15 |

| | |
|---|---|
| FURY | 5 |
| DAMAGE | 18 |
| FIELD ALLOWANCE | C |
| VICTORY POINTS | 5 |
| POINT COST | 74 |
| BASE SIZE | MEDIUM |

# HOARLUK DOOMSHAPER, RAGE OF DHUNIA
## TROLLBLOOD TROLLKIN EPIC WARLOCK CHARACTER

*They sought to put me in a cage like an animal, to judge me by human law.*
*Let the rage of Dhunia fall upon them!*

—Hoarluk Doomshaper

Hoarluk Doomshaper spent a century gathering strength and delving into the deepest mysteries of the Trollblood's essence. His power is so great it has shaken the communities of the Gnarls and the Thornwood to their roots, earning the fear and reluctant respect of countless elders. In many circles trollkin talk about him as a force of nature—implacable and incomprehensible, yet impossible to ignore. He is a creature they must appease and placate rather than persuade. Those who fear him once thought he had reached the peak of his power and that a shaman of his age could learn no more. They will soon discover the scope of their error.

Even as many hot-blooded trollkin flocked to Hoarluk Doomshaper to hear his violent rhetoric and fight at his side, he has remained focused on a deeper goal. It has never been enough for Doomshaper to be a simple war shaman or to lead his people in battle. He seeks the fundamental connection between all trolls, the power invested by Dhunia in their blood. After

| SPELL | COST | RNG | AOE | POW | UP | OFF |
|-------|------|-----|-----|-----|----|----|
| AGITATION | 3 | SELF | CTRL | - | | |

Doomshaper's controller places one fury point on each enemy warbeast currently in Doomshaper's control area.

| SPELL | COST | RNG | AOE | POW | UP | OFF |
|-------|------|-----|-----|-----|----|----|
| MAYHEM | 3 | SELF | CTRL | - | | |

Friendly Trollblood warbeasts currently in Doomshaper's control area may charge, slam, or trample without being forced this turn. Affected models charge, slam, and trample at SPD +5".

| SPELL | COST | RNG | AOE | POW | UP | OFF |
|-------|------|-----|-----|-----|----|----|
| MOB MENTALITY | 2 | 10 | - | - | | X |

When target enemy model is hit, one friendly Trollblood model/unit in Doomshaper's control area may move up to 2". Affected models cannot end this movement farther from the enemy model than they began and cannot end this movement out of formation or cause other models in the unit to no longer be in formation.

| SPELL | COST | RNG | AOE | POW | UP | OFF |
|-------|------|-----|-----|-----|----|----|
| PRIMAL SHOCK | 2 | 8 | - | * | | X |

Select a friendly Trollblood warbeast in Doomshaper's control area. Target a model within 8" of the selected warbeast and make a magic attack against it. This attack does not suffer the target in melee attack roll penalty when the selected model is in melee with the target. Doomshaper is still the attacker, but use the warbeast to determine the LOS of the attack and the spell's point of origin. A model hit by the attack suffers a damage roll with a POW equal to the warbeast's base STR.

| SPELL | COST | RNG | AOE | POW | UP | OFF |
|-------|------|-----|-----|-----|----|----|
| SUNDER SPIRIT | 2 | 10 | - | 12 | | X |

Target enemy warbeast damaged by Sunder Spirit loses its animus for one round. Doomshaper can cast that warbeast's animus as a spell this turn. Replace specific faction references with Trollbloods.

learning all he could from scrolls rubbed from ancient krielstones and venturing into every significant Molgur ruin, Doomshaper decided to take a more direct approach.

Accordingly he plunged himself into the depths of dire troll consciousness, unshackling his mind and freeing himself of all restraint to merge with the most violent and powerful of these creatures. He has run as one of them, lived as they do, and been accepted almost as their god. This has allowed him to tap into reserves no shaman has ever known, and his power has grown accordingly. Doomshaper proved it to himself in a ritual witnessed by the most ancient of dire trolls. At the height of the ceremony, he cut off his own hand and then regenerated it—accomplishing in seconds what would have taken months for another trollkin.

Not only has he unlocked unprecedented regenerative powers, but he has also gained insight into the primal nature that binds warbeast to warlock. This has given him unprecedented influence over his enemies, going beyond the blood of trolls to steal the essence of other beasts and employ their powers for his own use. His newfound mastery of natural lore now rivals even the druids of the Circle Orboros.

Indeed, so focused was Hoarluk on attaining these powers that he did not anticipate the treachery that nearly unraveled his efforts. A conspiracy within the Gnarls sought to sell him out in order to cement a truce with Cygnaran authorities. Doomshaper's subsequent capture and imprisonment have unleashed the full fury of this ancient shaman. No prison can hold him, not when the dire trolls of the wild can hear his call from miles away. When he regains his freedom, there will be nothing to mitigate Doomshaper's wrath. Those who feared him before cannot imagine what lies ahead of them now.

## SPECIAL RULES

### Feat: Scroll of Grimmr

| DOOMSHAPER | | | | | CMD 7 |
|-----|-----|-----|-----|-----|-----|
| SPD | STR | MAT | RAT | DEF | ARM |
| 5 | 6 | 5 | 4 | 13 | 14 |

| WILLBREAKER | | | |
|-----|-----|-----|-----|
| | SPECIAL | POW | P+S |
| Multi | | 7 | 13 |

| FURY | 7 |
|------|---|
| DAMAGE | 16 |
| FIELD ALLOWANCE | C |
| VICTORY POINTS | 5 |
| POINT COST | 67 |
| BASE SIZE | MEDIUM |

*Hoarluk Doomshaper's obsessive investigations into the roots of his people have led him to unearth forgotten works of spiritual power. Doomshaper wields the Scroll of Grimmr, a parchment writ on tanned hide that preserves the epithets of that venerated trollkin hero from the time of the Molgur. Invoked aloud this defiant challenge imbues trolls with a surge of vitality. Eager to kill and glut their appetites, they surge forward in frenzied haste.*

Doomshaper and friendly Trollblood warbeasts currently in his control area double their SPD for this turn.

### Doomshaper

**Calming Effect** - When a friendly Dire Troll in Doomshaper's control area frenzies, it never selects a friendly model to attack.

**Goad** - Immediately after a friendly Dire Troll destroys an enemy model with a melee attack in Doomshaper's control area, Doomshaper may force the warbeast to move up to 2".

**Hyper Regeneration** - At the beginning of his controller's Control Phase, Doomshaper removes d3 damage points.

**Tough** - When Doomshaper suffers sufficient damage to be destroyed, his controller rolls a d6. On a 5 or 6, Doomshaper is knocked down instead of being destroyed. If Doomshaper is not destroyed, he is reduced to one wound.

**Warbeast Bond** - One non-unique Dire Troll in Doomshaper's controller's horde may begin the game bonded to him. While in Doomshaper's control area, this warbeast may make double-hand throw, head-butt, headlock/weapon lock, rend, and throw power attacks as normal melee attacks but cannot make power attacks in place of a charge attack. To make a power attack with this ability, the Dire Troll must be able to make the power attack normally.

### Willbreaker

**Dominator** - When Doomshaper damages an enemy warbeast with a Willbreaker attack, immediately after the attack has been resolved, Doomshaper's controller takes control of the warbeast and turns it to face any direction. The warbeast then charges a model chosen by Doomshaper's controller. Doomshaper loses control of the warbeast after the charge attack is resolved.

**Reach** - 2" melee range.

## TACTICAL TIPS

**Goad** – You are forcing the warbeast to do this, so it gains a fury point.

**Warbeast Bond** – The warbeast may make one of the listed power attacks each time you force it to make an additional attack. Also be aware that if the warbeast has two claws, it can make a two-handed throw for each of its initial attacks.

**Dominator** – Doomshaper cannot force the warbeast.

**Sunder Spirit** – If a warbeast has more than one animus, Doomshaper gains access to all of them, and the warbeast loses all of them.

# CALANDRA TRUTHSAYER, ORACLE OF THE GLIMMERWOOD
## TROLLBLOOD TROLLKIN WARLOCK CHARACTER

*The future is never set, even when carved in stone.*

—Calandra Truthsayer

TROLLBLOODS

| SPELL | COST | RNG | AOE | POW | UP | OFF |
|---|---|---|---|---|---|---|
| BEFUDDLE | 3 | 8 | - | - | X | X |

On a hit, Truthsayer's controller immediately moves target enemy model/unit up to 3". During each of Truthsayer's controller's Control Phases after this spell is upkept, the affected model/unit must make a command check. If the check fails, Truthsayer's controller immediately moves the affected model/unit up to 3". Units must end this movement in formation. Affected models cannot be targeted by free strikes during this movement. A model can move only once per turn as a result of Befuddle.

| | | | | | | |
|---|---|---|---|---|---|---|
| LUCKY DAY | 2 | 6 | - | - | X | |

Target friendly Trollblood model gains Precognitive Awareness.

| | | | | | | |
|---|---|---|---|---|---|---|
| MISFORTUNE | 2 | 10 | - | 11 | | X |

A model damaged by Misfortune is knocked down.

| | | | | | | |
|---|---|---|---|---|---|---|
| SOOTHING SONG | 1 | SELF | CTRL | | - | |

Truthsayer's controller may remove one fury point from each friendly Trollblood warbeast currently in her control area. Fleeing friendly Trollblood models/units currently in her control area immediately rally.

| | | | | | | |
|---|---|---|---|---|---|---|
| STAR CROSSED | 3 | SELF | CTRL | | - | |

While in Truthsayer's control area enemy models roll an additional die on attack rolls. Discard the highest die in each roll. Star Crossed lasts for one round.

Calandra Truthsayer is a revered Dhunian shaman whose protective impulses have endeared her to many disparate tribes. Chiefs and elders alike have learned to trust her guidance and draw strength from her hopeful message. In this time of war she remains a beacon of hope and optimism who can always find an encouraging word to bolster the spirits of her followers. At the same time, battered refugees whom Calandra ministers are sometimes shocked to witness her raw ferocity in battle. Her maternal drive compels her to strike with merciless resolve against any who would harm those she has vowed to protect.

As Oracle of the Glimmerwood, she is more than a simple shaman. She possesses the rare gift of true sight and is able to discern glimmers of possible futures through divination and augury. Calandra is familiar with all forms of prognostication and feels each has its place. She may cast bones or runes, shuffle cards, check the alignment of the stars and moons, watch the flight of scattered sparrows, or gaze at the patterns in a flickering camp fire or the spilled entrails of her foes. All contain glimmers of the essential truth.

By these signs she is determined to guide the trollkin through this time of tragedy and help them find the best of all possible futures. She flatly refutes the grim omens circling both Madrak Ironhide and Hoarluk Doomshaper. She joined the embattled kriels to loan her unique vision and her leadership in battle. Calandra has pulled her allies from the brink of certain defeat often enough that her followers no longer see her as naively optimistic. They have begun to believe, and she draws strength from their faith in her.

Calandra made her name in the Glimmerwood, but she is a wanderer at heart and rarely stays in any one place long. She considers this her one essential failing as a Dhunian shaman even though the communities she visits across western Immoren appreciate her visits. She receives a warm welcome anywhere she journeys, whether it be the frost-bitten kriels of the Scarsfell, the deeply insular communities of the Gnarls, or the scattered environs of trollkin who have adapted to life alongside mankind.

## SPECIAL RULES

### Feat: Good Omens

*Calandra Truthsayer's unique affinity with Dhunia lets her perceive the vagaries of fate and twist their strands to aid the goddess' favored sons and daughters. Her blessing to beleaguered kith and kriel serves as a tangible manifestation of her irrepressible faith and optimism. Warriors who once would have fallen to grievous injuries instead laugh off the killing blows to fight on.*

While in Calandra's control area, friendly Trollblood models cannot be knocked down and are not destroyed on a Tough roll of 3, 4, 5, or 6. Good Omens lasts for one round.

### Truthsayer

**Fate Bound** - When a friendly Trollblood model makes an attack or damage roll while in Truthsayer's control area, Truthsayer may spend a fury point to allow the model to re-roll the roll. Each roll may only be re-rolled once due to Fate Bound.

**Precognitive Awareness** - Truthsayer gains +2 DEF against ranged and magic attacks. Once per turn, any time except during her activation, when an enemy model misses Truthsayer with a ranged or magic attack, Truthsayer may immediately move up to her current SPD in inches. If the attack has an AOE, Truthsayer moves before deviation for the AOE is resolved.

**Prognostication** - Truthsayer's controller gains +1 on the starting roll to determine the first player and turn order.

**Tough** - When Truthsayer suffers sufficient damage to be destroyed, her controller rolls a d6. On a 5 or 6, Truthsayer is knocked down instead of being destroyed. If Truthsayer is not destroyed, she is reduced to one wound.

### Salt

**Finisher** - Truthsayer gains an additional die on damage rolls against damaged models.

**Visions of War** - When Truthsayer destroys an enemy model with Salt, friendly Trollblood models currently in her control area can re-roll missed attack rolls. Each roll may be re-rolled once as a result of Visions of War. Visions of War lasts for one round.

| TRUTHSAYER | | | | CMD 8 | |
|---|---|---|---|---|---|
| SPD | STR | MAT | RAT | DEF | ARM |
| 5 | 6 | 5 | 4 | 14 | 14 |

| SALT | | | |
|---|---|---|---|
| | SPECIAL | POW | P+S |
| | Multi | 4 | 10 |

| FURY | 7 |
|---|---|
| DAMAGE | 16 |
| FIELD ALLOWANCE | C |
| VICTORY POINTS | 5 |
| POINT COST | 63 |
| BASE SIZE | MEDIUM |

The Oracle never travels alone, for the bright spark of her destiny has attracted an odd but dedicated band of followers and bodyguards. Each is drawn to her for different reasons, but their motley backgrounds and personalities do not detract from their fighting prowess, particularly when Calandra shapes the very strands of fate around them. Accidental windfalls and miraculous recoveries are a matter of course when fighting at her side. Her apparent reliance on luck has rubbed some trollkin the wrong way—the more pragmatic Grissel Bloodsong views it as pure folly—but others see her existence as proof that hope has a power of its own.

# MULG THE ANCIENT
## TROLLBLOOD DIRE TROLL UNIQUE HEAVY WARBEAST

*He is as timeless and immovable as the mountain, a walking monument to the strength of our blood.*

—Hoarluk Doomshaper

| ANIMUS | COST | RNG | AOE | POW | UP | OFF |
|---|---|---|---|---|---|---|
| Primal Stupor | 2 | Self | * | - | | |

While within 3" of the model using this animus, enemy warbeasts suffer -2 THR. If an affected warbeast frenzies, it forfeits its activation. Primal Stupor lasts for one round.

Thanks to their regenerative capabilities dire trolls can live for centuries, becoming increasingly dangerous and tenacious. As reputedly the most ancient and ferocious dire troll ever to walk Caen, Mulg embodies that reputation. Indeed, he is old enough to have seen the Orgoth with his own eyes. He has wandered the wilds of the southern mountains like a craggy troll king, accepting the homage of all other trolls who cross his path. Even highly aggressive young dire trolls will meekly back away when Mulg's heavy tread approaches their domain, laying fresh-killed deer or wild boar in his path to assuage his endless hunger.

Mulg had experienced only limited interactions with trollkin before he first descended from his mountain centuries ago to demand tribute. Envious of their sigils of power, he ordered runes to be carved into the stony flesh of his back depicting his many great deeds and ancient history. Mulg can focus his inhuman rage into these runes to stifle the power of enemy beasts before him.

It was Hoarluk Doomshaper who recognized the common threads in the folk tales of scattered Cygnaran kriels. In legends Mulg was described as a tremendous troll, a "walking piece of the mountain." Doomshaper became obsessed with him and made finding Mulg a personal quest he pursued fruitlessly for years. It was not until 603 AR that his relentless efforts bore fruit. Making his way to one of the deepest and most remote areas of the Wyrmwall, the shaman did not realize his passage created a stir among other full-blood trolls who followed to observe Mulg's reception.

A number of trolls gathered near Mulg when Doomshaper finally presented himself. The small and stooped trollkin startled those present by invoking the traditional dire troll greeting ceremony. He put on a display of aggression and invited Mulg to punch him in the chest. Mulg consented and smashed his fist straight into Doomshaper's torso, shattering his upper body and sending him flying across the clearing. Hoarluk lay still as death until he could muster enough power to mend his battered flesh and stand. Though he coughed blood with every breath, he still spoke words of respect to the great troll. No creature had ever survived such a blow, and the ancient was so impressed he named the shaman "Krol." In a primal ceremony they shared their blood, and since that time a special bond has existed between Mulg and Krol, whom Mulg considers a tiny brother.

The precise meaning of "Krol" is disputed, but the most likely translation is "not food." This represents a profound abstract concept to dire trolls, which are inclined to eat almost anything. Mulg imparted so much respect to Hoarluk Doomshaper through this blessing that the shaman gained the obedience of other dire trolls, an unprecedented feat.

Mulg has stayed out of the trollkin wars, content to roam his mountains on the prowl for food. Hunger gnaws at him constantly, even when he has eaten his fill. But in recent

# SPECIAL RULES

## Mulg

**Affinity (Doomshaper): Cantankerous** - At the end of Mulg's combat action while in Doomshaper's control area, if the last model Mulg hit with a melee attack during his combat action this turn is still in his melee range, Mulg may immediately make one normal melee attack targeting that model.

**Are You Going to Eat That?** - Once per turn, when a living model is destroyed within 4" of Mulg, before the model is removed from the table, Mulg may move up to his current SPD in inches directly toward the destroyed model. If Mulg ends this movement in base-to-base contact with the model, his controller may remove d3 damage points from anywhere on Mulg's life spiral.

**Regeneration [d3]** - Mulg may be forced to remove d3 damage points from anywhere on his life spiral once per activation. Mulg cannot regenerate during an activation he runs.

**Runebreaker Scars** - Mulg may be forced to use Runebreaker Scars. When Mulg uses Runebreaker Scars, enemy warbeasts lose their animus while within 5" of Mulg. Runebreaker Scars lasts for one round.

## Rune Club

**Critical Slam** - On a critical hit, instead of making a normal damage roll, Mulg may slam the target model d6" directly away from him. The model suffers a damage roll equal to Mulg's current STR plus the POW of his Rune Club. If the slammed model collides with another model with an equal or smaller-sized base, that model suffers a collateral damage roll equal to Mulg's current STR.

**Reach** - 2" melee range.

## Big Meaty Fist

**Claw** - Mulg's Big Meaty Fist has the abilities of a Claw.

| MULG | | | | CMD 6 | | |
|---|---|---|---|---|---|---|
| SPD | STR | MAT | RAT | DEF | ARM | |
| 4 | 12 | 6 | 3 | 11 | 19 | |

| LFT | RUNE CLUB | | |
|---|---|---|---|
| | SPECIAL | POW | P+S |
| | Multi | 6 | 18 |

| RT | BIG MEATY FIST | | |
|---|---|---|---|
| | SPECIAL | POW | P+S |
| | Claw | 4 | 16 |

| FURY | 5 |
|---|---|
| THRESHOLD | 11 |
| FIELD ALLOWANCE | C |
| VICTORY POINTS | 4 |
| POINT COST | 138 |
| BASE SIZE | LARGE |

## TACTICAL TIPS

**Affinity (Doomshaper): Cantankerous** – Because it is still his activation, Mulg can boost this attack.

**Runebreaker Scars** – Since a warbeast loses its animus while within 5" of Mulg when he uses Runebreaker Scars, an enemy warlock cannot use the affected enemy warbeast's animus.

**Primal Stupor** – Forfeiting its activation means the affected warbeast does nothing when it frenzies.

months, he has felt the blood-bond to Krol and heard the shaman's voice as a constant tug in his mind. When humans captured Krol and locked him behind their steel bars, a surge of rage overwhelmed Mulg's ancient brain. He gave a single great bellow that echoed across the Wyrmwall before marching toward Krol's prison. Younger dire trolls followed after him, compelled to join his blood-fueled crusade. Anything living that did not flee from their path was grabbed in meaty fists and eaten alive.

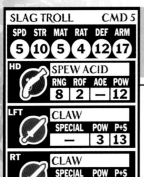

# SLAG TROLL
## TROLLBLOOD LIGHT WARBEAST

| SLAG TROLL | | | | CMD 5 | |
|---|---|---|---|---|---|
| SPD | STR | MAT | RAT | DEF | ARM |
| 5 | 10 | 5 | 4 | 12 | 17 |

| HD | SPEW ACID | | | |
|---|---|---|---|---|
| | RNG | ROF | AOE | POW |
| | 8 | 2 | — | 12 |

| LFT | CLAW | | |
|---|---|---|---|
| | SPECIAL | POW | P+S |
| | — | 3 | 13 |

| RT | CLAW | | |
|---|---|---|---|
| | SPECIAL | POW | P+S |
| | — | 3 | 13 |

| FURY | 3 |
|---|---|
| THRESHOLD | 9 |
| FIELD ALLOWANCE | U |
| VICTORY POINTS | 2 |
| POINT COST | 70 |
| BASE SIZE | MEDIUM |

*In some perversity of spirit they persist in consuming that which pains them. They are stubborn and thick-skulled even by troll standards.*

—Professor Viktor Pendrake

### Slag Troll

**Cast-Iron Stomach** - When the Slag Troll destroys an elemental construct or warjack with a melee attack, the Slag Troll gains boosted melee damage rolls for one round and may remove d6 damage points from anywhere on its life spiral.

**Regeneration [d3]** - The Slag Troll may be forced to remove d3 damage points from anywhere on its life spiral once per activation. The Slag Troll cannot regenerate during an activation it runs.

**Vitriol** - The Slag Troll may be forced to gain Vitriol for one round. While the Slag Troll is affected by Vitriol, non-Slag Troll models that hit the Slag Troll with a melee attack suffer Corrosion unless the Slag Troll is destroyed or removed from play by the attack.

### Spew Acid

**Corrosion** - A model hit by Spew Acid suffers Corrosion. Corrosion is a continuous effect that slowly erodes its target. Corrosion does one damage point each turn to the affected model during its controller's Maintenance Phase until it expires on a d6 roll of 1 or 2.

**Erosion** - The Slag Troll rolls an additional damage die on Spew Acid attacks against non-living models.

| ANIMUS | COST | RNG | AOE | POW | UP | OFF |
|---|---|---|---|---|---|---|
| **Acidic Touch** | 2 | 6 | - | - | | |

When a non-living model hits target friendly Trollblood model with a melee attack, after the attack has been resolved the attacking model suffers d6 damage points. Acidic Touch lasts for one round.

Slag trolls arose near hostile mountainous and volcanic environments and seem to prefer living near semi-active volcanic vents and old cooled lava flows. Their peculiar diet has given them a reputation for stupidity, but other trolls admire their intestinal fortitude. The tremendous acids they can build up in their gullets make them formidable adversaries, particularly against warjacks, wolds, and the walking dead.

Trolls do not have a typical relationship with their environment compared to natural animals. In hostile regions where there is no food and life is difficult to sustain, other species will leave to find better homes or die. Trolls prefer to tough it out, even if this means eating stone and metal. Slag trolls are living proof that the adaptable species can and will eat anything. With a taste for metal, the slag troll has metabolized powerful acids that can rapidly dissolve iron or even tempered steel. The species is notoriously ornery, constantly tormented by the metal shards perpetually growing through their flesh. Their habit of spitting corrosive bile at their foes has not endeared them to the enemies of the Trollbloods.

TROLLBLOODS

*Though they will come upon you like a tide of thunder, their storm will break upon your blades.*

—Chief Mortor of the Fennblades, during the Last Charge of the Calacians

Trollkin called Fennblades calmly wait shoulder to shoulder with wicked hooked greatswords raised at the ready while listening to the approach of thundering hooves. Even as the earth trembles with the rush of oncoming cavalry, they stand resolute and move only at the last minute. Some duck lances to sweep their blades through the legs of mounts—bringing down both man and steed—while others swing their blades straight into the chests of the riders while sidestepping their weapons. The result is always the same, as Fennblades stare down at the moaning and dying who foolishly sought to shatter their lines.

Around the time of the first Trollkin Wars, a large number of kriels within the Fenn Marsh northeast of Mercir banded together for mutual protection and safety. These southern battles never quite gained the fame or notoriety as the larger wars in the Thornwood, but the warriors who participated in them made a lasting mark on the way trollkin would fight in future conflicts.

| KITHKAR | | | | | CMD 9 | |
|---|---|---|---|---|---|---|
| SPD | STR | MAT | RAT | DEF | ARM | |
| 6 | 7 | 7 | 4 | 12 | 14 | |

| WARRIOR | | | | | CMD 7 | |
|---|---|---|---|---|---|---|
| SPD | STR | MAT | RAT | DEF | ARM | |
| 6 | 7 | 6 | 4 | 12 | 14 | |

| HOOKED GREAT SWORD | | | |
|---|---|---|---|
| | SPECIAL | POW | P+S |
| | Multi | 6 | 13 |

| FIELD ALLOWANCE | 2 |
|---|---|
| VICTORY POINTS | 2 |
| LEADER AND 5 TROOPS | 61 |
| UP TO 4 ADDITIONAL TROOPS | 9 ea |
| BASE SIZE | MEDIUM |

### Kithkar
**Leader**

**Warm Reception (Order)** - When a model that receives this order is targeted by an impact, charge, or slam attack made by an enemy model, before the enemy model makes its attack roll, the model that received this order may make one normal melee attack against the enemy model. The model that received this order gains +2 on this attack roll.

### Unit
**Hard** - A Trollkin Fennblade does not suffer damage or effects from impact attacks or collateral damage.

**Tough** - When a Trollkin Fennblade suffers sufficient damage to be destroyed, his controller rolls a d6. On a 5 or 6, a Trollkin Fennblade is knocked down instead of being destroyed.

### Hooked Great Sword
**Reach** - 2" melee range.

**Snag & Slash** - A Trollkin Fennblade gains an additional die on damage rolls against cavalry models. A cavalry model damaged by a Trollkin Fennblade is knocked down.

When word of the Fenn Marsh uprising reached Caspia, the king did not wish to divert his armies, which were otherwise engaged, so he sent his most prestigious cavalry battalion to deal with the "trollkin rabble." Named in honor of the ancient city predating Caspia, the famed Calacian Heavy Horse Battalion had never met defeat until they charged into the midst of the awaiting Fennblades. In a few minutes of churning hooves followed by screaming horses and the sound of metal on metal, the battalion lay annihilated. By twilight there was so much horse meat on the field that even the gathered trolls fighting alongside the local kriels could eat no more. In later battles the Fennblades repeated their successes, and by their efforts the human soldiers failed to subjugate the region.

As the stories of their victory spread, other kriels adopted similar methods. They took the name of Fennblades in honor of those who stood against Caspia's finest. Their techniques require long hours of drilling and greater discipline and coordination than trollkin normally exhibit. This makes these warriors ideally suited for the more cohesive army that the trollkin leaders are attempting to forge.

# TROLLKIN RUNESHAPERS
## TROLLBLOOD TROLLKIN UNIT

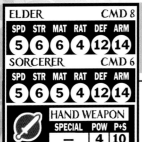

| ELDER | | | | | CMD 8 | |
|---|---|---|---|---|---|---|
| SPD | STR | MAT | RAT | DEF | ARM | |
| 5 | 6 | 6 | 4 | 12 | 14 | |

| SORCERER | | | | | CMD 6 | |
|---|---|---|---|---|---|---|
| SPD | STR | MAT | RAT | DEF | ARM | |
| 5 | 6 | 5 | 4 | 12 | 14 | |

| HAND WEAPON | | |
|---|---|---|
| SPECIAL | POW | P+S |
| — | 4 | 10 |

| FIELD ALLOWANCE | 2 |
|---|---|
| VICTORY POINTS | 2 |
| LEADER AND 2 TROOPS | 38 |
| BASE SIZE | MEDIUM |

**Tough** - When a Trollkin Runeshaper suffers sufficient damage to be destroyed, his controller rolls a d6. On a 5 or 6, the Trollkin Runeshaper is knocked down instead of being destroyed.

## Magic Ability

As a special attack or action, a Trollkin Runeshaper may cast one of the following spells during his activation. Determine the success of a magic attack by rolling 2d6 and adding the Trollkin Runeshaper's Magic Ability score of 6. If the roll equals or exceeds the target's DEF, the attack succeeds. A Trollkin Runeshaper cannot make additional attacks after making a magic attack.

- **Rock Hammer (★Attack)** - Rock Hammer is a RNG 6, AOE 3, POW 14 magic attack. On a critical hit, models in the AOE are knocked down. Rock Hammer never damages or affects models in this unit.

- **Stone Storm (★Attack)** - Stone Storm is a RNG 10, POW 12 magic attack. An enemy model hit by Stone Storm is pushed d3" directly away from the attacking model.

- **Stonewall (★Action)** - The Trollkin Runeshaper gains cover and +4 ARM.

### Elder
Leader

### Unit

**Confluence** - When making a magic attack roll, Trollkin Runeshapers gain a cumulative +1 bonus on the attack roll for each other model in this unit within 1" of it.

*This is the fundamental rune, Kora, which denies the pull of the earth and makes even the heaviest stone as light as a feather.*

—Runeshaper Elder Gorkalis of the Shaded Creek Kriel

such youths by aptitude and direct each to a path suiting his inclinations. The more aggressive sorcerers become tremendous assets on the battlefield, using their arcane strength to batter the enemy.

While such evocations may seem similar to druidic power, Runeshapers feel no affinity for human blackclads. The religious among them believe trollkin sorcery is a gift of Dhunia, not the Devourer Wurm, linked to the seasons that represent the goddess' manifestation on Caen. Earth power belongs to spring, fire to summer, ice and water to winter, and storms to autumn. Runeshapers are not priests, but many believe their power is a sign that they are destined to deliver Dhunia's wrath. Others ignore such spiritualism to focus on the raw arcane power of the runes themselves.

Runeshapers are among the most formidable of the trollkin sorcerers, having learned to manipulate rocks and stones with their minds. A focus for their power, runes are inscribed both on the ceremonial charms they wear and the countless weighty stones that respond to their will. At a Runeshaper's call these heavy pieces of rock rise to form floating patterns around him, ready to be hurled with killing force or interposed against incoming attacks as a whirling protective barrier.

Sorcerers born among the trollkin kriels have one significant advantage over their human counterparts: whereas humans must discover their gifts later in life, trollkin with this ability are immediately recognizable. Born as albinos, they soon separate from their peers and begin to learn how to master their inborn potential. Among larger collections of kriels, elders sort

# STONE SCRIBE ELDER

## TROLLBLOOD TROLLKIN KRIELSTONE BEARER & STONE SCRIBE UNIT ATTACHMENT

*The stories carved upon the krielstone fill it with the spirit of the deeds of our greatest heroes. It thirsts for battle and honor as much as you do.*

—Elder Stone Scribe Gylys Riverheart

| STONE SCRIBE ELDER CMD 9 | | | | | |
|---|---|---|---|---|---|
| SPD | STR | MAT | RAT | DEF | ARM |
| 5 | 7 | 6 | 4 | 12 | 13 |

| BATTLE AXE | | |
|---|---|---|
| SPECIAL | POW | P+S |
| — | 4 | 11 |

| | |
|---|---|
| ELDER'S DAMAGE | 5 |
| FIELD ALLOWANCE | 1 |
| VICTORY POINTS | +1 |
| POINT COST | 18 |
| BASE SIZE | MEDIUM |

Decades of experience with the krielstones have imparted the deepest of secrets to the eldest of the stone scribes. Such elders have spent decades making pilgrimages to the most important stones of all the trollkin kiths. At each site they study the inscribed tales and seek out the kith's shaman for further illumination about the local heroes. These years of study give the stone scribe elders rare insight into the heroism that powers the krielstones.

What separates elders from novices is more than just deeper lore but true respect for the art of rune carving and the place in history a krielstone represents. When scribes are young they must focus solely on the craft, learning how to expediently carve marks for famous heroes and mastering shortcuts in expression representing key moments. A single rune can convey the sequence of an entire battle. Elders know they are not simply historians: the power they bring to bear in the krielstones is an art. The shape of each hero's runes must convey the spirit of that great individual if his power is to become manifest.

### Stone Scribe Elder

**Unit Abilities** - The Stone Scribe Elder has Krielstone Bearer & Stone Scribe unit abilities.

### Stone Warp

If the Stone Scribe Elder is within 3" of the Krielstone Bearer, when the Krielstone Bearer makes a Protective Aura special action, the Stone Scribe Elder may use one of the following abilities. Stone Warp abilities last for one round.

- **Combat Warding** - Continuous effects on friendly Trollblood models affected by the Krielstone Bearer's Protective Aura expire. Instead of gaining an ARM bonus, while affected by the Krielstone Bearer's Protective Aura, friendly Trollblood models do not suffer continuous effects or blast damage and can only move or be moved during their activations.

- **Spirit Chaser** - Attacks made by friendly Trollblood models affected by the Krielstone Bearer's Protective Aura may damage models only affected by magic attacks. Affected models may charge incorporeal models.

- **Stone Strength** - Instead of gaining an ARM bonus, while affected by the Krielstone Bearer's Protective Aura, friendly Trollblood models gain +2 STR.

### TACTICAL TIPS

The Elder is a Stone Scribe.

**Stone Warp** – Remember, a model can benefit from only one Protective Aura at a time.

Laden with scrolls and rubbings taken from the numerous krielstones they have tended, stone scribe elders invoke a variety of supportive enhancements for the armies they accompany. Tapping directly into the heroism of their people, the elder scribe draws forth an echo of ancient prodigies and heroes of valor, blessing the gathered warriors with incredible strength or resilience.

TROLLBLOODS

# TROLLKIN HERO
## TROLLBLOOD TROLLKIN CHAMPION SOLO

| HERO | | | | CMD 9 | |
|---|---|---|---|---|---|
| SPD | STR | MAT | RAT | DEF | ARM |
| 5 | 8 | 8 | 4 | 12 | 17 |

| GREAT AXE | | |
|---|---|---|
| SPECIAL | POW | P+S |
| Multi | 5 | 13 |

| | |
|---|---|
| HERO'S DAMAGE | 10 |
| FIELD ALLOWANCE | 2 |
| VICTORY POINTS | 1 |
| POINT COST | 38 |
| BASE SIZE | MEDIUM |

*For hours he held his ground until the very earth was soaked with the blood of their dead. I lost count of how many fell before they ended him.*

—Helgin Kith Elder Bortas, after fighting in the Thornwood

### Hero

**Battle Formation** - While in base-to-base contact with one or more friendly Trollkin Champion models, the Hero gains +2 DEF against melee attacks and cannot be knocked down.

**Commander** - The Hero has a command range equal to his CMD in inches. Friendly Trollblood models/units in his command range may use the Hero's CMD when making command checks. The Hero may rally and give orders to friendly Trollblood models in his command range.

**Fearless** - The Hero never flees.

**Furious Charge** - The Hero may charge at SPD +5 and cross rough terrain though he suffers normal movement penalties.

**Inflamed** - The Hero gains a cumulative +1 on attack and damage rolls each time a friendly Trollkin Champion model in the Hero's command range is destroyed by an enemy attack. This bonus lasts for one round.

**Retaliatory Strike** - When a model hits the Hero with a melee attack, after the attack is resolved, the Hero may immediately make one melee attack against the attacking model.

**Tough** - When the Hero suffers sufficient damage to be destroyed, his controller rolls a d6. On a 5 or 6, the Hero is knocked down instead of being destroyed. If the Hero is not destroyed, he is reduced to one wound.

### Great Axe

**Back Swing (★Attack)** - The Hero may immediately make two Great Axe attacks.

**Reach** - 2" melee range.

### TACTICAL TIP

**Retaliatory Strike** – If the Hero is destroyed, he cannot make this attack.

This is not to say all trollkin heroes are the same; to be sure, they are as different from one another as all great leaders must be. Some are bloodthirsty berserkers with sour tempers whose presence in times of peace is a strain on their kith. Others are brooding and introspective, speaking little and avoiding all company. Still others are vain chieftains filled with pride and arrogance, suspicious of the young who emulate them. Yet each of these heroes is alike when life and death is on the line, for they put aside all thoughts except waging war to protect kith and kriel. They find it impossible to turn from battle, for it is only there that they can stand side by side with their brothers in arms and prove that one axe in a strong hand can make a difference even when opposed by a hundred swords.

Trollkin heroes are great champions whose deeds have spread by word of mouth throughout the kriels. They are living legends amongst their people, and just as the regular warriors of kith and kriel stand aside in awe as the champions walk into their midst, there are those few whose glory makes even proud champions bow their heads and kneel in respect.

Hardened by countless battles, these heroes' shoulders have held the weight of entire kriels, and they have offered themselves as sacrifices for those who rely on their strength. They know death awaits them every time they step into the fray and must content themselves with the knowledge they will live on in the memories of those for whom they have fought and bled. It is some comfort to know that song and stone will immortalize their deeds even as the crows pick at their bones.

TROLLBLOODS

*You've got to be kidding me. Was that thing its leg?*

—Sergeant Jarretty, 284th Trencher Company

| TROLL WHELP | | | | CMD | 1 |
|---|---|---|---|---|---|
| SPD | STR | MAT | RAT | DEF | ARM |
| 5 | 2 | 2 | 2 | 12 | 11 |

| FIELD ALLOWANCE | 3 |
|---|---|
| VICTORY POINTS | 0 |
| 5 WHELPS | 20 |
| BASE SIZE | SMALL |

Whelps are one of the inevitable consequences of the tremendous regenerative powers of full-blood trolls: short-lived degenerate creatures arising from severed limbs or other substantial pieces of disconnected tissue. It is difficult for humans even to comprehend the existence of these creatures. When a man loses a hand, foot, arm, or leg, that flesh becomes dead meat, no more than a reminder of what is missing. The tenacious resilience of full-blood trolls, however, is so strong that even severed limbs can take on a life of their own. A hand cut from a troll will soon regenerate its own head, torso, and limbs—matching the troll from which it arose—and thereafter follow after its progenitor by blood instinct.

Though the rapid growth of a whelp is amazing, it does not produce a full-fledged troll. The creatures are smaller, with disproportionate limbs matching the appendage from which they are spawned, and without the mental faculties of a true troll. Troll whelps are not particularly dangerous, and they rarely live longer than a few years.

Occasionally particularly dim-witted dire trolls mistake a whelp for a real offspring, but such misconceptions are rare and last only until it becomes obvious the whelp will never grow past a certain size. Most trolls consider whelps

### Troll Whelp

**Alternate Food Source** - At any time during its activation, a friendly Trollblood warbeast may devour any number of Troll Whelps within 1" of the warbeast. The warbeast may immediately remove d3 damage points from anywhere on its life spiral for each Whelp devoured. Remove devoured Troll Whelps from play.

**Annoyance** - While in melee with one or more Troll Whelps, living enemy models suffer -1 on attack rolls.

**Big Brother** - While within 10" of a friendly Trollblood warbeast, Troll Whelps never flee and automatically rally.

**Spawn Whelps** - Troll Whelps do not have to be put in play at the start of the game. The Troll Whelps' controller may put one Troll Whelp that did not begin the game in play into play when a friendly Trollblood warbeast is damaged by an enemy attack. The Troll Whelp's controller may place it anywhere completely within 3" of that warbeast. There must be room for the Whelp's base.

**Wrong Place, Wrong Time** - When a friendly Trollblood warbeast must make a threshold check, a Troll Whelp in its melee range may be removed from play to allow the warbeast to automatically pass the threshold check.

nothing more than an external part of their own body and treat them accordingly. Though their progenitors are benevolently tolerant and often allow whelps to do as they please, these hapless creatures rarely live out even their generally abbreviated lifespan. If caught with no other food source handy, trolls will eat their whelps with no more regard than for any other chunk of meat. Indeed, whelps make a ready source of emergency nourishment to fuel the troll's own regenerative powers. It is not at all uncommon to see a troll chuckling at the comical antics of a whelp one moment and then picking him up to toss into his mouth as a tasty snack the next.

TROLLBLOODS

# Horthol, Long Rider Champion
## TROLLBLOOD TROLLKIN LONG RIDER DRAGOON CHARACTER

*That one is all heart. If I put him at the front of battle, victory is certain. If I ask him to watch my family, I sleep assured of their safety.*

—Madrak Ironhide

TROLLBLOODS

Among the gathered kriels who wage war for survival many great names have come and gone, but fate holds a special place for those linked to Madrak Ironhide. Horthol is one of these champions. Once a proud chieftain in his own right, he has given up the leadership of his own kriel to serve the one trollkin he believes is destined to reshape the world. Horthol has proven loyal above all else, standing at Madrak's side even when others betrayed him.

Horthol has adapted to the needs of war with good humor and surprising resiliency, taking to the Long Rider saddle as if born to it. Now the bison riders look to him for direction and are ready to follow him unflinchingly wherever the war takes him. Increasingly Horthol has come to the realization that he serves Ironhide best at a distance by speaking on the great chieftain's behalf. While it pains him to fight so far from the leader to whom he swore his life, he does as duty compels him. With his great hammer in hand and astride his ground-shaking steed he has proven to be an unstoppable force.

Those who ride with Horthol find it hard to believe he has not always lived and slept in the saddle like the others of this tradition originating on Khador's southern plains. Instead Horthol's shared past with Madrak Ironhide took place in the northern Thornwood, where he was raised to hunt amid the dense knotted trees. His kriel was one of the first to fall to the deprivations of Cryxian horrors that plundered the forest in the wake of human wars. What few of Horthol's kin survived those dark days owe their lives to Madrak Ironhide, who nearly killed himself in a desperate attack to drive the walking dead away. When Horthol saw Madrak fighting so ardently for strangers, he knew a true chief stood before him, one who made his own claim to that title hollow. As the kriels gathered to listen to Madrak's plea for unity, Horthol was the first to step forward and offer his hammer in service.

Since that time Horthol has witnessed much, becoming both wiser and warier of the failings of humanity and his fellow kin. He stood by Ironhide when the chieftain humbled himself to ask aid of King Leto Raelthorne, and he saw hope die in Ironhide's eyes when the human sovereign refused the heartfelt plea. The heaviest blow came later, when the blackclads attempted Madrak's assassination and Horthol's fellow champion Pokrul—oath-brother and friend—betrayed them. This shocking treachery demonstrated clearly to Horthol that even blood-sworn kin could fall prey to follies he thought to be human weaknesses. It was a lesson he has never forgotten. Countless battles lay between where they began and where they now stand, and each brought a lesson and a steep blood price.

Even now, as a shadow falls across the great chieftain and elders openly refer to him as "World Ender," Horthol's allegiance has not shifted. When he looks at Madrak he sees only the face of his old friend and leader. At Madrak's request he has accepted the mantle of leadership for the Long Riders in Ironhide's service and has gone forth to loan his strength to Grissel Bloodsong and others who lead the trolls to war.

## SPECIAL RULES

### Horthol

**Brace For Impact** - While mounted, when Horthol is slammed, reduce the slam distance rolled by 3. If the total distance rolled is 0 or less, Horthol is not knocked down. Horthol is not knocked down when he suffers collateral damage from a slam.

**Cohort** - Friendly Long Riders in a horde with Horthol gain Follow Up and Line Breaker.

**Dragoon** - While mounted, Horthol has base SPD 7 and base ARM 18. Dismounted, Horthol has base SPD 5 and base ARM 16.

**Fearless** - Horthol never flees.

**Follow Up** - After hitting a model with a slam attack, after the slammed model is moved, Horthol may immediately move directly toward the slammed model up to the distance the slammed model was moved. Horthol stops moving if he contacts another model.

**Line Breaker** - When making impact attacks, this model rolls an additional die on the attack rolls.

**Slam** - While mounted, Horthol can perform power attack slams. A slammed model suffers a damage roll equal to the current POW of the Mount. If the slammed model collides with another model with an equal or smaller-sized base, that model suffers a collateral damage roll with a POW equal to the current POW of the Mount. After resolving the slam attack, Horthol may make one Long Hammer attack.

**Tough** - When Horthol suffers sufficient damage to be destroyed, his controller rolls a d6. On a 5 or 6, Horthol is knocked down instead of being destroyed. If Horthol is not destroyed, he is reduced to one wound.

### Mount

**Critical Knockdown** - On a critical hit, the model hit is knocked down.

### Long Hammer

**Critical Stagger** - On a critical hit, the model hit loses its initial attacks for one round.

**Reach** - 2" melee range.

| HORTHOL | | | | CMD 9 | |
|---|---|---|---|---|---|
| SPD | STR | MAT | RAT | DEF | ARM |
| 7/5 | 9 | 8 | 4 | 12 | 18/16 |

| LONG HAMMER | | | |
|---|---|---|---|
| | SPECIAL | POW | P+S |
| | Multi | 6 | 15 |

| MOUNT | | | |
|---|---|---|---|
| | SPECIAL | POW | P+S |
| | Critical | 14 | — |

| | |
|---|---|
| MOUNTED HORTHOL'S DAMAGE | 8 |
| DISMOUNTED HORTHOL'S DAMAGE | 8 |
| FIELD ALLOWANCE | C |
| VICTORY POINTS | 2 |
| POINT COST | 66 |
| MOUNTED BASE SIZE | LARGE |
| DISMOUNTED BASE SIZE | MEDIUM |

It was not easy for Horthol to obey Madrak's orders and shun the chieftain's company, but he understands Madrak asks this only because he fears what could happen to those closest to him as Rathrok's curse continues to manifest. Horthol knows in time they will reunite. He intends to stand at Ironhide's side in the end, even if it means sacrificing his life to preserve the chieftain's destiny. Until that hour—until he receives the summons for the last great battle—he rides with the Long Riders to bring victory to the gathered kriels.

TROLLBLOODS

## MADRAK IRONHIDE, WORLD ENDER
### EPIC WARLOCK

## HOARLUK DOOMSHAPER,
## RAGE OF DHUNIA
### EPIC WARLOCK

## CALANDRA TRUTHSAYER
### WARLOCK

**SLAG TROLL**
LIGHT WARBEAST

**TROLL WHELPS**
SOLOS

**STONE SCRIBE ELDER**
KRIELSTONE BEARER & STONE SCRIBE UNIT ATTACHMENT

**TROLLKIN HERO**
SOLO

**MULG THE ANCIENT**
UNIQUE HEAVY WARBEAST

TROLLBLOODS

# PAINTING TROLLBLOODS

## WHELP SKIN TONES

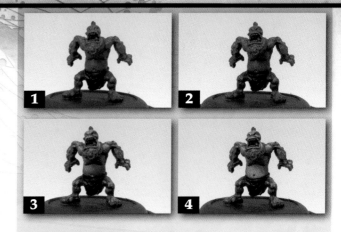

Whelps grow from the flesh cut from a pureblood troll's body, and as a result they take on the physical characterics of the progenitor. This offers a Trollblood player the chance to customize his whelps to match the trolls in his horde. Here are some steps for painting your whelps to match the Earthborn, Pyre, and Winter Trolls.

## PYRE TROLL WHELP

1—Basecoat the miniature with a mix of Sanguine Base and Trollblood Base.

2—Add Thornwood Green and Thamar Black to the basecoat color for the shadows.

3—To create the highlight color, add Trollblood Highlight and Khardic Flesh to the basecoat color.

4—Finally, paint the belly with Khardic Flesh.

### Colors Used:

- ⬤ Sanguine Base
- ⬤ Thornwood Green
- ⬤ Trollblood Base
- ⬤ Khardic Flesh
- ◯ Trollblood Highlight
- ⬤ Thamar Black

## WET BLENDING BISON FUR

Wet blending is a fast and fun technique that looks great on the finished miniature. Basically it involves mixing different colors of paint on the miniature itself while the paint is still wet. Do not thin your paints; pull them straight from the pots; and move quickly to prevent your paints from drying prematurely.

### Colors Used:

- ⬤ Beast Hide
- ⬤ Battlefield Brown
- ⬤ Bootstrap Leather
- ◯ 'Jack Bone
- ⬤ Thamar Black
- ◯ Mixing Medium

Apply Beast Hide at the top of the fur area as your first base color. Keep the paint heavy and thick so it will stay wet for the next steps.

Apply Bootstrap Leather near the Beast Hide as the second base color. Keep it wet and leave a space of the basecoat showing between the two colors to create a mixing field.

Use a clean, moist brush to mix the two colors in the mixing field. Be careful not to mix the two colors entirely into just one color. You should leave the two base colors alone on either side and mix only the area between them.

Apply Battlefield Brown as your third base color next to the Bootstrap Leather that remains unmixed. Leave a mixing field between the two colors. (You may notice there is a pattern here.)

TROLLBLOODS

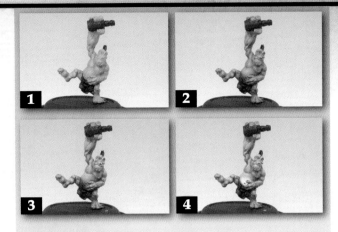

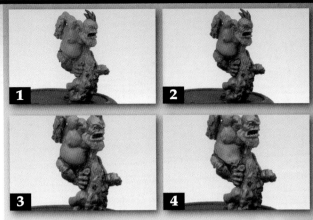

## WINTER TROLL WHELP

1—Basecoat the miniature with a mix of Frostbite and Trollblood Base.

2—Add Meredius Blue and Thornwood Green to the basecoat color for the shading.

3—Add Trollblood Highlight and Morrow White to the basecoat color for the highlights.

4—Finish the belly with a coat of Morrow White.

**Colors Used:**

- Thornwood Green
- Trollblood Base
- Meredius Blue
- Frostbite
- Trollblood Highlight
- Morrow White

## EARTHBORN TROLL WHELP

1—Basecoat the miniature with a mix of Trollblood Base and Gnarls Green.

2—Add a mix of Thornwood Green and Umbral Umber to the basecoat color to use for shading.

3—Add a mix of Trollblood Highlight and Traitor Green to the basecoat color and use it as the highlight.

4—Finish the belly with a coat of Thrall Flesh.

**Colors Used:**

- Thornwood Green
- Gnarls Green
- Traitor Green
- Trollblood Base
- Umbral Umber
- Trollblood Highlight
- Thrall Flesh

Mix the Battlefeild Brown and Bootstrap Leather in the second mixing field. Remember, both colors must be wet in order for them to mix properly.

Repeat the process once more by applying Thamar Black to the bottom of the fur as the last base color. Then mix it with the unmixed Battlefield Brown. Let this dry completely before the next step.

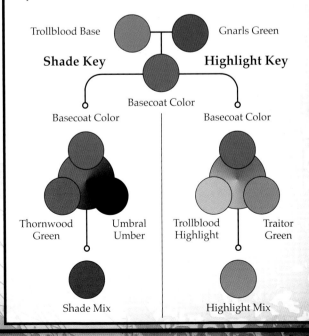

Mix a wash of Battlefield Brown, Mixing Medium, and a touch of water. Apply this wash to the upper half of the fur.

The final stage is drybrushing. Drybrush 'Jack Bone over the Beast Hide, Beast Hide over the Bootstrap Leather, Bootstrap Leather over the Battlefield Brown, and Battlefield Brown over the Thamar Black. *Voila!*

## Mixing Paints to Maintain Harmony

When mixing paints to create highlight and shading colors, include the basecoat color in the mix to help create a harmonious blend. For example, when painting the Earthborn Whelp we mixed Thornwood Green and Umbral Umber together with the basecoat (Trollblood Base) to create the shading color, and we mixed Trollblood Highlight and Traitor Green together with the basecoat to create the highlight color. Mixing paint this way helps tie the colors closer together and improves the overall look of the miniature.

Trollblood Base — Gnarls Green

**Shade Key**     **Highlight Key**

Basecoat Color

Basecoat Color     Basecoat Color

Thornwood Green     Umbral Umber     Trollblood Highlight     Traitor Green

Shade Mix     Highlight Mix

TROLLBLOODS

# CHASING THE STORM

Krueger's lightning bolts exploded in the trees ahead, narrowly missing the swiftly moving Scrapjack as it darted into the shelter of the trees. He could hear the Old Witch's laughter. He knew he was stretching his forces thin as he plunged deeper into enemy territory—but each time he got closer to cornering her.

He was beginning to think his adversary saw their clashes as some form of twisted diversion. Although Zevanna Agha appeared to be on the run, she also seemed content to give up territories while provoking him into one battle after another. Krueger smelled an ambush. He called his forces to pull back; they would have to swing around and approach from a different direction.

The next day they almost cornered her again as they clashed with a pocket of 3rd Border Legion reserves southeast of the Vescheneg Headlands. Kromac was in his full bestial glory, a chest and head taller than the Winter Guard he waded into. They were helpless lambs to the slaughter before his whirling axes. Tharn raged around him and quickly encircled the Khadoran lines to cut them to pieces.

This sight might have pleased Krueger at another time and place. Now he would have preferred the Tharn king fighting in his more human form, deliberately gauging the advance of his tribe and invoking powerful blood magic. The enticement to slaughter infantry never failed to draw out Kromac's more savage side, but that left Krueger to chase their true quarry on his own. Already the Tharn line was in chaotic disarray, engaged in bloody revelry. His larger contingent of Wolves of Orboros had fallen farther behind, bogged down by Iron Fangs, Kossites, and Widowmakers closer to the nearest ring of stones. He could hear the howls of their war wolves even at this distance. With Wolf Lord Morraig leading those men Krueger had every confidence they would emerge victorious, but he disliked his forces so scattered.

"Where is the Witch?" Krueger muttered as he scanned the tree line ahead. Agha had vanished after sacrificing a Juggernaut to take out one of his most reliable and oldest woldwardens, leaving him with two. He had forced her to abandon her other 'jacks. Only the Scrapjack had managed to keep up with their running battles, although Krueger knew he could not count on that for much longer. The Witch took unpredictable precautions. He was being led somewhere, and he suspected it boded ill.

They pushed on to the northwest as reeves reported sighting the hag. Kromac had fallen behind, but Krueger pressed on. With a familiar crackle Wayfarer Telvoso appeared next to him and offered a respectful nod. "We have sent 'wyrds and 'watchers ahead into the nearest glades," he reported.

"Very well." They walked together at a swift pace. Krueger remained alert to his surroundings and continued scanning the darkness between the trees.

The wayfarer went on, "Several stonewards and their stalkers were also sent ahead, but against the Witch . . ." He did not have to explain further. They both knew all too well the futility of trying to target the elusive Scrapjack or the Old Witch herself within the boundaries of the forest. Attempts to force her out of the trees had thus far failed. "It seems she has destroyed all the shifting and sentry stones in this region," he continued. "It will get worse from here."

"Find Kromac and tell him to make haste." Telvoso raised a dubious eyebrow at this, as both of them knew the futility of ordering Kromac to do anything, but the wayfarer did not question the command. He vanished in another crackle of shimmering air.

Krueger had little warning before a man in furs leapt out at him from the cover of the nearest trees. He was tall and thick enough to be a Kossite and wielded a pair of brutal axes. Krueger managed to block the first axe with Wurmtongue but received an off-handed strike below his left ribcage that cut savagely upward. He yanked away and tumbled even as he instinctively diverted the wound to the nearest woldwarden, several paces behind him and rushing to reach its master. The force of that energy crumbled the stone of its torso; pieces of granite fell to the ground, and several connective vines withered to dust.

Krueger snarled, struck back hard, and drove Wurmtongue deep into the attacker's chest. Lightning shimmered along the spear's length and then exploded into the nearest tree and set it afire. Krueger yanked the spear loose and let the manhunter fall to the ground. As the life left his assailant Krueger breathed deeply; he felt his foe's vitality flow into his own limbs.

Krueger remained wary in case this was an opening gambit. As expected, the Scrapjack appeared to his left and sprang forward on clanking legs. Krueger could almost hear the Witch's laughter as her enormous toy moved in for the kill. It closed with unnatural speed, seeking to crush him under its extended metal foot.

He swept his left hand outward with a rush of invoked power to gather a blast of swirling wind. Hammering the lanky 'jack with its full force, he sent it tumbling to thrash on the ground with a smashed torso. Krueger rushed forward with his spear arcing sparks to stab into the 'jack's exposed boiler. Lightning danced along its frame as he impaled it repeatedly. Steam hissed like a last breath from the holes he had pierced, and the light of its eyes and arcantrik relay faded as its engine ground to a halt.

An inhuman shriek burst from the trees nearby. Krueger crouched to leap into the sky, intending to ride the wind and gain a better vantage on his quarry, but the ground around him suddenly erupted with an impossible profusion of jagged metal barbs. Several of the wicked talons ensnared his flowing robes, pinning him in place. He could feel his strength draining away as a palpable aura of dread descended. Crows flew from the trees with a cacophony of hungry cawing to bite at him. He flailed at them with his spear even as cruel metal barbs dug into his legs. He saw a pair of gleaming eyes in the darkness through the trees, but when he blinked she was gone.

He should have stopped and gathered his forces. A rational corner of his mind knew this. But after the crows scattered and the metal barbs fell back into the earth, Krueger felt a rage he could not put down. He took to the air and let the wind fling him forward to soar after her. He sought her shadow among the trees and reached out to the simple minds of snakes and birds of prey to catch hints of her passage. He left his wolds behind and soared into the lowland hills of the cursed Vescheneg Headlands. Something glittering caught his eye in a blackened vale, and he descended with spear in hand and lightning at the ready. The air around him crackled, and dark clouds surged overhead.

Looking around at the strange clearing, Krueger realized the witch had led him to a grave site. There was evidence of old violence here. Shattered stones carved with ancient runes lay half-buried and overgrown with oddly twisted vines and moss. The creeper thorns were so thin and elongated they looked like sharpened claws. What trees remained were stooped and painfully gnarled, and one had a knot that eerily resembled a howling face. Krueger recognized the signs of old blight: a dragon had bled here once. The lingering poison set his nerves on edge.

A small cairn of rocks sat at the center of this clearing. Stacked atop the stones rested tarnished bronze armor pieces, a scythe blade broken into three pieces, and a bit of woven metal. Krueger felt his hackles rise and his rage burn as he recognized the weapon and a necklace upon the cairn. They had belonged to Salestria. He had no doubt. Their complex relationship may have been difficult at best, but he never saw her without that chain after the day he gifted it. A potent of his order, she had been dead for ten years now. Ten years, and Dahlekov had never provided a satisfactory accounting of her death.

"Foolish boy." A voice skittered in his ear, and suddenly Krueger felt razored claws along his throat. He gasped as he realized Agha had come up from behind him without a sound. "Shh, be quiet. This vill be over soon."

Is this how Salestria had been defeated? Looking down at the cairn in front of him Krueger felt the certainty of his own death. He had reason to curse himself for allowing his rage to drive his actions. It had been rash, even stupid, to outpace his woldwardens and enter this place without a single beast at hand to suffer his injuries. He could try to lash out at the Witch but knew he could not strike quickly enough.

She laughed. "I could kill you, yes? I see in your eyes you know. How foolish you have been. You are pawns in a larger game. Never do you learn. This land is mine. You cannot steal this land. I let you use it, sometimes. Vhat I need, I take. It is that simple." She made a little noise between her teeth. "How I vould enjoy adding your skull to my collection." Her claws traced gently along his bald head and rivulets of blood trickled down into his eyes. "But I vill give you a chance, yes? There is vork for you to do, I think."

Krueger gritted his teeth. "I will not serve you."

"Oh, this I know, little *vorona*." She cackled and traced another thin line along his throat with a single claw. It was a Khadoran word that meant "crow." "But vhy are you here? Think on this. My sons and daughters think they have given me the Thornwood, but it is rotten. Toruk stirs. The final feast comes between the great serpents. Poison eats the land. You see it here, smell it on these stones. Two thousand years since this blood spilled, yet still it taints the land. It is a scar on my flesh as much as on your Orboros. If you do not vish to fall," her clawed hand pointed toward the cairn, "go to the Shadoveald Barrow. There they keep the Vyrmstone. You have heard of this, yes? It holds your order's scratchings about the world-eaters. But it is more than you think. Study its lessons. After that, if you vish to dance vith me again, I vill be here."

He felt her claws on his throat for several seconds more before realizing it was a phantom sensation caused by numerous small cuts made along the skin of his neck and head. She was gone. Krueger stared back at the cairn and considered her words. He loathed the thought of that ancient crone manipulating him, but something in what she had said resonated. He imagined the games she had played with Dahlekov and his predecessors, back for thousands of years. He stood on the same ground as Salestria. He had nearly perished as well, but he had not. What had changed?

The mention of the Wyrmstone stirred an undeniable curiosity in him. He had never heard it described as more than a simple artifact from another era. He had seen it once while meeting Dahlekov, but he had not had occasion to examine it closely. It was a hemisphere of stone almost a foot and a half across, its curved surfaces inscribed inside and out with ancient runes. Such a relic might indeed contain secrets, perhaps known only to the omnipotents. Even before he took to the air to return to his army he had decided he very much wanted to examine that rune-laden stone.

Gaining access to the Wyrmstone was not difficult. Krueger had been at the forefront of the fighting that just recently had restored the Shadoweald to Circle hands and was known to its keepers. They welcomed him warmly to the sacred site atop the hill at the forest's center. When he mentioned a desire to study the stone, they led him to its chamber and left him with scrolls and ink.

To his frustration, the stone's secrets would not be easily deciphered. Its runes formed a grid through which ran a series of intersecting lines. Each of these lines comprised a distinct sentence, and they overlapped with a multitude of interpretations. Eventually he tired of transcription and blithely packed up the stone to take it with him. Its keepers would surely suffer when Dahlekov learned of his theft, but then again, they should learn better vigilance.

After rejoining his army, Krueger kept largely to himself. He punctuated his long hours of isolation with bursts of frantic activity spent increasing and preparing his forces. That he had found renewed purpose and dedication was clear to all his followers. He made liberal use of the wayfarers bound to his service to foment smaller cabals of younger druids scattered across his disparate territories. He sent Wolf Lord Morraig to gather more Wolves of Orboros and Kromac to call the Tharn wherever they traveled. He had begun to make his way south with his army when Dahlekov finally tracked him down.

Krueger was not surprised when a vaguely human shape coalesced out of the smoke gathered from several nearby fires to stand imperiously in front of him. Dahlekov favored these smoke sendings in times of war. Krueger was no longer even sure where the omnipotent was physically located. "Krueger Stormwrath. What is it you think you are doing?"

Krueger made a small gesture with his right hand, and the subordinates nearest him gratefully slipped away. He then addressed the smoke with its glowing eyes. "That is no longer your concern, Dahlekov."

Smoke sendings had no facial details, but the anger in the voice was unmistakable. "I tasked you to push Zevanna Agha back to the headlands. Not only did you disobey, you also stole a piece of our order's history. Return to the Shadoweald *now*." Agitation made Dahlekov's Khadoran accent more pronounced.

"I'm sorry, Omnipotent," Krueger answered smugly, "but I won't be obeying your orders any longer. You can handle the Old Witch yourself. We recovered several sites near the Kalhesh Glades. Make use of them as you see fit. Consider it a parting gift."

"What nonsense is this, Stormwrath? What use is the Wyrmstone to you?"

"It seemed more convenient to take it with me to study at my leisure. I will return it when I'm finished. Have you read it, Dahlekov?"

"Of course. Its relevance—"

"Escapes you. I know. I am still puzzling through a few details myself. But it provides remarkable insight into the minds of our forebears. I was amazed to discover they spent time planning the theoretical destruction of the dragons. In those days, so soon after Toruk's brood drove him from the mainland, the risks of action were too great. But now, with what we know? It inspires me to think of the vision our order once possessed. When did we become such cowards? Why preserve these words only to ignore them?"

"The verses on that stone contradict themselves. It is a lesson in folly. We preserved it only because it is all that survives describing the alliance of the dragon brood against their progenitor. It has no other importance."

Krueger laughed. "I couldn't disagree more! I found it very enlightening."

"Return the stone and resume your duties, and I will forgive this lapse," Dahlekov growled.

Krueger responded calmly, "My army will leave your territory shortly. You can avoid confronting me if you prefer. If you wish to press the issue, I welcome the opportunity to debate your claims of authority." He waved his hand and sent a gust of wind to tear the smoke sending apart.

He felt eyes upon him and saw Wayfarer Telvoso watching him from a polite distance as he leaned on his great voulge. Krueger addressed him. "Do you take issue with what you just heard?"

"No, Potent. Your will is my command."

"I have no more use for that title. Address me as Stormlord." Behind Krueger's voice rolled the hint of thunder.

One task Krueger entrusted to Wayfarer Telvoso was to deliver a meeting request to his old mentor, a druid who maintained an isolated existence near the ruins of Acrennia. He had not made such an invitation for nearly a decade, but he did not doubt there would be a response. Contact came while crossing through the bogs of central Ord. They were keeping to the remote areas on the fringes of the Thornwood as they continued south collecting reinforcements loyal to the Stormlord. His message was taking hold among the younger druids in particular. Word of his defiance to Dahlekov had spread rapidly.

---

## "Toruk stirs. The final feast comes between the great serpents. Poison eats the land."

---

It was a typically overcast and dismal day, but soon a narrow slit in the clouds allowed the sun to gleam forth like a burning eye, and it quickly assumed a powerful intensity. The temperature increased with such ferocity that it caused the nearest thick ponds to start bubbling froth. The Stormlord sensed a familiar sensation of remote regard and stopped walking.

Around him there was a buzzing exodus as startled insects fled, confused by the unnaturally rapid shift in climate. The air felt leeched of moisture, and the colors around him were bleached by the oppressive glare. Krueger shifted in his heavy robes as sweat rolled down his bald head.

"Krueger." A voice spoke from the nearest mirage-like haze, arising from above a low mossy boulder now roasting beneath the sun. "Why do you disturb me?"

Dealing with Mohsar the Desertwalker was always tricky, even face to face. Mohsar had saved Krueger from the parents who had attempted to burn him alive and had later awakened his powers as a druid, but he was hardly nurturing. Every day spent with his mentor had been a lesson in enduring torture both mental and physical. There was no one on Caen Krueger respected, feared, or hated more.

Krueger turned to face the shimmering haze. "Forgive me, Omnipotent Mohsar. I assure you it is important. I have a question regarding the Wyrmstone."

Seconds stretched into minutes with no answer. Krueger scowled and wondered if their communication had gone astray, yet the oppressive heat remained and the blinding light of the sun beat down to remind him of his insignificance. As his patience wore thin he felt compelled to ask carefully, "What occupies you, Omnipotent?" He never would have hazarded such a question if Mohsar had been present in person.

---

## "You appear to be in open defiance of our order. What would possibly motivate me to help you?"

---

The omnipotent answered at once. "Skorne. They meddle with things they do not understand. I have put aside my isolation, for now." This sent a chill down Krueger's back even as he blinked against the sweat beading from his eyebrows. *I have put aside my isolation.* The words echoed ominously in his mind. Where Mohsar walked, the cruel desert followed. After a pause Mohsar spoke again, "The Wyrmstone? Do you fear I will come to regain that worthless piece of rock? You have chosen an opportune time to defy us. It is unlikely we will be in a position to reprimand you personally—yet. Take what comfort you wish from that."

It was the first indication that Mohsar was aware of Krueger's recent misdeeds. He was not exactly displeased to hear the Desertwalker would not be coming for him immediately. "This stone includes the names of the dragons that formed a compact against Toruk sixteen centuries ago. But the names are not the same as the ones we call them by today."

"Did you think their names have not changed?" Mohsar snapped. "Get to your point."

The churlish tone reminded Krueger unpleasantly of his youth. "The fact that they changed was not surprising, no, but it makes the interpretation difficult. I have worked out several of them, including a few I believe are now gone. But I could not find any description that ties to Ethrunbal. Which of these names is his? Do you know?"

"Ethrunbal was not involved in that compact, so far as we are aware. There is no mention of him in the Wyrmstone." His voice conveyed escalating irritation. "Why are you wasting my time?"

Krueger felt a thrill of excitement at this confirmation of his theory, but he managed to keep his voice calm. "Which dragon was it who arranged this compact? Halfaug?" He deliberately chose an unlikely candidate knowing it would irritate Mohsar.

"No, it was Blighterghast, you fool. That much is clear. I have had enough of this, Krueger. I feel no need to discuss ancient history with you. Do not trouble me again." Mohsar severed the contact. The haze vanished and in seconds the air returned to normal. The damp mugginess and sudden chill were almost more shocking than the heat had been.

Krueger mopped his sweating brow and smiled. He turned to Wayfarer Telvoso. "Our destination is confirmed. The southern Wyrmwall."

The next visitation came weeks later by way of rain and thunder shortly after they had entered the northern edge of the lengthy chain of the Wyrmwall Mountains. The cold was biting at this elevation, and wind gusts tugged at their robes. Krueger's assemblage had become truly a force to be reckoned with, a far larger army than even he had anticipated. He was eager to test them in battle, but thus far he had fought the temptation to divert from their path. He had felt the pull most strongly as he crossed northern Cygnar, with collections of trollkin so close on either side. There would be time for such battles soon enough.

Krueger knew he would not be able to take the entire army all the way to the southern Wyrmwall. He would need to establish proper base camps while he considered the stages ahead. A part of him had expected Omnipotents Dahlekov or Lortus to send someone to challenge him, perhaps even Morvahna. The lack of such a confrontation was almost disappointing.

Northeast of Rimmocksdale Lake a sudden downpour hit the company with great force. Krueger immediately sensed something unnatural in the storm. He might have bent his will to disperse it, but each lick of lightning and wind-tossed sheet of rain added to his strength and felt like an extension of his body. He sent his senses into the howling wind, and no matter how darkly or furiously the weather raged he never found his vision troubled. He saw other druids and even Wolf Lord Morraig duck away from the biting rain, huddled in their cloaks. The sight made him grin maliciously at their weakness. Only Kromac seemed unperturbed, walking in his human guise near Krueger with his face raised calmly to the rain as if he too sensed it was unnatural.

The heavy water drops in front of Krueger swirled into cohesion to assume the likeness of a man, like some liquid phantom. The lightning flashed again, striking so close the thunder exploded into his ears and set his heart racing. A man emerged from the watery shape in front of him, scattering the droplets. Kromac made a noise deep in his throat and stepped forward, axes in hand, but Krueger stayed him with a gesture. The rest of the slowly advancing column behind them ground to a gradual halt.

The slender, pale man facing Krueger was a familiar sight. His sharp and angular features were almost elven, and his left hand was missing two fingers. What remained was thick with mottled scar tissue. Thin black lines radiated from this injury and ran up his left arm, spreading up his neck and onto his left cheek in a delicate web. Rumor asserted this injury was the result of some unexplained contact with Blighterghast years ago, a blight that lingered. He wore the bronzed armor and heavy dark robes of their fellowship, but no weapon was immediately apparent. Krueger knew better than to take comfort from this.

Krueger leaned upon Wurmtongue, offering the smallest nod of his head in greeting. "Omnipotent Lortus, welcome. This is a rare honor. You prove perspicacious; I needed to speak with you."

"Did you?" The omnipotent sounded amused.

"Yes. It occurred to me you may be in a unique position to assist me."

"You appear to be in open defiance of our order. What would possibly motivate me to help you?" There was a definite edge to the question despite the man's otherwise amiable tone.

"So you are here to rebuke me for my disagreement with Dahlekov?" Krueger asked.

Lortus shrugged but his posture suggested alertness. Krueger could sense strands of the other druid's power all around him, for their natural affinities were similar. Lortus had long been an acknowledged master of storm and wind. "Dahlekov's territories are his own to manage. Now you are in mine. What brings you to my mountains, marching at the head of an army?" The omnipotent glanced behind Krueger. "There is no enemy of ours near here."

"We are only passing through. A temporary imposition." Krueger assured him.

"You are not here to challenge me?" Lortus asked with a raised eyebrow.

"What would be the point of that?" Krueger chuckled. "Nothing could be further from my mind. You always expect the worst of me. No wonder Morvahna is closer to your heart."

Krueger saw Kromac's lip twitch the tiniest bit and his posture become rigid at the mention of the name.

"Morvahna is in the habit of pitting her gathered forces against our enemies, which I appreciate," Lortus admitted. "Is this about her? You march in the wrong direction, if so."

Krueger shook his head. "No. She is not important. I require an audience with Blighterghast. I believe you are in a position to arrange this?"

The smile on Lortus' face vanished and he stared at Krueger with new intensity. "No. Absolutely not." His voice held the unmistakable echo of thunder.

Krueger was unmoved. "I will find him. But things will go more smoothly if you provide an introduction. I know you are acquainted." His eyes went to the druid's disfigured hand.

"Dragons exist entirely outside the natural order," Lortus reminded him condescendingly. "Their minds are not the same as ours. Nothing beneficial could possibly arise of such a meeting."

"I have a proposal the dragons need to hear, and Blighterghast seems the most likely to listen. The time has come to initiate a dialog."

"A remarkable assertion. If you believe this to be the case, share your insights with me. I will appraise their worth and determine how best to proceed."

Krueger shook his head. "No, I must talk to him directly. It is the only way." His gaze returned to Lortus' old injury. "You were not an omnipotent when you earned that. I trust you had your reasons; I am willing to afford you that much respect. Did you gain approval from Ergonus before you acted? I think not."

Lortus' eyes showed the first spark of true anger. "Direct contact is strictly forbidden. Do not test me." Krueger saw no hint of movement, but there were obsidian blades in each of Lortus' hands as he stood with his arms folded across his chest. Krueger scowled and tightened his grip on Wurmtongue.

Kromac stepped suddenly forward, moving to interpose himself. He had not yet called on the Devourer to adopt his more physically imposing form, but he had his axes in hand and looked ready to use them. He was of a similar height to Lortus, but even as a human his bulk was considerably larger. Lortus was a frail twig in comparison.

The air sizzled, and Lortus was suddenly no longer there. A brilliant glowing afterimage displayed his silhouette bathed in the white fire of lightning as his body became a pillar of pure electricity screaming up into the boiling sky. The explosion of blazing tendrils and the sound wave of thunder passed smoothly over Krueger and left him untouched, but Kromac was hurled backward fifteen yards to shatter a nearby evergreen tree. He did not look badly hurt as he staggered back to his feet, but threads of smoke rose from his hair and studded leathers. Wolf Lord Morraig and two of the nearest warpwolves rushed forward, but there was no enemy to battle.

Krueger shook his head as he walked to Kromac. "That was rash."

Kromac growled in his throat and scratched at the blackened streak across his bare chest. "Perhaps." He paused. "That did not go well."

Krueger gave a satisfied smile. "Actually, it went perfectly."

The Tharn king stared at him dubiously. "Oh?"

"I know Lortus. He is cautious and patient by nature and did not wish to challenge my army without further support. He will retreat to observe our actions before confronting us again. Meanwhile, he will stay as close to Blighterghast as possible so he can ensure intercepting us. He is probably on his way to somewhere proximate to the dragon's lair now."

"This is good for us how?" Kromac puzzled.

Krueger smiled again, feeling his plans fall into place. "I might have difficulty finding Blighterghast. He is slippery if he chooses to be, or so I hear. But I can certainly find Lortus. All I have to do is follow the storm." He took a deep breath, tasting the ozone in the air. "Come. A dragon awaits."

# Kaya the Moonhunter
## CIRCLE ORBOROS EPIC WARLOCK CHARACTER

*Despite all attempts to shelter and control her, this one's destiny blazes with the power of the unconquered sun.*

—Krueger the Stormlord

| SPELL | COST | RNG | AOE | POW | UP | OFF |
|---|---|---|---|---|---|---|
| DOG PILE | 2 | 10 | - | - | X | X |

Friendly Circle warbeasts may charge or slam target enemy model at SPD +5" without being forced and regardless of LOS. When a friendly Circle warbeast charges or slams the affected model, it may move across rough terrain and obstacles without penalty.

| FORCED EVOLUTION | 2 | 6 | - | - | X | |
|---|---|---|---|---|---|---|

Target friendly living Circle warbeast gains +2 STR and DEF.

| MIST WALKER | 3 | SELF | CTRL | - | | |
|---|---|---|---|---|---|---|

Kaya and friendly Circle warbeasts currently in her control area gain Stealth for one round. Attacks against a model with Stealth from greater than 5" away automatically miss. If a model with Stealth is greater than 5" away from an attacker, it does not count as an intervening model.

| MUZZLE | 2 | 10 | - | 12 | | X |
|---|---|---|---|---|---|---|

An enemy warbeast damaged by Muzzle cannot end its normal movement closer to Kaya than it began. Muzzle lasts for one round.

Countless battles in recent months have honed Kaya to perfect fighting form, proving repeatedly she has the will and strength to survive against impossible odds. She fights with a visceral joy for the rush of battle but also with a determined belief that her enemies deserve destruction. Her clarity of purpose springs from the same wild spirit that allows her effortlessly to control the beasts accompanying her, including the great wolf Laris who keeps constant vigil at her side. She stands on the precipice of greatness and has proven her willingness to leap into the unknown—regardless of the dangers—to seize it.

Kaya has learned from hard experience that some of her peers will try to exploit her potential for their own benefit. Her confidence in herself has grown, and she has begun to see how she can put her power to proper use without becoming the tool of another. However she is not a schemer and prefers to rely on intuition to guide her steps. As she ages and gains experience, Kaya has refined these instincts such that they rarely lead her astray.

Once she moved from one battle to the next without thought beyond the moment, answering the imperatives of her wilding. She has since learned to transcend this, still tapping her youthful reserves but mastering deeper rites and rituals gained from the lore of beast masters who preceded her. These techniques helped sharpen her arsenal of weapons to a razor's edge.

She has gone forth to wage war in the Circle's name all along the Hawksmire River, the Castle of the Keys, the Thornwood, Khador's northern reaches, the Gnarls, and the Wyrmwall. The soil of every wild place has tasted the blood of Kaya's enemies. In battle she moves with fluid grace and amazing speed, seeming to prefer being surrounded by her foes. As Kaya leaps into the midst of her enemies warpwolves, satyrs, and Laris suddenly appear out of the shadowy darkness, their limbs infused with fresh vitality. Never has carnage achieved such

# SPECIAL RULES
## Feat: Call of the Hunt

*Kaya the Moonhunter can immerse herself into the minds of her beasts to fuse their efforts into a single flawless execution of her will. Kaya can unleash her beasts in a seemingly reckless assault where they rend and kill anything they find. Calling on ancient rites based on the conjunctions of the moon, Kaya can then instantly summon her companions back to her side to stand watchful vigil.*

| KAYA | | | | CMD 8 | |
|---|---|---|---|---|---|
| SPD | STR | MAT | RAT | DEF | ARM |
| 6 | 5 | 6 | 4 | 16 | 14 |

| GLIMMER | | |
|---|---|---|
| SPECIAL | POW | P+S |
| Multi | 6 | 11 |

| FURY | 6 |
|---|---|
| DAMAGE | 16 |
| FIELD ALLOWANCE | C |
| VICTORY POINTS | 5 |
| POINT COST | 94 |
| BASE SIZE | SMALL |

Friendly Circle warbeasts currently in Kaya's control area gain The Calling. Kaya can force a model with The Calling even if it is outside of her control area. At the end of an affected warbeast's activation, it may be placed anywhere within 3" of Kaya. There must be room for the model's base in its new location. Call of the Hunt lasts for one turn.

## Kaya

**Against the Odds** - When Kaya makes a melee attack, she gains +1 to her melee attack and damage rolls for each enemy model after the first that she is in melee with when the attack is declared. This bonus lasts for the attack.

**Alpha** - When Kaya runs, friendly living Circle warbeasts with LOS to her when she ends her normal movement may run without being forced this turn. When Kaya charges, friendly living Circle warbeasts with LOS to her when she ends her normal movement may charge or slam without being forced this turn.

**Calm** - Friendly Circle warbeasts in Kaya's control area make threshold checks at +1 THR.

**Pathfinder** - During her activation, Kaya ignores movement penalties from, and may charge across, rough terrain and obstacles.

**Sympathetic Transference** - Kaya may transfer damage to a friendly living Circle warbeast even if the warbeast has a number of fury points equal to its FURY.

## Glimmer

**Rapid Strike** - When Kaya hits an enemy model with a Glimmer attack during her activation, she may make an additional Glimmer attack. Attacks gained from this ability cannot generate further additional attacks from this ability.

**Reach** - 2" melee range.

sublime perfection as when Kaya and her beasts unleash themselves, holding nothing in reserve and accepting that rest will come when every enemy lies shattered and bleeding across the forest soil.

The more Kaya joins the Circle battles, the more she appreciates the solid foundation given to her by Baldur the Stonecleaver. She intends to heed Baldur's example by focusing squarely on the enemy and ignoring all other distractions. So long as her beasts are at her side she knows she can achieve any victory, even those which her peers have consigned to defeat.

| LARIS | | | | | CMD 7 |
|---|---|---|---|---|---|
| SPD | STR | MAT | RAT | DEF | ARM |
| 7 | 8 | 6 | 1 | 15 | 14 |

**HD** | **JAW**

| SPECIAL | POW | P+S |
|---|---|---|
| — | 4 | 12 |

| FURY | C |
|---|---|
| THRESHOLD | 10 |
| FIELD ALLOWANCE | C |
| VICTORY POINTS | 2 |
| POINT COST | 0 |
| BASE SIZE | MEDIUM |

## Laris

**All Terrain** - During Laris' activation, Laris ignores movement penalties from, and may charge and slam across, rough terrain and obstacles.

**Companion** - Laris is included in any horde that also includes Kaya the Moonhunter. Laris cannot be included in a horde that does not include Kaya the Moonhunter. If Kaya the Moonhunter is destroyed or removed from play, remove Laris from play.

**Guard Dog** - While Laris is within 3" of Kaya and not stationary, Kaya cannot be targeted by free strikes, gains +2 DEF against melee attacks, and models attacking Kaya do not gain back strikes bonuses.

**Mystic Bond** - While Laris is in Kaya's control area, Kaya may measure her spells' ranges from Laris rather than from herself. Kaya must have LOS to her target. All modifiers are based on Kaya's LOS.

**Scent** - Laris may ignore LOS when declaring a charge or slam.

**Spirit Bond** - Laris is bonded to Kaya. Laris never attacks Kaya. When Laris frenzies, it never selects Kaya to attack. Other models cannot use Laris' animus, force, heal, transfer damage to, or leach or reave fury from Laris.

**Wolf Shepherd** - While Laris is in Kaya's control area, friendly living Circle warbeasts within 6" of Laris may be forced, leached, reaved, healed and transferred damage by Kaya.

| ANIMUS | COST | RNG | AOE | POW | UP | OFF |
|---|---|---|---|---|---|---|
| **Spirit Shift** | 2 | Self | - | | - | |

When Laris uses this animus, immediately place it within 2" of Kaya. When Kaya uses this animus, immediately place her within 2" of Laris. There must be room for the placed model's base in the new location. A model cannot move after being placed as a result of this animus.

Laris is far more than a ferocious wolf standing vigil at Kaya's side. He is a creature as preternatural as he is wild and a cunning and adaptive reflection of some inner portion of Kaya's predatory spirit. He is the answer to Kaya's call for the other half of herself, and the bond between them is essential and profound. The link that joins their minds and emotions allows them to accomplish otherwise impossible feats. Kaya's power flows naturally through Laris, and Laris feels her wounds more keenly than any injury to his own flesh. Outside of battle his mind is a calm and soothing influence on Kaya's inner turmoil, and his instinct to preserve her life perfectly contrasts her sometimes reckless courage. He is a manifestation of Orboros with a wisdom and personality all his own.

Connecting to Laris was no simple feat, requiring Kaya to stretch herself in a way she never had before. One key to unlocking this deeper power was for Kaya to learn the role of celestial influences empowering the Circle Orboros. Under Morvahna's tutelage she began to tap into the moons' mystical pull on the blood of all predators. Morvahna initiated Kaya into these elder rites by urging her to undertake a strenuous ordeal, climbing to one of the highest peaks in the Wyrmwall Mountains. The introspection and patience required for such a task went against Kaya's natural inclinations, but on some level she sensed that something vital awaited her.

Atop the mountain peaks she arrived at a nearly forgotten sacrificial site. She spilled her blood on ancient stones as lightning crackled across a storm-tossed sky. Then the black clouds parted and the three moons of Caen illuminated the tableau. She did not undertake this journey to find Laris but sought instead to unlock her inner strength and predatory awareness. She was therefore startled and awed when a ghostly white wolf emerged from the wilds at the climax of the ritual. With a single look, Kaya knew the wolf's mind and could sense its greeting. It invited her to hunt and she readily accepted. She joined the wolf in a lengthy prowl through the mountain passes—running like siblings of the same pack—and in these hours the two bonded inextricably. It was only later that Kaya discovered how profoundly the link amplified her already formidable powers.

The wolf has stayed at her side ever since. She named him Laris after the second of the three moons orbiting Caen. The ignorant call this moon baleful and wicked, and it is associated with storms and ill fortune. Laris has in fact proven to be a calming influence on the beasts accompanying Kaya into battle, serving as a bridge and mystical conduit between Kaya and her pack. Through the bond they share, Kaya can feel the complex flow of his emotions and thoughts, receiving warnings and sometimes seeing through his eyes. Laris does not filter the world through language but boasts a keen perception and insight, picking up on the subtlest reactions.

When Kaya first descended the mountain and met again with the Autumnblade, the senior druid was surprised and unsettled by the way she had clearly exceeded her expectations. The appearance of the wolf marked a rite of passage for Kaya, showing she had transcended the mentorship of elder druids to walk her own path. This was the placement of the first stones laid by her own hand in the path of her destiny.

Laris is an accomplished mountain and forest hunter and a brave guardian. Though Kaya has become calmer since bonding with him, the cold predatory stare of a wolf is sometimes reflected in her eyes. A wolf feels no sorrow or compassion for its prey, and Kaya has put aside such human feelings, knowing hesitation could mean death in the dangerous days ahead.

# Laris

## CIRCLE ORBOROS UNIQUE LIGHT WARBEAST

> *He is flesh put to Kaya's inner nature, a guardian pulled from her very soul.*
>
> —Kromac the Ravenous

Circle Orboros

# Krueger the Stormlord
## CIRCLE ORBOROS EPIC WARLOCK CHARACTER

*With knowledge and power illimitable, it is inexcusable that this order remains content to stand idly as the world crumbles.*

—Krueger the Stormlord

Even the three omnipotents of the Circle Orboros begrudgingly admit that Krueger is among the most powerful of their number. So far as they are concerned he stands subordinate to them, however, not because of lack of ability but because of temperament. Krueger cares little what they feel he is worth. He knows that greatness does not come as a reward for humility or silent dedication. To

truly change the world—to seize victory from inevitable defeat—Krueger must act boldly and never look back. He intends to rattle the Circle Orboros like a creaky house caught in a storm. If he makes enemies of the most powerful individuals in western Immoren in the process, so be it. Krueger will endure that storm and rise above it as lord and master.

He lost patience with the omnipotents some time ago after the death of Ergonus. He expected to join their number at that time but was denied. His path would have been easier with the proper rank and authority, but that which they

Circle Orboros

| SPELL | COST | RNG | AOE | POW | UP | OFF |
|---|---|---|---|---|---|---|
| LIGHTNING STORM | 3 | 8 | 3 | 13 | X | X |

Lightning Storm is a cloud effect that stays on the table as long as upkeep is paid. Models entering or ending their activation in the cloud suffer an unboostable POW 10 damage roll. While in the cloud, models cannot make ranged attacks.

| | | | | | | |
|---|---|---|---|---|---|---|
| RAG DOLL | 2 | 10 | - | 11 | | X |

Target enemy model is pushed d3" directly away from or toward the spell's point of origin. Krueger's controller chooses the direction the model is pushed before determining the distance it is pushed. On a critical hit, after being pushed, the model is knocked down.

| | | | | | | |
|---|---|---|---|---|---|---|
| STORM WALL | 3 | SELF | CTRL | - | | |

While in Krueger's control area, enemy models suffer -5 RNG on their ranged attacks. When an enemy AOE ranged attack deviates from a point in Krueger's control area, after determining the deviation distance, Krueger's controller chooses the direction the AOE deviates. Storm Wall lasts for one round.

| | | | | | | |
|---|---|---|---|---|---|---|
| VOICE OF THUNDER | 3 | SELF | CTRL | - | | X |

Krueger gains Terror. Enemy models/units in melee range of a model with Terror and enemy models/units with a model with Terror in their melee range must pass a command check or flee. Additionally, while in Krueger's control area, friendly Circle models/units automatically rally and never flee.

| | | | | | | |
|---|---|---|---|---|---|---|
| WIND BLOWN | 2 | 6 | - | - | | |

Target friendly Circle model gains +2" of movement during its normal movement this turn.

stole he can seize instead. The work ahead is too important for internal bickering to stand in his way.

It was after he came to the aid of Kromac the Ravenous in the Thornwood that Krueger began to realize how insular he had become because of his constraints. How could he grasp the overall situation when tied down to meaningless errands and petty scheming? He knows now that this has been the omnipotents' game all along. They sit in the background pulling strands of their spider's web while keeping their subordinates ignorant of the deeper follies into which the Circle has tumbled.

This realization came like a welcome flood of cleansing rain after a long and troubled period. Even his struggles with Morvahna took on a new light in the wake of it. Krueger still loathes that manipulative woman, for he sees in her a miniature reflection of troubles endemic to the Circle. He no longer desires to compete for the approval of men who do not deserve respect. The issue at hand is the fundamental purpose of the Circle Orboros. Although Krueger did not join Morvahna's fruitless struggle to stop Everblight at the Castle of the Keys, he is far from blind to the threat the dragons pose. In fact, Krueger believes himself to be the only man in a position to make a lasting change. He is willing to risk all to bring decisive victories to the Circle. He will take the steps the rest of his peers are too cowardly to attempt. If the omnipotents wish to enforce his obedience and stop him, they can come to him and test their strength against his.

Krueger has been gathering his own army, often attracting those either discontented with their place in the hierarchy or drawn to Krueger's bold and uncompromising vision. He claims he is not seeking violence against his peers and that it is not civil war he intends. In good time he will settle other old debts—repay the trollkin for their

## SPECIAL RULES

### Feat: Hurricane

*The air itself bows to Krueger's will. In the blink of an eye even the stillest calm becomes a raging hurricane. Enemies are powerless to advance against the howling wind. They labor for every inch they gain as they suffer the Stormlord's fury.*

Enemy models currently in Krueger's control area suffer -2 SPD and are pushed 3" directly away from Krueger. Krueger's controller determines the order models are moved. Hurricane lasts for one round.

### Krueger

**Consume Vitality** - When Krueger destroys a living enemy warrior model with a melee attack he gains +2 STR and ARM for one round.

**Elite Cadre** - Tharn Ravagers included in an army with Krueger gain +1 MAT, RAT, and CMD and the Jump ability. After advancing but before performing an action, a model with Jump may move up to 5". During this movement, the model may move through other models if it has enough movement to move completely past their bases, cannot be targeted by free strikes, and ignores rough terrain, obstacles, and other movement penalties and effects. The model may perform its action normally after this movement. Any effects that prevent charging also prevent Jump.

**Flight** - Krueger ignores movement penalties from rough terrain and obstacles. Krueger may move through another model if he has enough movement to move completely past the model's base. Krueger may charge across rough terrain and obstacles or through other models. Krueger cannot be targeted by free strikes.

### Lightning Bolt

**Sustained Attack** - Once Krueger hits a target with a Lightning Bolt attack, additional attacks with it against the same target this turn automatically hit. No additional attack rolls are necessary.

### Wurmtongue

**Lightning Leap** - When a model is hit, lightning arcs from the model hit to the nearest enemy model within 4". That model is automatically hit and suffers an unboostable POW 10 damage roll.

**Reach** - 2" melee range.

### TACTICAL TIP

**Consume Vitality** – The bonus is not cumulative.

| KRUEGER | | | | CMD | 9 |
|---|---|---|---|---|---|
| SPD | STR | MAT | RAT | DEF | ARM |
| 6 | 5 | 5 | 6 | 15 | 15 |

| LIGHTNING BOLT | | | |
|---|---|---|---|
| RNG | ROF | AOE | POW |
| 10 | 3 | — | 12 |

| WURMTONGUE | | |
|---|---|---|
| SPECIAL | POW | P+S |
| Multi | 7 | 12 |

| | |
|---|---|
| FURY | 7 |
| DAMAGE | 16 |
| FIELD ALLOWANCE | C |
| VICTORY POINTS | 5 |
| POINT COST | 71 |
| BASE SIZE | SMALL |

impertinence, gain vengeance against Zevanna Agha, and put Morvahna in her place—but larger matters have occluded those petty goals.

Once his army is assembled, Krueger the Stormlord intends to resolve the stalemate of the dragons by forcing them to act. He knows he must act now before it is too late. He promises his followers to return the Circle to its primordial roots, where the weak make way for the strong and druids are free to drink deeply of nature's unchecked power. He brings lightning and storm, blood and battle, the crashing power of the earth, and the chance to make Caen itself tremble beneath their tread.

# Mohsar the Desertwalker
## CIRCLE ORBOROS WARLOCK CHARACTER

*Where Mohsar walks, he brings the desert. He is not a force idly woken, nor is he easily quelled. I'd sooner endure an avalanche than Mohsar's wrath.*

—Baldur the Stonecleaver

Of the three omnipotents presiding over the Circle Orboros, the eldest and most enigmatic is Mohsar the Desertwalker. Other druids speak his name in hushed tones, as if invoking his title might attract his unwelcome attention. Mohsar is the least directly involved in internal struggles of the Circle and takes no part in the administrative distractions of conveying orders to subordinate potents. He has largely stayed far to the southeast, alone in his contemplation of the howling wastes, the blinding sands, and the merciless heat.

Not many of his fellow druids share Mohsar's appreciation for this harsh environment, but the Desertwalker sees it as the perfect mirror to reflect the myriad nature of Orboros. In the desperate struggles of the desert animals and plants, the relationship between predator and prey is absolutely preserved.

| SPELL | COST | RNG | AOE | POW | UP | OFF |
|---|---|---|---|---|---|---|
| CREVASSE | 4 | 10 | * | 10 | | X |

When target enemy model is hit, draw a 6" line in any direction from it. All models whose bases are crossed by this line suffer a POW 10 damage roll. Models destroyed by Crevasse are removed from play.

| DEATH TO DUST | 2 | 8 | - | 12 | | X |
|---|---|---|---|---|---|---|

A model suffering sufficient damage to be destroyed is removed from play.

| MIRAGE | 3 | 6 | - | - | | X |
|---|---|---|---|---|---|---|

During its controller's Control Phase, target friendly Circle model or models in target friendly Circle unit may be placed completely within 2" of their current location. If Mirage targets a unit, only models in formation may be placed and models must be placed in formation.

| PILLAR OF SALT | 2 | CTRL | 3 | | | - |
|---|---|---|---|---|---|---|

Place a 3" AOE pillar template anywhere completely within Mohsar's control area. The AOE cannot be placed touching a model's base, an obstruction, or an obstacle. The AOE is an obstruction that blocks line of sight and provides cover. The AOE is a structure and has ARM 18. The AOE leaves play if it takes one or more damage points. Pillar of Salt lasts for one round.

| SANDS OF FATE | 2 | CTRL | - | - | | - |
|---|---|---|---|---|---|---|

Remove a friendly living Circle trooper model in Mohsar's control area from play and replace it with Mohsar. Mohsar cannot move after being placed by Sands of Fate this activation.

| SUNHAMMER | 3 | SELF | CTRL | - | | X |
|---|---|---|---|---|---|---|

When an enemy warbeast/warjack moves more than 1" and ends its normal movement in Mohsar's control area, it suffers d3 damage points.

The raw elemental power of nature surrounds him, and in the desert it has conquered the feeble efforts of civilization to hold it at bay. No city can outlast the shifting dunes, and to Mohsar there is no beauty purer than the cleansing wrath of a sandstorm.

Mohsar has learned to manifest the tremendous powers of his environment. At the smallest wave of his fingers the land cracks open to swallow armies whole, pillars of salt erupt to block the only path through narrow passes, and impossible heat hammers down from the sky to punish any beast or machine that dares approach. Even more terrifying is the fact that all of these powers seem to cost him very little, as if the greatest feats of natural magic require nothing more than walking the shifting sands.

Mohsar's loathing of humanity is legendary, and he puts up with his fellows only when absolutely necessary. Any army he calls to battle is disposable, a force to be sacrificed to achieve his ends. Despite the callousness of his approach to conflict, other druids, Tharn, and the Wolves of Orboros are too terrified of him to refuse his summons. Those who learn that Mohsar tutored Krueger in the ways of Orboros immediately gain insight into the mettle of the Stormlord's soul. Yet even then, their imaginations cannot fully comprehend the cruel savagery inflicted by Mohsar on his former apprentice in an effort to grind him into perfection, to raze away his flaws, and to drag him bleeding and screaming to the dizzying heights of his inner potential. Mohsar is as unforgiving and relentless as the sun, and his presence reflects scornful disregard as palpable as the hot wind blowing across the dunes.

# SPECIAL RULES

## Feat: Disjunction

*Steeped in the energy flowing through Orboros, Mohsar the Desertwalker has learned to sense and disrupt spiritual manifestations. He sunders the bond between warlock and warbeast with almost casual disregard, and he can shred the delicate connection between warcasters and their arc nodes. His power ensures those who would hurl magic against the Desertwalker must do so face-to-face.*

While in Mohsar's control area enemy models cannot channel spells, leach fury, or have fury leached from them. Disjunction lasts for one round.

## Mohsar

**Blind Seer** - Mohsar has no back arc and his front arc extends 360°. Mohsar never suffers Blind. Mohsar ignores cloud effects, concealment, Invisibility, and Stealth when declaring charges or making attacks.

**Maltreatment** - During his controller's Control Phase, after leaching fury but before threshold checks are made, Mohsar may remove one or more fury points from friendly living Circle warbeasts in his control area. The warbeast suffers d3 damage points for each fury point removed.

**Pathfinder** - During his activation, Mohsar ignores movement penalties from, and may charge across, rough terrain and obstacles.

## Witherthorn

**Erosion** - Mohsar rolls an additional damage die on Witherthorn attacks against non-living models.

**Reach** - 2" melee range.

| MOHSAR | | | | CMD 8 | | |
|---|---|---|---|---|---|---|
| SPD | STR | MAT | RAT | DEF | ARM | |
| 5 | 4 | 5 | 6 | 14 | 14 | |

| DUST HOWLER | | | |
|---|---|---|---|
| RNG | ROF | AOE | POW |
| 10 | 1 | 4 | 13 |

| WITHERTHORN | | |
|---|---|---|
| SPECIAL | POW | P+S |
| Multi | 6 | 10 |

| FURY | 8 |
|---|---|
| DAMAGE | 15 |
| FIELD ALLOWANCE | C |
| VICTORY POINTS | 5 |
| POINT COST | 63 |
| BASE SIZE | SMALL |

Mohsar is a locus of calm and silence amid the gathered storm. At first glance it is easy to underestimate this man. Those who come close enough to see his eyes discover they are milky and clouded: Mohsar is blind. This hinders him little as his awareness of Orboros is perfect. He needs to extend no effort to let his consciousness flow from himself and take in the entirety of the landscape around him.

Mohsar apparently left his isolated retreat reluctantly, and those who have spoken to him claim that the interruption has aroused his temper. Without question, his appearance has troubled more than just his enemies. At first many of the veteran potents presumed he intended to deal with Krueger the so-called Stormlord. Mohsar has disappointed them by seeming less concerned with his former protégé than the other omnipotents are. Instead, Mohsar appears troubled by the skorne, perhaps seeing the shadow of a black cloud only visible to his blind eyes. He takes no one into his council and even those who serve him can only guess at his thoughts.

# Megalith
## CIRCLE ORBOROS UNIQUE HEAVY WARBEAST

*Sometimes the stone speaks to the shaper. Before I carved the first rune I knew this one would outlast me.*

—Baldur the Stonecleaver

| ANIMUS | COST | RNG | AOE | POW | UP | OFF |
|--------|------|-----|-----|-----|-----|-----|
| **Rooted** | 2 | 6 | - | - | | |

Target friendly Circle model cannot be knocked down and can move or be moved only during its activation. Incorporeal and trampling models cannot move through the affected model. Rooted lasts for one round.

All wolds are a juxtaposition of elements, blending the natural with the constructed. Their bodies are a fusion of massive stone blocks set into a skeleton framework of wood and vine. They walk swiftly through the forest as if part of the landscape, but the ground trembles under the weight of their step. The runes carved along their forms mark them as extensions of the druids who set them in motion. Among the myriad woldwardens one walks apart and distinct from the rest. It is Baldur's masterpiece, Megalith. The branches and vines holding its form together are still alive, and below its heavy stone tread its roots sink deep into the ground—both to steady its motion and to drink from the earth to power its massive form.

Megalith's eyes glow with something greater than the will of its master, something akin to self-awareness. It is more than an echo or remnant. This stone goliath sometimes wanders where it believes itself most needed, and it has a way of finding Baldur just when its master requires reinforcements. After being damaged in battle the cracks along its stones undergo some inexplicable reversal, sealing up of their own accord and vanishing as if the textured granite were living skin. Cracked branches in its understructure will seep sap that quickly hardens before falling away to reveal unblemished wood. Megalith can extend this restorative power to other woldwardens near to it, allowing them to advance together as a crushing wall while shrugging off inconsequential attacks by the enemy.

The process by which Baldur constructed Megalith required considerable time and resources beyond that of other wolds. Baldur needed to carefully shape and nurture the living elements constituting Megalith's form while sculpting enormous pieces of natural stone around them. He initiated the entire artifice to prove a long-held theory of blending living wood with rock. It was as much an expression of art as engineering, a contrast to the pragmatic approach Baldur typically takes when expediting other elemental constructs. He labored for almost a month without rest while completing the most delicate stages of the final fusion. He claims that Megalith drank an equal measure of his own blood.

In the end he had every right to be proud of such a creation, born from the tireless effort of his own hands. Megalith's roots tap into the fundamental nexus of power which comprises the capillaries of Orboros, a fount of

# SPECIAL RULES

## Megalith

**Affinity (Baldur): Weight of Stone -** While within Baldur's control area, Megalith's Rune Fists gain Weight of Stone. A model damaged by a weapon with Weight of Stone suffers -3 DEF, and its base SPD is reduced to 1 for one round.

**All Terrain -** During its activation, Megalith ignores movement penalties from, and may charge and slam across, rough terrain and obstacles.

**Bountiful Restoration -** Megalith may remove d3 damage points from anywhere on its life spiral during its controller's Maintenance Phase. When Megalith removes this damage, any friendly Woldwardens in base-to-base contact with it may also remove one damage point from anywhere on their life spirals.

**Elemental Construct -** Megalith is not a living model. Megalith never makes threshold checks, automatically passes command checks, and never frenzies or goes wild. Megalith cannot run or be healed.

**Natural Power -** Once per turn during its activation while in a friendly Circle warlock's control area, Megalith may cast one of the warlock's spells with a fury point cost of three or less without being forced or spending fury points. Megalith cannot cast spells with a RNG of Self or Ctrl. Megalith uses the FURY of the warlock whose spell it is casting to resolve all effects of the spell including attack rolls. Megalith may be forced to boost magic attack and magic damage rolls. The warlock may upkeep spells cast by Megalith. Spells cast by Megalith are considered to have been cast by the warlock. When Megalith casts an offensive spell, Megalith is considered to be the attacker.

## Rune Fist

**Claw -** Megalith's Rune Fists have the abilities of Claws.

| MEGALITH | CMD - | | | | |
|----------|-------|-----|-----|-----|-----|
| SPD | STR | MAT | RAT | DEF | ARM |
| 6 | 11 | 6 | 4 | 10 | 19 |

| LFT | RUNE FIST | | |
|-----|-----------|-----|-----|
| | SPECIAL | POW | P+S |
| | Claw | 5 | 16 |

| RT | RUNE FIST | | |
|-----|-----------|-----|-----|
| | SPECIAL | POW | P+S |
| | Claw | 5 | 16 |

| FURY | 4 |
|------|---|
| THRESHOLD | — |
| FIELD ALLOWANCE | C |
| VICTORY POINTS | 4 |
| POINT COST | 134 |
| BASE SIZE | LARGE |

endless elemental power. With its more sophisticated and dimly conscious mind, Megalith can utilize a broader spectrum of druidic magic. When employed directly by Baldur or loaned to one of his peers, it can extend their magical will in myriad ways other woldwardens cannot. Baldur admits he crafted Megalith as an act of pride, but there is no refuting its assets on the battlefield. What Baldur could never have predicted was the way in which the tenuous thread of his own life would one day be preserved by the nurturing grasp of his creation.

# Shadowhorn Satyr
## CIRCLE ORBOROS HEAVY WARBEAST

| SHADOWHORN SATYR | | | | CMD 6 | |
| --- | --- | --- | --- | --- | --- |
| SPD | STR | MAT | RAT | DEF | ARM |
| 6 | 10 | 5 | 3 | 12 | 17 |

| LFT | CLAW | | |
| --- | --- | --- | --- |
| | SPECIAL | POW | P+S |
| | — | 4 | 14 |

| RT | CLAW | | |
| --- | --- | --- | --- |
| | SPECIAL | POW | P+S |
| | — | 4 | 14 |

| FURY | 4 |
| --- | --- |
| THRESHOLD | 9 |
| FIELD ALLOWANCE | U |
| VICTORY POINTS | 3 |
| POINT COST | 94 |
| BASE SIZE | LARGE |

*Call them from the mountains and let us unleash their savagery upon the enemies of Orboros.*

—Krueger the Stormlord

## Shadowhorn Satyr

**Bounding Leap** - After advancing but before performing an action, the Shadowhorn Satyr may be forced to move up to an additional 5". During this movement, the Shadowhorn Satyr may move over other models if it has enough movement to move completely past their bases. During this movement the Shadowhorn Satyr cannot be targeted by free strikes and ignores rough terrain, obstacles, and other movement penalties and effects. Any effects that prevent charging or slamming also prevent the Shadowhorn Satyr from using Bounding Leap. The Shadowhorn Satyr may use Bounding Leap once per activation.

**Chain Attack: Pitch** - If the Shadowhorn Satyr hits with both of its initial Claw attacks against the same model in the same activation, after resolving the attacks it may immediately make an additional melee attack against the target. If the attack succeeds, instead of suffering a normal damage roll, the model is thrown d6" with the same effect as a throw power attack and suffers a damage roll equal to the Shadowhorn Satyr's current STR. Do not make a deviation roll when determining the thrown model's point of impact. If the thrown model collides with another model with an equal or smaller-sized base, that model suffers a collateral damage roll equal to Shadowhorn Satyr's current STR.

**Hold Ground** - The Shadowhorn Satyr and friendly models in base-to-base contact with it gain +2 DEF against charge and slam attacks originating from the Shadowhorn Satyr's front arc.

**Reversal** - When a model misses the Shadowhorn Satyr with a charge attack or slam attack, the attacking model is knocked down.

| ANIMUS | COST | RNG | AOE | POW | UP | OFF |
| --- | --- | --- | --- | --- | --- | --- |
| **Virility** | 2 | 6 | - | - | | |

Target friendly living Circle warbeast gains +2 on melee attack rolls. A model slammed or thrown by the affected warbeast is moved an additional +2". Virility lasts for one round.

The shadowhorns' love of battle is evident even in their clashes in the wild. As with other satyrs, many of these contests take place between mature males competing to mate. While their bodies are leaner, their nimble athleticism makes them capable of impressive feats such as using the momentum of an attacker against it. Where the gnarlhorns clash head-to-head with impacts that sound like lightning, the shadowhorns engage in a leaping dance of melee, springing off tree trunks while passing one another in blurs of motion. Foes who close with a shadowhorn are often sent flying through the air, their bodies shattering against the nearest trees.

The satyrs are elusive creatures who have learned their survival depends on avoiding the sight of mankind. It is only recently that the druids have called them forth from their deep mountain and forest lairs to join the battles abroad. There are a number of hardy breeds of these creatures, some better equipped for warfare than others. From the forest comes the swift-moving and agile shadowhorn, a variety that has entered the fray with particular enthusiasm. Their build is more slender than the gnarlhorn's, but their energetic personalities are even more aggressive, and they often display savage glee when closing with the enemy.

# Tharn Bloodweavers
## CIRCLE ORBOROS THARN UNIT

*Fresh blood pumped by a frantic heart carries a magic of its own. With each cut we claim that blood for our own.*

—Kyrie Scarmaker, Tharn Bloodweaver Priestess of the Devourer Wurm

| PRIESTESS | | | | | CMD 8 | |
|---|---|---|---|---|---|---|
| SPD | STR | MAT | RAT | DEF | ARM | |
| 7 | 6 | 6 | 4 | 14 | 11 | |

| BLOODWEAVER | | | | | CMD 6 | |
|---|---|---|---|---|---|---|
| SPD | STR | MAT | RAT | DEF | ARM | |
| 7 | 6 | 5 | 4 | 14 | 11 | |

| SACRAL BLADES | | | |
|---|---|---|---|
| | SPECIAL | POW | P+S |
| | — | 3 | 9 |

| FIELD ALLOWANCE | 2 |
|---|---|
| VICTORY POINTS | 2 |
| LEADER AND 5 TROOPS | 58 |
| BASE SIZE | SMALL |

The Tharn women who practice the rites of the Bloodweavers are true masters of bloodletting. Their devotion to the Devourer Wurm is absolute, killing with the visceral immediacy of sacral blades wielded in their own hands.

Bloodweavers conduct ritual hunts according to the celestial conjunctions of the Eye of the Wurm, drenching themselves in the blood of the slain while chanting praises to the Devourer. The specifics of these rites are of little consequence to their victims but involve offerings corresponding to the stars. Rarer celestial events coincide with greater offerings of blood and flesh and sometimes bring larger gatherings of individual sisterhoods. Each of these tight-knit cabals has learned to fight side by side with smooth practiced movements, relying solely on non-verbal cues for coordination. The silence with which they kill is followed by the chilling sound of their ecstatic chanting.

Civilized humans might dismiss the existence of these Tharn as superstition were it not for the gruesome remains marking their passage. Witnessing them in battle can drive pious Menites and Morrowans to madness. The Bloodweavers close in for the kill while the shadows move like living things to cloak

### Priestess
Leader

### Unit
**Blood Rites** - Each Tharn Bloodweaver begins the game with one blood token. A Tharn Bloodweaver may have up to three blood tokens at any time. When a Tharn Bloodweaver directly hits and destroys a living enemy model with a melee attack, she gains one blood token. A Tharn Bloodweaver may spend blood tokens during her combat action to make additional melee attacks. While she has a blood token, a Tharn Bloodweaver has Stealth. Attacks against a model with Stealth from greater than 5" away automatically miss. If a model with Stealth is greater than 5" away from an attacker, it does not count as an intervening model.

**Blood Work** - When a Tharn Bloodweaver targets an enemy model with a melee attack, before making the attack roll she may spend one blood token to gain one of the following effects.

• **Blood Burst** - When a living model is destroyed by this attack it is removed from play. Before the model is removed from the table center a 5" AOE on the model. Enemy models in the AOE suffer a blast damage roll with a POW equal to the destroyed model's current STR.

• **Blood Spiller** - The attacking model gains an additional die on this attack roll and damage roll.

• **Weaver's Curse** - When a model is hit, before damage is rolled for the attack, enemy upkeep spells on the model/unit hit expire. If the attack damages a model, that model cannot attack a model in the Bloodweaver's unit for one round.

**Gang** - A Tharn Bloodweaver gains +2 to attack and damage rolls when making a melee attack targeting an enemy model in melee range of another model in this unit.

**Pathfinder** - During her activation, a Tharn Bloodweaver ignores movement penalties from, and may charge across, rough terrain and obstacles.

their motions. As the blades taste flesh, primal power causes a victim's heart to race frantically before the blood suddenly ignites and vaporizes into expanding mist. The victim's entire body will rupture and explode with sickening force, sending bone fragments and boiling gore splattering around them.

# Stoneward & Woldstalkers
## CIRCLE ORBOROS UNIT

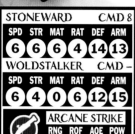

| STONEWARD | | | | CMD | 8 |
|---|---|---|---|---|---|
| SPD | STR | MAT | RAT | DEF | ARM |
| 6 | 6 | 6 | 4 | 14 | 13 |

| WOLDSTALKER | | | | CMD | – |
|---|---|---|---|---|---|
| SPD | STR | MAT | RAT | DEF | ARM |
| 6 | 4 | 0 | 6 | 12 | 15 |

| ARCANE STRIKE | | | |
|---|---|---|---|
| RNG | ROF | AOE | POW |
| 10 | 1 | — | 12 |

| VOULGE | | | |
|---|---|---|---|
| SPECIAL | | POW | P+S |
| Reach | | 4 | 10 |

| FIELD ALLOWANCE | 2 |
|---|---|
| VICTORY POINTS | 2 |
| LEADER AND 5 TROOPS | 63 |
| BASE SIZE | SMALL |

*They think us too few to raise armies, yet our reserves are as boundless as the sticks and stones of the forest.*

— Stoneward Nalosar

### Stoneward

**Fearless** - The Stoneward never flees.

**Leader**

**Pathfinder** - During his activation, the Stoneward ignores movement penalties from, and may charge across, rough terrain and obstacles.

### Geomancy

The Stoneward may cast one of the following spells at anytime during his unit's activation.

• **Concerted Fire** - A Woldstalker in this unit gains +1 cumulative bonus to ranged attack and ranged damage rolls for each other model in his unit that has hit an enemy model with a ranged attack this activation.

• **Obscurity** - Every model in this unit gains +2 DEF against ranged and magic attacks for one round.

• **Zephyr** - Models in this unit may immediately move up to 3". During this movement, models cannot be targeted by free strikes. A model cannot end this movement out of formation or cause other models to no longer be in formation.

### Woldstalker

**Construct** - A Woldstalker is not a living model, never flees, and automatically passes command checks.

**Floating** - During its activation, a Woldstalker ignores movement penalties from rough terrain and obstacles.

### Arcane Strike (Woldstalker Only)

**Wraith Bane** - Arcane Strike attacks may damage models only affected by magic attacks.

### Voulge (Stoneward Only)

**Reach** - 2" melee range.

in the event of his death: the woldstalkers carry forward his last impulses and hunt down their prey with inhuman perseverance.

Woldstalkers are simple in form and function, being essentially floating conduits of concentrated energy. The firepower they can unleash as a collective is formidable. Each woldstalker trembles violently as glowing energy coalesces below them to flow up through their wooden frames, focused into a small crystal orb before unleashing a devastating blast.

Adapting to the pace of the escalating wars, the druids have turned their craft to animating even greater quantities of inert materials and creating legions made of earth and stone. Once used to hunt those who despoiled places of significance to the Circle Orboros, woldstalkers are now appearing in ever greater numbers. The stonewards who create these fast and efficient killers also lead them to battle.

Guided by his mental commands and protected by his druidic enchantments, each woldstalker acts as an extension of the stoneward's will. He steers their movements and chooses the targets of their searing attacks. Through his constructs, a single blackclad magnifies his power fivefold. It requires a particular sort of discipline and concentration to guide multiple attackers operating with loose independence at the same time, a practiced skill for the stonewards. A stoneward's guidance lingers even

# Druid of Orboros Overseer

## CIRCLE ORBOROS DRUIDS OF ORBOROS UNIT ATTACHMENT

> *That you intruded here in ignorance matters not. You cannot depart. Every action has consequences. You may have a moment to pray to your god.*
>
> —Overseer Miredor, Mistress of a Hundred Talons

| OVERSEER | | | | | CMD 9 |
|----------|----|----|----|----|----|
| SPD | STR | MAT | RAT | DEF | ARM |
| 6 | 6 | 7 | 4 | 14 | 13 |

| VOULGE | | |
|--------|----|----|
| | SPECIAL | POW | P+S |
| Reach | 4 | 10 |

| | |
|---|---|
| DAMAGE | 5 |
| FIELD ALLOWANCE | 1 |
| VICTORY POINTS | +1 |
| POINT COST | 28 |
| BASE SIZE | SMALL |

Overseers occupy the vital central tier in the hierarchy of the Circle Orboros, not yet recognized as potents but possessing more impressive abilities than the inexperienced warders. Those who reach this rank have proven they possess the ambition and drive required to master their wilding. This is a time of testing by the higher ranks. An overseer must learn not only to apply his strength to further the goals of the Circle but also to lead others effectively. Superiors entrust them with essential tasks in the complicated schemes of the omnipotents. An overseer may not always understand how his mission plays into the higher plans, but the consequences for failure become increasingly dire.

Potents task overseers to watch specific territories and regulate the lesser druids operating within them. They must travel between sacred sites and protect them from interlopers who would defile them, calling on their subordinates and nearby Wolves of Orboros to present a show of force. An overseer moved to wrath is like the darkening sky before a thunderstorm, the rumbling earth during an earthquake, or the approaching roar of a torrential flood.

Druids at this level have experienced all of the essential paths of Orboros. Tapping into these abilities provides a heady rush and the first hint of what a druid can eventually become. The earth opens at their call, wind becomes a sharp-edged weapon unleashed at the wave of a hand,

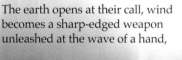

## Overseer

**Beast Master** - The Overseer can force friendly Circle warbeasts within a number of inches of him equal to his current CMD as if he were a warlock.

**Spell Thrower** - Once per game during his unit's activation the Overseer may use Spell Thrower. This activation, models in his unit that perform a special action or special attack may perform one additional special action or special attack.

### The Devouring (Order)

**Officer** - The Overseer is the unit leader.

**Tactics: Spell Lore** - Models in the Overseer's unit gain the following Magic Ability spells:

- **Healer (★Action)** - Remove one damage point from a friendly living Circle warbeast within 8" of the model casting this spell.

- **Nudge (★Action)** - Target friendly Circle model within 8" of the model casting this spell may be moved up to 1". A model cannot end this movement out of formation. A model can be moved only once per turn by Nudge.

- **Wind Strike (★Attack)** - Wind Strike is a RNG 8 magic attack. Enemy models hit by Wind Strike are pushed d3" directly toward or away from the model casting this spell. The Druid's controller chooses the direction the model is pushed before determining the distance it is moved.

**Unit Abilities** - The Overseer has Druids of Orboros unit abilities.

## Voulge

**Reach** - 2" melee range.

### TACTICAL TIPS

**Spell Thrower** – Models in this unit can still cast spells after casting Counter Magic. Remember though, The Devouring is not a special attack or special action, so Spell Thrower will not allow the Druids to cast a spell after performing The Devouring.

**The Devouring (Order)** – Remember that the Overseer is the unit leader while he's in play.

wild beasts answer their unspoken summons, and they can draw on the life force surrounding them to seal the most grievous wounds. In the Circle Orboros only the strong endure, while the weak falter and fall behind.

# Tharn Ravager White Mane
## CIRCLE ORBOROS THARN RAVAGER SOLO

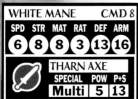

| WHITE MANE | | | | CMD 8 | |
|---|---|---|---|---|---|
| SPD | STR | MAT | RAT | DEF | ARM |
| 6 | 8 | 8 | 3 | 13 | 16 |

| THARN AXE | | | |
|---|---|---|---|
| | SPECIAL | POW | P+S |
| | Multi | 5 | 13 |

| | |
|---|---|
| DAMAGE | 8 |
| FIELD ALLOWANCE | 2 |
| VICTORY POINTS | 1 |
| POINT COST | 33 |
| BASE SIZE | MEDIUM |

*You are proud of your scars, of the few times you have tasted your prey's heart. Return to me when your axe-brides are beyond counting.*

—White Mane Morikai of Kival *tuath*

### White Mane

**Blood Assault** - Once per activation before performing an action, the White Mane may spend one heart token to move up to 5". During this movement, the White Mane may move through other models if it has enough movement to move completely past their bases, cannot be targeted by free strikes, and ignores rough terrain, obstacles, and other movement penalties and effects. Any effects that prevent charging also prevent the White Mane from using Blood Assault.

**Camouflage** - The White Mane gains an additional +2 DEF when benefiting from concealment or cover.

**Fearless** - The White Mane never flees.

**Grim Example** - When the White Mane destroys a living enemy model with a charge attack, friendly Tharn Ravager models with LOS to him may charge or run without receiving an order and gain an additional die on their first melee attack damage rolls this turn.

**Heart Taker** - The White Mane gains a heart token when he destroys a living model with a melee attack. The White Mane can have only up to three heart tokens at any time. The White Mane may spend heart tokens during his combat action to boost attack or damage rolls or to make additional melee attacks.

**Killing Rage** - The White Mane charges living models at SPD +5.

**Pathfinder** - During his activation, the White Mane ignores movement penalties from, and may charge across, rough terrain and obstacles.

**Tree Walker** - The White Mane's LOS is never blocked by forests. While within a forest, the White Mane gains +2 DEF against melee attacks and may move through obstructions and other models if he has enough movement to move completely past the obstruction or the model's base.

### Tharn Axe

**Powerful Charge** - When making a charge attack, the White Mane gains +2 to his attack roll.

**Reach** - 2" melee range.

also admire canny leaders who bring them prosperity. Slaughtering with abandon is not the only criteria for a revered *tuath* king. Tharn live to fight without question and to revel in the gifts bestowed on them by their unique relationship with the Devourer Wurm. Without the guiding hand of the White Manes, though, they would never gather in greater numbers or form such a formidable fighting arm of the Circle Orboros.

The eldest of White Manes have moved beyond mere killing. They know how to inspire loyalty in those who follow them, how to spread the legend of their deeds, and how a well-timed insult can deflate the hopes of young upstarts without having to kill them outright. Many call themselves chieftains but such a title means little. A White Mane may count only a dozen strong Tharn warriors as his faithful war band. There is no shame in banding together under such a great Tharn king.

Those few beast lords who survive dozens of hunts and surpass the odds by surviving to reach their senior years become White Manes. Younger kin look to these seasoned killers with both respect and fear. Seeing a White Mane charge into battle inspires ravagers to a frenzied state as they rush to follow his example. His scarred mien and grisly tokens proudly mark countless kills and many years of hard fighting.

Becoming a leader among the Tharn is a matter of gaining the absolute respect of one's warriors. In addition to raw battle prowess, the Tharn

## CIRCLE OROBOROS WOLVES OF OROBOROS SOLO

*Other families tremble at the howl of a wolf in the darkness. To us it means a brother returns home.*

—Kund, Huntsman of the Wolves of Orboros

| WAR WOLF | | | | CMD 7 | |
|---|---|---|---|---|---|
| SPD | STR | MAT | RAT | DEF | ARM |
| 8 | 7 | 6 | 0 | 14 | 12 |

| BITE | | |
|---|---|---|
| SPECIAL | POW | P+S |
| — | 4 | 11 |

| | |
|---|---|
| DAMAGE | 5 |
| FIELD ALLOWANCE | 3 |
| VICTORY POINTS | 1 |
| POINT COST | 16 |
| BASE SIZE | MEDIUM |

The Wolves of Orboros consider themselves kin of their namesake creature. This attitude extends to literally fighting side by side with half-wild animals and speaking of them as brothers. The hulking animals kept by the Wolves of Orboros are of a stocky mountain breed found in northern Khador and among the Cygnaran Wyrmwall Mountains. They bring speed, exceptional senses, and raw killing power as their natural assets.

The breeds of wolf chosen by the warriors of Orboros do not behave the same as their wilder kin, but neither are they tamed hounds bred for war. They are something between. Tales passed down through the older families of the Wolves of Orboros describe the animals hunting alongside mountain men of ancient Molgur tribes. Perhaps there was some ancient compact made between the ancestors of these men and wolves that bound them together. For reasons not well understood, the wolves immediately recognize their scent and seek them out. War wolves do not begrudge such hunters their pelts.

They do not respond to shouted commands but fight on their own initiative. They are cunning creatures however and do not need to be told to lie in wait until the spears of the Wolves have pinned an enemy in place. They circle at the ready and move from behind to take the enemy unaware. At the distinctive sound of the reeves' crossbows they leap from the trees as a blur of ghostly fur, their fangs bared to tear into tendons and muscle.

### War Wolf

**Flank** - When this model makes a melee attack against an enemy model that is in the melee range of another friendly Wolves of Orboros model, this model gains +2 to attack rolls and rolls an additional damage die.

**Kneel** - Friendly Circle models can ignore a War Wolf when determining LOS.

**Pathfinder** - During its activation, a War Wolf ignores movement penalties from, and may charge across, rough terrain and obstacles.

**Scent** - A War Wolf may ignore LOS when declaring a charge.

**Sic 'em** - Once per turn if this model is not in melee, when a friendly Reeve of Orboros hits an enemy model with an attack, immediately after the attack is resolved the War Wolf may charge the enemy model that was hit. The War Wolf's charge attack roll is boosted.

### TACTICAL TIP

**Flank** – This includes Reeves of Orboros.

# Wolf Lord Morraig

## CIRCLE ORBOROS WOLVES OF ORBOROS CHARACTER DRAGOON SOLO

*Morraig was born for war. The ancient hag who caught him as he fell from his mother's womb said it was the blood of enemies to come which stained his hair red.*

—Krueger the Stormlord

There are always men or women who appear to have been born in the wrong age. They enter the world like the perfect embodiment of ancestors from times long gone, equipped with instincts and dispositions setting them apart from the era in which they live. In some cases they find themselves remembering places and events forgotten by the living and never recorded in dusty tomes. Such images come to them in dreams or remembrances when they walk the places where their ancestors left an indelible imprint. Morraig is such a man, the inheritor of an ancient and proud bloodline whose steps seem to guide him toward some greater reckoning with the past.

Even among the most respected elder huntsmen of the Wolves of Orboros Morraig seems larger than life, a man whose voice crackles with the thunder of command. The war wolves who barely tolerate the touch of man gladly bear him into battle, accepting his weight and fighting to the death to defend him. He rides one of the most massive of the northern wolves, a line bred for size over many generations. This heavily muscled creature easily carries his weight in battle and lives for the hunt.

Morraig is a pragmatic warrior predestined to lead men in war. Despite the rumors surrounding him he feels little tolerance for mystical talk, shifting uncomfortably in his saddle when elder blackclads scheme and invoke their magic. He has become used to such sights as the warlord of nearly a third of the Wolves of Orboros in western Immoren, but his mind remains rooted in practical matters. His attitude perplexes some of his more spiritually minded peers. They find it remarkable that he would express barely restrained disdain for the rites of the druids while riding into battle astride an enormous war wolf that responds unerringly to the slightest shifts of his weight.

Morraig was born in the accursed Vescheneg Headlands of western Khador, but his stock derives from the Wyrmwall Mountains of southern Cygnar. His people trace their ancestry back to the Molgur, and they have ever been in the service of the Circle Orboros. While not precisely nomadic, they have uprooted themselves and moved where needed countless times, spreading their progeny across the entire region. Morraig finds cousins, nephews, aunts, uncles, and more distant relatives everywhere he travels. Sometimes he jokes that any wilderness man with a touch of flame in his hair is likely a kinsman. He considers no one place home and travels constantly, finding welcome among wild areas and rustic communities alike no matter the nation. There are few in the Wolves of Orboros who do not recognize him. Elders treat him like a long lost son, while those of fighting years embrace him as a brother and the young wish their fathers were a little more like him.

Perhaps it is his quiet humility and good humor that draws others to him and puts them at ease. Certainly Morraig has done more to expand the ranks of the Wolves of Orboros in recent years than any dozen of his peers. When he enters a snowed-in hunter's lodge or remote mountain feast hall and shares drinks and stories, invariably half the able-bodied men present will put aside old aspirations to join his brotherhood. Although he claims that the talk of destiny is nonsense, he seems to be working quite hard to prepare the Wolves for some coming conflict.

The companionable visage he bears when gathered around the fire with his brothers in arms contrasts with the utter ferocity and ruthlessness he embodies in war. He trains and drills his men until they can no longer stand, forcing them to march through forests in the dead of night as rain pours down around their heads. He is an uncompromising master, but those who follow him know he forges them into burnished weapons. They take inspiration from seeing him lead the charge against the enemies of Orboros. Few can match his cleft sword, and the enraged wolf beneath him snaps at any who evade his blade's edge. The motion of his steed is unusual to those expecting to face a horseman's charge and has thrown off more than one veteran adversary. Those thinking themselves his equal are often surprised to find his blade thrust through their breastplates.

The Wolf Lord has long been obedient to the druids, but in recent years he has come to view no man his master and only a few blackclads worthy of his respect. His ultimate fidelity is to the men he leads, yet on some instinctive level he knows he marches toward some larger purpose. When his path crossed that of Krueger the Stormlord, Morraig felt a thrill of recognition shooting like lightning to the marrow of his bones. He clasped hands with the arrogant druid and something beyond words connected in their stares.

Morraig has since taken his men into the service of the Stormlord even as emissaries from other potents have begun to send polite but increasingly agitated queries. He is convinced Krueger is the key to many unanswered questions and perhaps to the visions which haunt his dreams. Whether they journey to glory or to ruin, Morraig has made his choice and where he marches an army of the Wolves of Orboros follow.

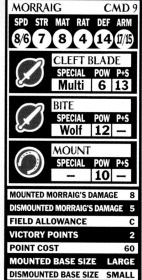

# SPECIAL RULES

## Morraig

**Cohort** - Wolves of Orboros in a horde with Morraig gain Prowl.

**Commander** - Morraig has a command range equal to his CMD in inches. Friendly Circle models/units in his command range may use Morraig's CMD when making command checks. Morraig may rally and give orders to friendly Circle models in his command range.

**Dragoon** - While mounted, Morraig has base SPD 8 and base ARM 17. Dismounted, Morraig has base SPD 6 and base ARM 15.

**Fearless** - Morraig never flees.

**Flank** - When Morraig makes a melee attack against an enemy model that is within the melee range of another friendly Wolves of Orboros model, Morraig gains +2 to attack rolls and rolls an additional damage die.

**Pathfinder** - During his activation, Morraig ignores movement penalties from, and may charge across, rough terrain and obstacles.

**Prowl** - While within a terrain feature that provides concealment, the AOE of a spell providing concealment, or the AOE of a cloud effect, this model gains Stealth. Attacks against a model with Stealth from greater than 5" away automatically miss. If a model with Stealth is greater than 5" away from an attacker, it does not count as an intervening model.

**Scent** - While mounted, Morraig may ignore LOS when declaring a charge.

## Cleft Blade

**Cleave** - Once each activation, after resolving a melee attack in which Morraig destroys an enemy model, he may immediately make an additional melee attack against a model in his melee range.

**Reach** - 2" melee range.

## Bite

**Wolf** - The Bite attack cannot be used to make a charge attack. Do not add Morraig's STR to the POW of the Bite attack. When dismounted Morraig loses this weapon.

### TACTICAL TIP

**Flank** – This includes Reeves of Orboros.

| MORRAIG | | | | | CMD 9 | |
|---|---|---|---|---|---|---|
| SPD | STR | MAT | RAT | DEF | ARM | |
| 8/6 | 7 | 8 | 4 | 14 | 17/15 | |

| CLEFT BLADE | | |
|---|---|---|
| SPECIAL | POW | P+S |
| Multi | 6 | 13 |

| BITE | | |
|---|---|---|
| SPECIAL | POW | P+S |
| Wolf | 12 | — |

| MOUNT | | |
|---|---|---|
| SPECIAL | POW | P+S |
| — | 10 | — |

| MOUNTED MORRAIG'S DAMAGE | 8 |
|---|---|
| DISMOUNTED MORRAIG'S DAMAGE | 5 |
| FIELD ALLOWANCE | C |
| VICTORY POINTS | 2 |
| POINT COST | 60 |
| MOUNTED BASE SIZE | LARGE |
| DISMOUNTED BASE SIZE | SMALL |

### KAYA THE MOONHUNTER
**EPIC WARLOCK**

### LARIS
**UNIQUE LIGHT WARBEAST**

### KRUEGER THE STORMLORD
**EPIC WARLOCK**

### SHADOWHORN SATYR
**HEAVY WARBEAST**

### MOHSAR THE DESERTWALKER
**WARLOCK**

**MEGALITH**
UNIQUE HEAVY WARBEAST

**DRUID OF ORBOROS OVERSEER**
DRUIDS OF ORBOROS UNIT ATTACHMENT

**STONEWARD & WOLDSTALKERS**
UNIT

**WAR WOLF**
SOLO

**THARN RAVAGER WHITE MANE**
SOLO

Circle Orboros

# Painting Circle Orboros

## LACQUERED BRONZE

This technique creates the appearance of bronze showing through a layer of translucent green. In the end it will appear like the green color barely covers the bronze underneath.

### Colors Used:

- Iosan Green
- Coal Black
- Meredius Blue
- Umbral Umber
- Radiant Platinum
- Molten Bronze
- Rhulic Gold
- Brass Balls
- Brown Ink
- Turquoise Ink
- Mixing Medium

**1** Begin with a basecoat of Molten Bronze mixed with a touch of Umbral Umber and thinned with a little Brown Ink and water.

**2** Wash the inner recessed areas with a mix of Meredius Blue, Iosan Green, Mixing Medium, and water.

**3** Paint thin shadow lines under the raised bronze areas with Coal Black. Paint the undersides only. Imagine a light is shining above the model and you're painting in the shadows under the raised sections.

## A DIFFERENT APPROACH TO SKIN TONES

When painting skin tones one normally starts with a midtone basecoat, then shades down, and finally highlights. Here, we instead create a transition of colors for the basecoat. Then we simultaneously shade down both areas without highlighting.

### Colors Used:

- Exile Blue
- Beast Hide
- Ironhull Grey
- Battlefield Brown
- Bloodstone
- Bloodtracker Brown
- Hammerfall Khaki
- Gun Corps Brown
- Menoth White Highlight
- Trollblood Highlight
- Thamar Black
- Mixing Medium

**1** Basecoat the skin and fur with a mix of Trollblood Highlight, Menoth White Highlight, and Hammerfall Khaki.

**2** Blend a mix of Beast Hide and Hammerfall Khaki into the skin areas that will become darker in color, like the hip area. Wash the fur near the hoof with a mix of Trollblood Highlight, Battlefield Brown, and Mixing Medium.

**4**

Glaze the recessed areas with Turquoise Ink. Glazes are essentially very thin layers of paint or ink with a heavy dilution of water. You don't want to wash the area and have pools of watery paint, so use just enough to make a thin layer in order to tint the area you are glazing. Aply multiple coats to get the desired effect.

**5**

Blend Molten Bronze onto the central raised portions of the lacquered areas. This will lend translucency. Paint the bronze trim with Molten Bronze to act as a highlight and clean up any messes caused when creating the lacquered look.

**6**

Lightly glaze a shadow with Brown Ink in the lacquered areas that would have a shadow cast on them from the raised bronze areas. Again, imagine a light is shining above the miniature and paint in the shadows.

**7**

Highlight the bronze with a mix of Rhulic Gold and Brass Balls.

**8**

Apply a final highlight to only the upper edges with a mix of Brass Balls and Radiant Platinum.

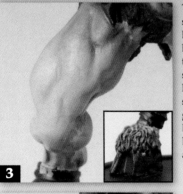

**3**

Take the mix used in step 2, add Gun Corps Brown and Bloodtracker Brown, and blend it onto the skin. As the blending steps get darker, paint less and less surface area so the color shifts have a good transition to them. Blend pure Battlefield Brown into the bottom area of the fur.

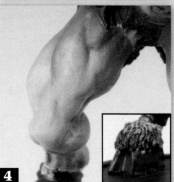

**4**

Continue blending the skin, this time using pure Bloodstone. Paint the tips of the fur area with a thinned Thamar Black.

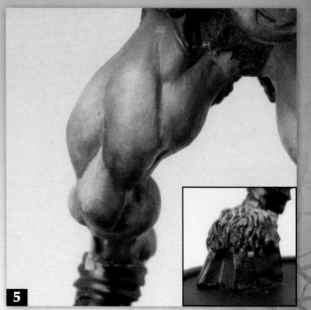

**5**

To complete the skin, shade under the muscles with a mix of Ironhull Grey, Menoth White Highlight, and Hammerfall Khaki. Follow with a final blend of Exile Blue and Battlefield Brown.

# THRONE OVER THE ABYSS

With her army stretched out behind her in perfect columns, Archdomina Makeda of House Balaash stared ahead to the darkening clouds of the Stormlands. The blazing desert heat mixed with the strong winds and the crackle of lightning from the ceaseless storms ahead. She could not see it yet, but Makeda felt the presence of the Abyssal Fortress lurking within that haze of clouds and lightning like a living thing. It should have felt like a homecoming. She had spent so long mustering her army and preparing its soldiers for war there. Ahead was the hall where the Conqueror awaited, as if daring her to commit the ultimate act of defiance.

Her army had weathered the return crossing with fewer casualties than anticipated, which Makeda took as a good sign. They had received good guidance by the likes of Saxon Orrik and learned their lessons well. It helped that supply fortresses at periodic intervals across the trackless waste had been able to provide shelter, water, and food. These outposts were small, and the demands of her army had depleted several. Makeda already had plans in mind to expand them, having seen several points as yet untapped that would serve as useful sites for future construction. But it was premature to begin thinking that way.

The crossing had taken long months—months she was entirely cut off from communication with the small reserves she had left behind to hold their forward bases, established at such high cost closer to the Black River. Anything might have happened in this time, and Makeda wondered if she would return to discover Lord Tyrant Hexeris had lost them all. Given the lack of interest the western kingdoms had shown in that territory, however, she considered the risk remote. Such disregard was one of the benefits of humanity's indulgent reliance on the overly ripe and fertile lands west of the Black River. They were blind to the thousands of square miles of perfectly useful lands between the river and the Bloodstone Desert. For thousands of years the skorne had been exploiting worse lands.

Makeda almost wished she had ordered Hexeris to accompany her, and not only to keep him under closer scrutiny. His unique talents would have been a tremendous asset in the battle ahead, as Vinter had no one of comparable lore at his immediate disposal. By choosing to meet him with nothing but steel she was allowing him his preferred method of engagement. Against someone like the Conqueror, superior numbers were an illusionary advantage. If fortune was on her side, though, the advance placement of her own people within the fortress garrison would result in a swift and relatively painless overthrow.

Atop the throne occupying the central hall of the Abyssal Fortress sat Supreme Archdominar Vinter Raelthorne IV, also called the Conqueror and the Reborn. The greatsword Kingslayer, never out of his sight, was ceremonially placed flat upon the stone tiles three paces in front of his throne. Its position meant any supplicant would be forced to peer down at its cruel length when genuflecting. In this posture its apparent distance from the hand of its wielder was hardly reassuring.

"Rise, Lord Tyrant Khetor," Vinter instructed the skorne currently in that posture. Aside from Vinter and Khetor the hall was empty and silent. "You have gathered them, as I asked?"

"Yes, Supreme Archdominar. They await your summons." Lord Tyrant Khetor rose at his command but seemed slightly uncomfortable standing straight while speaking to his liege and master. He was large even by skorne standards, though not quite so massive as the cataphracts.

"Excellent. How far away is the Army of the Western Reaches?"

"Several hours at best, if they push hard and take no time to properly organize for siege. Tomorrow is more likely, or the day after."

"Very well." Vinter was silent for a time. Khetor waited dutifully at perfect attention, unmoving. "We stand at the division between what was and what will be. This will be a difficult time for you, Lord Tyrant, and for those of you who have remained loyal. Are you prepared?"

Khetor did not hesitate. "I believe so, Great Lord." He used the most formal of a dozen words in skorne for that particular honorific. It might have seemed falsely sycophantic from anyone else.

"I have never embraced or approved of fanaticism. I find it distasteful. Yet repeatedly it is fanatics who best serve me. I know, Lord Tyrant, that you ignored Dominar Xyvell's orders to put aside your faith. Indeed my sources indicate you are something of a preacher of that particular philosophy. You have continued to insist to all who will listen I am the Reborn."

The Lord Tyrant bowed his head as if rebuked. "I did disobey that order, Great Lord. I will accept whatever punishment you deem necessary."

"It was a test, Lord Tyrant. I wished to see how conveniently you could put aside those beliefs. That you hold fast is unfathomable but gratifying. For that reason I have left crucial matters in your hands. The days ahead will be a trial for your sect. They will not understand the choices I have made. By necessity none of your followers can be privy to the plans I have set in motion."

"It is not our place to understand your plans, Great Lord. We will endure and persevere. We will prepare for your call and stand vigilant regardless of how long it takes. I will make sure of this." Khetor bowed his head once again.

"We shall see," Vinter replied. "My trust is not easily won. Only time will tell if you prove to be a less fragile implement than so many others before you." He waved to the closed doors. "Now invite them in. Stay to witness."

Khetor bowed again and went to open the great doors to the hall. Dozens of highly decorated senior skorne lords and officers approached to bask in the presence of the Conqueror. They wore their full regalia, which for their rank included both elaborate armor and weapons. Proud and dignified, each was certain of their place in the world and reveled in the honor of this invitation. They were the most esteemed and veteran soldiers of the army defending the Abyssal Fortress and were sworn to protect the supreme archdominar. Most were house lords or heirs to house lords, the aristocracy of the evolving Skorne Empire. Several had played key roles in the Second Unification. They each bowed before Vinter before moving to take their places.

"I am honored to receive you, officers, Tyrants, Lord Tyrants, and Dominars. I thank you for indulging me at this crucial hour."

Vinter continued after a pause, "All of you know the Army of the Western Reaches returns to us. We did not order them here, so this is no joyous reunion. Treachery compels them. Archdomina Makeda of House Balaash, who once served me ably, now leads her army against me. Knowing her as I do, I am certain she believes her cause is just. This makes her treachery all the more unfortunate. We cannot reward betrayal with mercy or compassion. Loyalty is not a scale where the heavy weight of previous fidelity counterbalances defiance. Loyalty must be absolute, or it is false."

Most of the faces raised to him were as receptive and confident as when he first spoke. But in the eyes of the shrewder officers he began to see the first shimmer of worry. "I know many of you have served with Archdomina Makeda, even recently. This must be a difficult situation for those of you recently returned to accept a deserved rest from the western front. Duty compels you, and I trust in that sense of duty to guide you now. You have been asked to fulfill tasks distasteful to you, but you hold duty and honor as your shields." He had lost some of them. They were confused but kept their expressions carefully blank.

"Dominar Xyvell, step forward." The senior skorne who responded was a veteran of countless battles, a living weapon as comfortable in his armor as his own skin. His movements were graceful and strong in spite of his age. The blades at his waist gleamed with the sacral stones of his ancestors. He bowed deeply before the throne. "Supreme Archdominar."

Vinter smiled. "You have served me very well, Dominar Xyvell, supervising my fortress army. It must have been an indignity to let your battle skills languish here, so far from the front. I appreciate your devotion to the cause of our defenses. No one could imagine we would have reason to test them so soon."

The dominar bent even lower. "The thought of battle pleases me, Supreme Archdominar, but I would be better pleased had no enemy arisen to test this fortress."

"Because of your diligence," Vinter continued, "I was puzzled when you failed to bring to my attention a matter relevant to our defenses. When we learned Makeda marched here, you did not see fit to discuss some of the recent changes in personnel implemented at the archdomina's request. It seems a natural question: if she intended to move against me, why send her most reliable officers here first? Very strange. Then again, Makeda of House Balaash is a soldier. Deception does not come naturally to her. Clearly she did not expect me to notice these changes. Understandable, given I am occupied with weightier matters. But she could not have expected them to escape your notice, Dominar."

Xyvell had frozen into stone, and a number of the gathered officers stopped breathing as they heard these words. Vinter chuckled, a deep and malicious sound. "Let us be done with these deceptions. Like Makeda, you are a lord and a soldier. It must have been galling to lower yourself to lying, even if you believed it necessary. I am sure you would prefer to face your adversary honestly in combat, following the *hoksune* code. So. Dominar Xyvell, do you deny conspiring with Archdomina Makeda?"

The dominar stood and faced Vinter with a neutral expression. The heartbeat he paused seemed long moments to the honored officers watching in horror. "I do not deny it." He said the words as if grateful to voice them at last.

Vinter stood abruptly. A gasp went up from the assemblage, and the other skorne took a step back, perhaps not even realizing they did so. Dominar Xyvell alone stood still, his eyes empty of fear. Vinter smiled again. "Because of your caste and your standing, I will grant you a warrior's death. Come at me, Xyvell. Kill the enemy who stands before you, as Vuxoris would ask of you."

Xyvell did not hesitate but immediately adopted his combat stance. He had half drawn his primary blade when Vinter crossed the tiles between them, the motion a blur despite his heavy plated armor. He did not stoop to recover Kingslayer but came directly to the dominar, stepping against him to shove him with his shoulder as they both reached for the hilt of the skorne's secondary blade. The compact man easily knocked Xyvell's hand away and drew that sword in a single motion, slicing the dominar's hand open. Xyvell finished drawing his primary blade and resumed his stance, but his eyes were wide with surprise. Vinter was standing casually before him holding one of his house swords. A single drop of blood from his hand hit the tiles before the dominar sprang to attack, releasing his war cry.

Xyvell was skilled, fast, and strong. Vinter parried his first three attacks but was glad he had deprived the adversary of his second blade. He knew, however, that the dominar's fighting had a fundamental weakness. While it emphasized speed and skill, the Praetorian style did not embrace the concept of feints.

The technique was not unknown to the skorne—paingivers were versed in them, and others used them to varying degrees—but it was inevitable that the deeper a soldier committed to *hoksune*, the more direct his style became. Xyvell certainly knew what feints were, but he had never honed his reflexes to confront them. This approach served well on the battlefield where he would be seeking to destroy numerous enemies expediently while surrounded by allies, but it was insufficient in an advanced duel.

In truth, Vinter rarely bothered with such tricks when wielding Kingslayer. It was a massive weapon not ideally suited for such niceties. Fortunately his borrowed blade was light and maneuverable in comparison.

He feinted a slash to Xyvell's throat. As the dominar raised his blade to block, Vinter shifted to lunge into his adversary's exposed armpit. The blade slid between Xyvell's ribs to

Skorne

pierce his lung and rob him of his strength. Xyvell attempted a feeble counterattack, but with a twist of the blade Vinter set the hilt loose from weakening fingertips.

Vinter caught the falling primary sword with his off hand even as he spun to plunge the other one through the center of Xyvell's breastplate. The simple sword displayed finer quality than the armor, as Vinter exploited a groove in its ornamentation to anchor his sword and allow him to leverage his strength to pierce its metal. The sword penetrated breastplate, sternum, heart, and even spine. Vinter yanked sharply at the hilt and broke it free of the blade with a single loud snap. He tossed the hilt with its sacral stone pommel to clatter across the floor as Xyvell slumped at his feet.

With the fallen lord's primary sword still in his hand, the Conquerer looked to the others. They had been silent witness to the death of one of their most senior peers, but they did not have sufficient presence of mind to attack in a single rush. Many were convinced that the death of Dominar Xyvell had been a lesson on the consequences of betrayal. Why would Vinter invite so many of them armed in one place if he meant them harm?

Others had no such failure of imagination. At the front Dominar Lykash shared a look first with his brother, Senior Primus Xosan, and then with Lord Tyrant Korsaar on his other side. Freshly returned from Makeda's army, these three had extensive experience fighting side by side. Vinter's lips twitched with admiration as they leapt to attack, united in purpose without a single word. Dominar Lykash brandished both his two swords. Korsaar held a single-edged skorne greatsword in both hands. Xosan sought to exploit the reach and penetrating power of a massive red-tasseled war spear.

Vinter reacted as if he had choreographed their approach in his mind. He came forward low, allowing a spear thrust to rasp off the curved spaulder protecting his left shoulder. Ignoring Xosan, he instead focused on the other two. Korsaar was coming forward on his left and closing a bit too quickly in his eagerness, sweeping his greatsword in a mighty cleaving cut. Lykash converged from the other side, his pointed teeth bared as he lunged with each of his shorter blades.

The Conqueror deflected Korsaar's slash off his left vambrace and thrust Xyvell's sword straight through the lord tyrant's throat. He could hear the skorne gargle in an eruption of blood even as he released the hilt. This attack left Vinter's right side open to Lykash, but his armor saved him from the worst of it. Though the dominar's first blade found flesh between the overlapping plates, it managed only an inconsequential wound. The other blade skittered ineffectually across the edge of the his breastplate. Vinter recovered the greatsword dropped from Korsaar's dead fingers. Gripping it in both hands he spun it in a single smooth motion to hew through Xosan's approaching spear haft and left wrist just as Lykash attempted his second strike. Xosan's dismembered hand still gripped the severed shaft as the blade of the spear clattered to the floor.

Vinter turned on Dominar Lykash and abandoned subtlety to leverage all his weight and strength in a massive overhead slash. Lykash crossed his swords and raised them to intercept, barely catching the heavier blade in time.

Vinter grimaced; Kingslayer would have shattered one or both of those swords. Still, the strength of the blow almost knocked Lykash off his feet.

Vinter kicked out with his right armored boot into the dominar's left knee. Armor protected the joint, but the impact sent his leg skidding. Lykash spun to try to regain his balance but Vinter was already in motion, his sword a silver blur as it swept cleanly through the dominar's neck, sending his head toppling.

Before the head smacked wetly to the floor, Vinter turned on the senior primus who had drawn a sword from his belt. Whether due to resolve or mortitheurgy, Xosan's attack came at full strength despite the blood still pouring from his left stump. Vinter met his advance with cold assessment; the skorne was skilled but projected his moves with his eyes. After two parries Vinter made quick work of him with a downward chop through the collarbone and into his chest. This wedged Korsaar's greatsword in place, locked between shattered vertebrae. Vinter released the weapon without regret. It had served his purpose.

---

## "We cannot reward betrayal with mercy or compassion. Loyalty must be absolute, or it is false."

---

The steps of the Conqueror echoed in the great hall as he crossed the bloodied stones and bent to retrieve Kingslayer. No one else moved to attack. The remaining officers held defensive stances with their weapons at the ready and naked fear on their blanched faces. A few backed toward the doors but found them sealed closed. Vinter did not speak but simply waded into the assembly, cutting down one skorne soldier after another in a blinding rush. He was not even breathing hard by the time he halted, leaving alive just five lesser officers whom he did not believe had conspired against him. They accepted his mercy gratefully; the floor of the hall was thick with blood.

"Lord Tyrant Khetor," he called above the remains of the butchery. Khetor rushed forward at the sound of his name. He had witnessed the carnage with an expression of growing awe. He stared at Vinter as if seeing a god made flesh. "You are Dominar Khetor now." Vinter then spoke to those who remained. "You are all promoted. Now, prepare to offer Makeda a proper welcome."

Archdomina Makeda had prepared her soldiers for siege, entrusting much of the detailed preparations to Tyrant Xerxis. The fact that she and her soldiers knew the Abyssal Fortress well aided them considerably. Though it was an imposing structure, its function was first and foremost to shelter a large army during lengthy training. Its defenses largely faced east, the most likely origin of any attack, particularly in the early years when the Second Unification was fresh. Such attackers would have had to utilize the great bridges crossing the Abyss and connecting the Defiant

Plateau. With the Bloodstone Desert and the Stormlands as formidable geographical barriers to the west, the fortress architects had never expected a great threat to arise from that direction.

Makeda had left many of their warbeasts in the west with the border forts and garrisons, knowing they would slow her army too much. Instead she had brought as many titan cannoneers as her force could support, along with numerous cyclopes and basilisks. The cannoneers were armed and ready, but as she closed on the fortress Makeda felt reluctant to employ their full strength.

She turned to Tyrant Xerxis. "Is it foolish arrogance that makes me hesitate to destroy the fortress I hope to seize?"

Xerxis' face was carefully expressionless. His was the realm of tactics; he left the overall strategy to Makeda. If she asked that the fortress be preserved, he was prepared to do it whatever the cost in lives. If she ordered it obliterated, he would raze it to cinders. After weighing the options he answered, "The fortress will serve you here, as it did him. Repairing whatever destruction we reap will consume time and resources we cannot easily spare."

## The legacy of their individual wounds painted a vivid story of the battle here—the seamless perfection of a single untouchable warrior.

Morghoul clearly preferred to examine the situation from a different perspective. "The Abyssal Fortress is a powerful symbol to the empire, as is its throne."

A runner slave approached and groveled at Makeda's feet until bidden to rise. He passed a lacquered tube to the archdomina and moved to a respectful distance to await her call. Makeda read its contents and announced, "Vinter requests parley at the gate."

"Ignore it," Morghoul suggested. "He will arrange your death if he sees a way."

Makeda shook her head. "The army must take strength from knowing I do not fear him. I will take a guard of cyclopes with me." Xerxis nodded at this prudent measure. Several of those present had witnessed the duel twelve years ago that had ended with House Balaash at last bowing to the Conqueror.

Morghoul insisted, "I will come." Makeda gave him an appraising look but did not object.

"Makeda of House Balaash," Vinter addressed her. His deliberate omission of her title was not surprising, nor was the fact that he did not even acknowledge Morghoul.

His voice carried clearly despite the intermittent explosions that streaked across the darkened sky. Enormous metal rods and spires engineered to divert that energy periodically attracted the blazing lightning to send it into the soil. Most of the swirling storm's chaos raged beyond the fortress perimeter, forced away by the difficult and patient arts of many lore masters and occultists. They had poured a small fortune into the sands to help regulate these phenomena, creating a wide hemisphere of molten metal patterns around the fortress.

Instead of meeting her at the gate, Vinter stood atop the outer wall of the fortress just above the primary gatehouse. Even at this distance she could feel the urge to engage him, to repay him for long years of devoted service forwarding his selfish plans. Memories of their futile attacks on Fort Falk were still painfully vivid in her mind.

Vinter continued, "After our long friendship I am surprised you would seek my downfall without offering terms."

"What would be the point of terms?" Makeda asked. "I know you will not surrender. I followed you in the past because of who I believed you to be. I heeded your lies, lies that would have brought our army and our empire to ruin. You have betrayed my entire people and shown your true face, and now I understand my role as a protector of my people. Our fate is no longer yours to direct. Our destiny is once again our own."

Vinter's expression was strangely companionable, but Makeda saw the malice beneath. "It is unfortunate you did not seek me out before embarking on this course. I might have explained many things to you. So quickly you abandon the work we shaped together. You have lost your faith, and I know that is painful. In truth, I am proud of you, as faith is a disease. There were great conquests ahead of us. But you lacked patience."

He paused as if expecting a response, but Makeda's expression only hardened.

He shrugged. "No matter. You have only accelerated my plans. You were but one weapon in my arsenal. Take this fortress, if you can. I will not stand directly in your way. The next time fate crosses our paths, perhaps we will have a reckoning."

It sounded suspiciously like a farewell, and Makeda glanced to Morghoul with a scowl. He only mouthed, "More lies." When she looked back up to the ramparts, Vinter was gone.

The skorne atop the fortress walls proved determined to make them pay for their assault. The siege proceeded at a rapid pace, led by the archdomina and Tyrant Xerxis. The defenders were stalwart and well equipped with Venator reivers and cannons but were also greatly outnumbered, and their fixed positions gave them limited options. Makeda saw little to indicate whether the efforts of her officers inside the fortress had come to anything, but clearly they had been unable to open the main gates. Her cannons brought it down soon enough.

Skorne

Xerxis' command of the situation was impeccable. He applied precisely enough force to achieve their objectives, and each component of the army played its part with expert precision. Ranks of Praetorian Karax and Cataphract Cetrati drew fire as clustered Venator teams and basilisks picked apart weapons crews atop the walls. Praetorians bearing ladders made their courageous assault and quickly scoured the battlements. Following them, Morghoul made his way into the fortress and deep into the heart of the defenders to sow terror among the officers and weaken the enemy's resolve.

On their side, the defenders seemed possessed of an almost suicidal intensity. Several times in pitched battles along the walls small knots of defenders fought to the last. Xerxis led the cataphracts in a bold strike past the shattered gates into the large central courtyard that had once been the assembling field for the western army itself. There his clubs quickly annihilated all who stood in his way. Makeda bloodied her own sword in this last assault, even as alongside her the cyclops giant Molik Karn wielded a great scimitar in either hand, reaping death. Yet still there was not a single surrender as the defending army fell to the forces of the archdomina.

As she led a small company to the throne room, Makeda turned the battle over in her mind. Vinter had not shown himself at all after he disappeared from the battlement, a fact she found increasingly troublesome. Nor had she seen any sign of her men sent to open this fortress to her. Something she could not see had happened here. A stench pervaded the whole fortress. They reached the sealed doors of the great central audience hall, and she stood aside as Xerxis shattered the locks.

The reek of recent death assaulted her even as the doors swung open. Her face grim, Makeda stepped into the chamber. The floor was tacky with the aftermath of slaughter. By now she could not even register surprise as she saw the familiar faces of great skorne lords and vassals. The legacy of their individual wounds painted a vivid story of the battle here—the seamless perfection of a single untouchable warrior. This was a dance with which she was intimately familiar. Morghoul soon joined her and she saw in his eyes that he was also recreating the battle as his eyes scanned the carnage.

"Sending them here was a mistake," Makeda stated simply, without emotion.

Morghoul disagreed. "A tactical risk. Had they succeeded we would have considered it the height of wisdom. It might have worked."

"Not against him," Makeda asserted. "I forgot who he was, for a time. I could not see him."

She turned, and officers shouted for subordinates to clear the corpses. She walked through the drying blood to the dais with Xerxis and Morghoul behind. The sudden activity in the great room paused as those gathered witnessed Makeda sit upon the throne.

She spoke to the silent hall, her voice clear and strong. "This day, I declare myself Supreme Archdomina of the Skorne Empire. I swear upon the legacy of my ancestors that I will forge our people into one nation, one army. Thus united, our imperishable dominion will claim the world."

A collective cry went up, and the soldiers raised their weapons and banged their armor in salute. Makeda accepted their laudation even as in her bones she felt an undeniable weight: Vinter still lived. They would not find him as they continued to search the fortress. Looking over what he had left in this chamber, she knew he had chosen to leave. For now, though, she would give her people this victory, this idea that the Conqueror had fled like a coward rather than face her. No longer would they view him as invincible. Let her soldiers believe they had driven him forth, if it gave them strength.

As the din continued, Makeda called Morghoul to her side with a look. He leaned forward to catch her words. "The next and perhaps most important task lies ahead. We must reclaim the capital before they hear word of this. Too easily the houses there will fall into chaos and feuding if we allow it. It may be a long while before we return to the west to continue our advance."

Morghoul listened closely but then shook his head. "No, consolidate your power and place someone here you consider incorruptible. But the army should return west. Send me to Halaak. Alone. I will deliver the capital, far more swiftly and surely than if you marched an army into its streets. I will seize control of my caste and turn them on any who would oppose you. The capital is as good as yours." The fingers of his left hand touched the hilt of his sword.

Makeda stared at him for a long moment, wondering if what he promised was even possible. A single paingiver against all of Halaak? After a moment she nodded, her eyes flashing with the certainty of destiny. "Yes. Go east. Inform them they have a new ruler. Be wary: some will bow, but the plotting will begin. In secret will traitors conspire to seize this throne for themselves."

"Leave those who whisper in the shadows to me." Morghoul's smile was sincere.

# Supreme Archdomina Makeda
## SKORNE EPIC WARLOCK CHARACTER

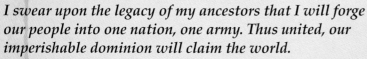

*I swear upon the legacy of my ancestors that I will forge our people into one nation, one army. Thus united, our imperishable dominion will claim the world.*

—Makeda of House Balaash, when adopting the title of Supreme Archdomina

By proclaiming herself supreme archdomina, Makeda has assumed the mantle of leadership over all the skorne people. The adoption of this title cements the fact that she no longer recognizes any higher authority. She has risen in the skorne people's hour of need as a peerless leader whose vision of their mutual destiny has inspired her soldiers to ever greater efforts. Her army faces tremendous challenges, but by Makeda's iron will, they stand prepared to crush any enemy opposing them.

Recent turnabouts have forced Makeda to reevaluate not only her loyalties but also her perceived place in the world. Not so long ago her devotion to the Conqueror was absolute and unshakable, and she believed wholeheartedly in Vinter Raelthorne IV's status as the Reborn. She stood ready for the extreme challenge of leading the Army of the Western Reaches against the kingdoms of the west. She never suspected that her sovereign had laid the foundation for failure, undermining the very invasion he had initiated.

SKORNE

| SPELL | COST | RNG | AOE | POW | UP | OFF |
|-------|------|-----|-----|-----|-----|-----|
| FORTIFICATION | 2 | CTRL | 5 | - | | X |

Place a 5" AOE template anywhere completely within Makeda's control area. While in the AOE, friendly Skorne models cannot be knocked down or made stationary, treat rough terrain as open terrain, and never suffer blast damage.

| LEASH | 2 | 6 | - | - | | X |
|-------|------|-----|-----|-----|-----|-----|

Immediately after Makeda ends her normal movement, target friendly Skorne warbeast may move up to its current SPD in inches but cannot end this movement further from Makeda than it began.

| MISERY | 2 | 8 | - | 12 | | X |
|-------|------|-----|-----|-----|-----|-----|

Target model/unit damaged by Misery automatically fails its next command or threshold check. Misery lasts for one round.

| ROAD TO WAR | 3 | SELF | CTRL | - | | |
|-------|------|-----|-----|-----|-----|-----|

Models/units currently in Makeda's control area gain +2 movement when running or advancing this turn.

---

Morghoul was the one to bring to Makeda this startling and almost inconceivable fact, and at first she refused to believe him. The proof became incontrovertible during the hopeless attack on Fort Falk when she watched grief-stricken while her soldiers hurled like chaff against the walls on Vinter's orders. Were she a lesser person such a revelation might have left her empty and hollow, but as the inheritor of a long line of resolute leaders, Makeda has responded with renewed conviction and rage. Her example has lifted the flagging spirits of the army after their defeat at Fort Falk and the debacle at the Castle of the Keys, and her leadership ignited a new sense of purpose within them.

With the support of Lord Assassin Morghoul, Makeda worked with swift and quiet cunning to root out those still loyal to Vinter. They were soon eradicated and loyal vassals set up in their place. She next confronted the Conqueror himself and personally defied his authority over her people. Though he still lives, she managed to seize control of the Abyssal Fortress, which safeguards the passage back to the heart of the empire.

Makeda has vowed to impose order and forge the seeds of a new nation. Once the vital bridges connecting east and west were secure, the supreme archdomina sent Morghoul back to Halaak to deliver ultimatums in her name. She did not hesitate to spread the word of her rulership and the consequences for defiance, knowing the proud house lords would otherwise fall prey to internecine feuding. While many of them may be uncomfortable with this unexpected coup, they remember the lessons of the Second Unification delivered by Morghoul in the name of a different master. They would not have their seats had not Morghoul killed so many of their predecessors by excruciation. His presence underscores the threat and lends credence to Makeda's claims of absolute authority.

She has shown the will to go to any lengths to ensure the Skorne Empire will never again serve the interests of a foreign power. Makeda learned valuable insights from Vinter regarding the strength of empire, and she intends to adapt those lessons to remake skorne society while retaining its vital core. She has accepted the burden of this seemingly impossible goal, and her shoulders are strong enough to bear its weight. Solidarity will be the key to rising from the ashes and becoming an empire that spans the continent. Any who defy her conviction will fall to the wayside or feel her boots trampling them underfoot.

# SPECIAL RULES

## Feat: Gates of Death

*The greatest of dominars hold death itself at bay, deigning to answer its impetuous demands at their leisure. By invoking her will over the souls of her vassals, Supreme Archdomina Makeda throws open the very gates of death to prompt the slain to return to life.*

Immediately return all destroyed Skorne troopers to each friendly unit currently in Makeda's control area. These models must be placed in formation completely in Makeda's control area. Returned models cause their units to lose benefits or effects received from the original destruction of the models. Returned models cannot activate the turn they return to play. Returned models have one wound.

| MAKEDA | | | | CMD | 10 |
|--------|-----|-----|-----|-----|-----|
| SPD | STR | MAT | RAT | DEF | ARM |
| 6 | 7 | 7 | 4 | 15 | 17 |

| SWORD OF BAALASH | | |
|------|------|------|
| SPECIAL | POW | P+S |
| — | 5 | 12 |

| SWORD OF BAALASH | | |
|------|------|------|
| SPECIAL | POW | P+S |
| — | 5 | 12 |

| | |
|---|---|
| FURY | 6 |
| DAMAGE | 16 |
| FIELD ALLOWANCE | C |
| VICTORY POINTS | 5 |
| POINT COST | 77 |
| BASE SIZE | SMALL |

## Makeda

**Command Authority** - Makeda may issue any order to a unit that its original leader or officer could issue.

**Dauntless Aura** - Friendly Skorne models/units in Makeda's command range never flee and immediately rally.

**Elite Cadre** - Praetorian Swordsmen in an army with Makeda gain +1 MAT, RAT, CMD. When one or more models in a Praetorian Swordsmen unit are destroyed by enemy attacks, during the unit's controller's next Maintenance Phase the models in the unit may move up to their current SPD in inches. A model cannot end this movement out of formation or cause other models in the unit to no longer be in formation.

**Parry** - Makeda cannot be targeted by free strikes.

**Stay Death** - Once per turn, when a friendly living Skorne trooper model suffers sufficient damage to be destroyed while in Makeda's command range, she can spend one fury point to keep the model from being destroyed. If the model is not destroyed, it is reduced to one wound.

**Warbeast Bond** - One non-unique warbeast in Makeda's controller's horde may begin the game bonded to her. This warbeast does not suffer the effects of lost aspects while in Makeda's control area.

**Whirlwind of Death** - When Makeda hits an enemy model with a melee attack including the first, she gains a cumulative +1 bonus to melee attack and damage rolls. This bonus lasts for one turn. After resolving the attack, Makeda may move up to 1".

## TACTICAL TIP

**Warbeast Bond** – The warbeast is still destroyed if it loses its last aspect.

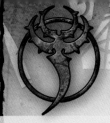

# LORD ASSASSIN MORGHOUL
## SKORNE EPIC WARLOCK CHARACTER

> *We stand at the crossroads of the glorious past and an uncertain future. My blade is ready to reveal the true path.*
>
> —Lord Assassin Morghoul

Morghoul stands ready to become an architect in a new skorne civilization. While others may not understand the workings of the mind behind his inscrutable mask, Morghoul has always acted to strengthen his people. Only those with simple aspirations place all their hopes on a single leader. In his long years of service, Morghoul has served many masters and feels no more regret for abandoning Vinter Raelthorne than he did when he left House Vokuul to serve the Conqueror during the First Unification. Morghoul has fully embraced the cause initiated by Supreme Archdomina Makeda, but few would suspect just how essential he was in realizing that vision. He employs every skill, tool, and secret at his disposal to bring about the transformation of the skorne.

Morghoul has approached his new place in society systematically, just as he would any task. First he stepped forward to seize control over the entire paingiver caste by accepting Makeda's offer to transform their loose affiliation into a true household. Though some of the more traditional paingivers resisted this radical move, Morghoul accepted that the consolidation of his authority might require some degree of bloodshed. He immediately began to forge the paingivers into a weapon wielded in his hand. Morghoul's blade Mercy was a priceless gift from Makeda, a Balaash treasure to symbolize his ascension as lord of his house. It serves as a symbol of his leadership and embodies his sanction and dominion over the lives of all paingivers.

To make his dominance over the caste a reality, Morghoul knew he could not limit himself to those serving the Army of the Western Reaches. When he volunteered to deliver word of Makeda's ascension to Halaak personally, Morghoul knew he must first confront the most proud and arrogant of those paingivers in residence. This challenge came in the form of Master Tormentor Jyvaash Komorn, the legendary leader of the notorious Bloodrunners.

| SPELL | COST | RNG | AOE | POW | UP | OFF |
|-------|------|-----|-----|-----|----|----|
| DEATH WARRANT | 2 | 10 | - | - | X | X |

Target enemy model/unit becomes Morghoul's prey. If Morghoul begins his normal movement within 10" of the prey, he gains +2" of movement that activation. Morghoul gains +2 to attack and damage rolls against the prey. If a friendly Skorne warbeast begins its normal movement within Morghoul's control area and within 10" of the prey, it gains +2" of movement that activation. While within Morghoul's control area, friendly Skorne warbeasts gain +2 to attack and damage rolls against the prey.

| SPELL | COST | RNG | AOE | POW | UP | OFF |
|-------|------|-----|-----|-----|----|----|
| FLESH HOOKS | 2 | 10 | - | 12 | X | X |

A non-warcaster/warlock model hit by Flesh Hooks cannot end its normal movement further from Morghoul than it began.

| SPELL | COST | RNG | AOE | POW | UP | OFF |
|-------|------|-----|-----|-----|----|----|
| SHADOW WALKER | 2 | 6 | - | - | | |

Target friendly non-warlock Skorne model/unit may move through other models if it has enough movement to move completely past the models' bases, cannot be targeted by free strikes, and ignores intervening models when declaring a charge or slam. During its activation, an affected model ignores movement penalties from, and may charge and slam across, rough terrain and obstacles. Shadow Walker lasts for one turn.

As expected, he decried Morghoul as an upstart and a heretic. Despite a dozen of Komorn's best hand-picked Bloodrunners standing guard, Morghoul did not hesitate. In moments Komorn and his inner guard lay eviscerated by Mercy's edge. Morghoul had taken the Fan of Shadows from Komorn's very fingers and thereby gained possession of an artifact of fearsome reputation long associated with the murderous craft of the Bloodrunners.

Assuming absolute control of the surviving Bloodrunners, Morghoul set about the immediate subjugation of the capital. With an army of shadow and silence, he delivered Makeda's demands. Once examples were made of the most impertinent, the other houses quickly saw the wisdom of accepting Makeda's rule and bowed to the banner of House Balaash.

Morghoul's subordinates now stalk the Skorne Empire and the Western Army enforcing absolute obedience. He has earned his role as one of Makeda's most valued advisors, and his presence has not gone unnoticed by even the highest-ranking officers serving the supreme archdomina. Morghoul cares not whether the submission of her followers arises from fear or respect.

What even Makeda does not understand—what no one has been able to discern—is that it is not ambition or individual loyalty that motivates Morghoul. Rather he carries a devotion to the deeper philosophies and destiny of his people. He truly believes in the ultimate glory and triumph of the skorne culture, a civilization forged in the crucible of destruction and hardship. He will go to any lengths to ensure that his people will rise to the position of ultimate dominance. In this regard, even Makeda does not escape his scrutiny. The lord assassin intends to watch her and weigh her by the same standards he once applied to Vinter Raelthorne. Should she fail to meet the challenge ahead or become an impediment to the skorne, she will meet her end by Morghoul's blade.

# SPECIAL RULES

## Feat: Blackout

*Lord Assassin Morghoul can call on his refined power of mortitheurgy to blind his enemies. With a single cruel wave of his fan, he calls down a curtain of darkness. His enemies are left reeling in pain, lost and betrayed by their own senses.*

Enemy models currently in Morghoul's LOS and control area suffer Blind for one round. Blind models cannot make ranged or magic attacks, suffer -4 MAT and DEF, cannot charge, run, or slam, and must forfeit either movement or action during their next activation.

## Morghoul

**Anatomical Precision** - If Morghoul's melee damage roll fails to exceed target living model's ARM, the target automatically suffers one damage point.

**Elite Cadre** - Paingiver units included in an army with Morghoul gain +1 MAT, RAT, and CMD and Perfect Balance.

**Perfect Balance** - Morghoul cannot be targeted by combined melee attacks, combined ranged attacks, or free strikes. Perfect Balance negates back strike bonuses against Morghoul. When knocked down, Morghoul may stand up during his activation without forfeiting his movement or action.

## Fan of Shadows

During his activation, Morghoul may spend one or more fury points to use one Fan of Shadows ability for each fury point spent. Fan of Shadows abilities last for one round. Each ability may only be used once per activation.

- **Entropy** - While in Morghoul's melee range, enemy models lose Tough, cannot transfer damage, cannot be forced to regenerate, and unspent focus points do not add to their ARM.

- **Shadowfall** - Place Morghoul anywhere completely within 4" of his current location. Morghoul cannot run in the same activation he uses Shadowfall.

- **Stealth** - Morghoul gains Stealth. Attacks against a model with Stealth from greater than 5" away automatically miss. If a model with Stealth is greater than 5" away from an attacker, it does not count as an intervening model.

## Mercy

**Dissection** - Damage exceeding a living or undead model's ARM is doubled.

| MORGHOUL | | | | CMD 8 | |
|----------|----|----|----|-------|----|
| SPD | STR | MAT | RAT | DEF | ARM |
| 7 | 6 | 8 | 4 | 17 | 13 |

| MERCY | | |
|-------|-----|----|
| | SPECIAL | POW | P+S |
| Dissection | 5 | 11 |

| FURY | 5 |
|------|---|
| DAMAGE | 16 |
| FIELD ALLOWANCE | C |
| VICTORY POINTS | 5 |
| POINT COST | 70 |
| BASE SIZE | SMALL |

## TACTICAL TIP

**Dissection** – Damage from Anatomical Precision is not damage that exceeds the target's ARM, so it is not doubled.

# VOID SEER MORDIKAAR
## SKORNE WARLOCK CHARACTER

*They fear him, but in time his name will outlast Voksune's. He has proven we can enslave death itself.*

—Tyrant Hexeris

The void seer is a walking contradiction whose very existence throws doubt on the most deeply held skorne beliefs. Though terrifying, his presence is also a reminder to those who follow Supreme Archdomina Makeda that in her army nothing is impossible. Among her chosen warlords Mordikaar has defied the ultimate power of death.

Void Seer Mordikaar should not exist. He was dead; his soul was torn from his body and hurled into the Void. By sheer determination and singular occult knowledge, he pulled himself back from that cold and horrible chasm to live again. His heart still beats, and his lungs still breathe. There is no question he is alive and not some undead mockery like the genzouls or kovaas. The exact methods of his resurrection are known only to him.

Mordikaar is tainted by the powers of death and annihilation. A seeping wound in reality lingers about him. Maddened and deranged spirits of the void—intangible yet boasting undeniable strength and presence—periodically slip through into Caen to haunt him. Mordikaar deals with them as casually as a warrior sharpening his sword, either banishing them or binding them into his service as befits his needs.

Before the event of his death, Mordikaar was a well respected but inscrutable mortitheurge known primarily to other masters of his field. He plumbed

| SPELL | COST | RNG | AOE | POW | UP | OFF |
|-------|------|-----|-----|-----|----|----|
| DOOM MARK | 3 | 10 | - | - | X | X |

Friendly Skorne models attacking target enemy model/unit gain an additional die on attack rolls.

| ESSENCE BLAST | 3 | SP | - | * | | X |
|---|---|---|---|---|---|---|

Select a friendly living non-warlock/warcaster Skorne model in Mordikaar's control area. Make a spray attack using that model as the spell's point of origin. That model is considered the attacker for purposes of determining LOS for the attack. Determine eligible targets and measure the spray from that model. Mordikaar does not suffer the target in melee attack roll penalty against models that are in melee with the selected model. Models hit suffer a damage roll with a POW equal to 5 + the base STR of the selected model. After the spell has been resolved, remove the selected model from play.

| MANIFEST VOID | 2 | SELF | CTRL | - | | |
|---|---|---|---|---|---|---|

While in Mordikaar's control area, enemy warbeasts cannot be forced to use animi, and enemy spell casters must spend one additional focus or fury point to cast or upkeep spells. Non-Skorne models cannot gain soul tokens for models destroyed while in Mordikaar's control area. Manifest Void lasts for one round.

| SPIRIT IN AMBER | 1 | | CTRL | - | | |
|---|---|---|---|---|---|---|

Return one friendly living destroyed Skorne trooper model to play. Place the model anywhere completely in Mordikaar's control area and within 3" of another model in its unit. Returned models have one wound and do not generate soul tokens when destroyed. The model is destroyed at the end of this turn.

| VOID WALKER | 2 | 6 | - | - | X | |
|---|---|---|---|---|---|---|

Target friendly Skorne model/unit gains Exorcist and Ghostly. A model with Ghostly may move, charge, and slam through any terrain and obstacles without penalty. A model with Ghostly may move through obstructions if it has enough movement to move completely past the obstruction. An affected model cannot be targeted by free strikes.

the depths of secrets in the first skorne city of Malphas and ventured into the deepest forbidden ruins. Mordikaar investigated an obscure heresy proclaiming that Voskune, Ishoul, and Kaleed never fell into the Void but persisted past death by force of will alone. Extollers repeatedly tried to expunge this heresy, but the belief proved tenacious among the city's lore masters, who preserved scrolls blatantly contradictory to traditional historical accounts.

Though Mordikaar never found the "Self Exalted Trinity," his occult research took him in a radically different direction. He has never accepted exaltation by sacral stone as anything more than a half measure and is determined to find a better solution to mortality. Key to his breakthrough was isolating the nature of the normally invisible light manifested by spiritual energy. Though his philosophy is antithetical to the extollers, his lanterns allow him to see with their vision. Rather than relying on a crystal eye, Mordikaar crafted arcane lanterns that focus and amplify his spiritual powers as well as revealing and manipulating the spirits gathered around him.

Just as Mordikaar does not speak of the events leading to his death, he is equally enigmatic about what drew him to join the Army of the Western Reaches. He has

## SPECIAL RULES

### Feat: Void Wind

*When Void Seer Mordikaar forced his way back to Caen after death, he left a perilous crack in the divide between this world and the unfathomable emptiness of the Void. With effort Mordikaar can seize that crack with his will and force it wide. Eager to escape their endless torment, maddened spirits rush through this opening with anguished spectral howls to wreak havoc on the living.*

While in Mordikaar's control area this turn, friendly Skorne models gain Poltergeist. Additionally, enemy models roll one less die on attack rolls against affected models. Void Wind lasts for one round.

### Mordikaar

**Exorcist** - Melee and ranged attacks made by Mordikaar can damage models only affected by magic attacks. Mordikaar may charge incorporeal models.

**Poltergeist** - When an enemy model misses this model with an attack, immediately after the attack has been resolved this model's controller may choose to have the attacking model pushed d3" directly away from this model.

**Void Lord** - While in Mordikaar's control area, friendly Void Spirits gain boosted attack rolls.

### Death Blast

**Spirit Rendering** - When Mordikaar destroys a living model with Death Blast, he may remove one damage point from himself. Living models destroyed by Death Blast are removed from play and do not provide soul tokens.

### Eidolon

**Parasitic Curse** - When Mordikaar damages an enemy model with an Eidolon attack, that model suffers -2 STR. While an enemy model suffering Parasitic Curse is in Mordikaar's control range, Mordikaar can replace his base STR with that model's base STR. Parasitic Curse last for one round.

| MORDIKAAR | | | | CMD 8 | |
|-----------|---|---|---|---|---|
| SPD | STR | MAT | RAT | DEF | ARM |
| 5 | 5 | 6 | 5 | 14 | 16 |

| DEATH BLAST | | | |
|---|---|---|---|
| RNG | ROF | AOE | POW |
| 10 | 1 | 3 | 13 |

| EIDOLON | | |
|---|---|---|
| SPECIAL | POW | P+S |
| Parasitic | 6 | 11 |

| FURY | 7 |
|------|---|
| DAMAGE | 16 |
| FIELD ALLOWANCE | C |
| VICTORY POINTS | 5 |
| POINT COST | 64 |
| BASE SIZE | SMALL |

### TACTICAL TIPS

**Parasitic Curse** – Base STR means that modifiers, such as the -2 from Parasitic Curse, are not included.

**Spirit in Amber** – You cannot return a model to play if no other models in its unit are in play, returned models do not regain expended once-per-game abilities, and the returned model can activate the turn it returns to play if its unit has not yet activated.

attached himself to Tyrant Hexeris with whom he shares many interests, but an undeniable tension and restrained hostility exists between the void seer and Supreme Aptimus Zaal. Makeda is inclined to put up with the eccentricities of these mystics so long as their collective power preserves the Western Army. Whether Mordikaar will prove to be a uniquely powerful asset or an apocalyptic catalyst is unknown.

# MOLIK KARN
## SKORNE CYCLOPS UNIQUE HEAVY WARBEAST

*Karn is an instrument of conquest. In another time he would have carved an empire. Now he serves mine.*

—Supreme Archdomina Makeda

The skorne have achieved a particular triumph by enslaving Molik Karn. Though he has borne the paingivers' lash and learned to obey, his will has never been broken. His service to Supreme Archdomina Makeda extends beyond mere slavery. He has some deeper loyalty to her and brings the full force of his deadly strength and barbaric nature to fight at her side. He is truly a cyclops lord—a giant of his species and cunning despite his brutishness. His single eye sees keenly into the future and allows him to evade the brunt of potential threats. With a falchion in each hand and thick armor covering him from head to toe, he has proven all but invincible in countless battles. He never tires of the sport and wakes each day eager to wet his blades in blood.

| ANIMUS | COST | RNG | AOE | POW | UP | OFF |
|---|---|---|---|---|---|---|
| Fate Walker | 3 | Self | - | - | | |

After all friendly models end their activations this turn, the model that used this animus may move up to its current SPD in inches.

Normally the skorne could count on dim-witted cyclops bands to hunt their prey in disordered groups, retreat from skorne forces, and generally steer clear of major settlements. Given their usefulness when conditioned for war, they were allowed to roam as wild breeding stock, but with the arrival of Molik Karn this changed. He first came to the attention of the skorne with a savage war cry that shook the stones of the Shroudwall Mountains followed by scores of maddened cyclopes charging down to obliterate the villages in their path. They hauled off dozens of skorne captives in these raids and subjected them to cruel blood sports before consuming them as food. At the heart of this trouble was Molik Karn, towering over his brethren and making his dominance clear. In one battle, the enormous chief shattered a half-dozen Cataphract Arcuarii with a single sweep of his club.

Even faced with the magnitude of this threat, the skorne knew they must capture the beast rather than slay him. House Kophar, led by Tyrant Xerxis, dispatched a small army that included some of  the finest beast handlers it could hire to capture this savage lord. Even in the face of horrific casualties, House Kophar saw the task as a point of pride and would not back down. They eventually succeeded in hauling Karn back to their camp but only after paying a heavy price. Paingivers exerted every trick at their disposal and every imaginable technique in their attempts to break him. All failed. Only exhaustion would overcome Karn after long nights of torment, and with the briefest rest he would rise again as ferocious as before.

At last the master tormentors admitted they had done all they could and that he was as tame was he would ever be. They believed they had failed and quaked in fear when Domina Makeda of House Balaash commanded them to bring this creature before her. They hauled Molik Karn to the Abyssal Fortress in the days when the Army of the Western Reaches mustered for their first major crossing. Makeda stepped alone into the courtyard fighting arena where Karn awaited and waved the attending paingivers away. The cyclops sneered at her and leapt forward to attack, but she latched onto his mind with a will that only the leader of House Balaash could muster, and she stopped the beast in his tracks. By mental strength alone Makeda forced him prostrate before her. The domina sensed his fighting spirit and nodded once to the paingivers, accepting this gift.

# SPECIAL RULES

## Molik Karn

**Affinity (Makeda): Dominating Presence** - While in Makeda's control area, Molik Karn gains +1 FURY.

**Cyclops Chieftain** - While within a number of inches of Molik Karn equal to his current CMD, friendly Cyclops models may use Molik Karn's current CMD and THR in place of their own current values.

**Fate Ward** - During his activation, Molik Karn can be forced to use Fate Ward. Attack and damage rolls made against Molik Karn cannot be boosted for one round.

**Future Sight** - Molik Karn may boost attack and damage rolls after making the rolls.

**Guided Strike** - When Molik Karn hits a non-stationary model with a melee attack during his combat action, he may be forced to use Guided Strike. When this ability is used, add the amount by which Molik Karn's attack roll exceeded the target's DEF to this attack's damage roll.

**Hyper Senses** - At the start of Molik Karn's activation, before his normal movement, he may turn to face any direction. When Molik Karn destroys a model with a melee attack, he may immediately turn to face any direction. When an enemy model ends its normal movement with Molik Karn in its melee range, Molik Karn may immediately turn to face the model directly.

## Falchions

**Reach** - 2" melee range.

## TACTICAL TIP

**Affinity (Makeda): Dominating Presence** – If Molik Karn's FURY is reduced because he is no longer in Makeda's control area, remove fury points in excess of his FURY.

| MOLIK KARN | | | | CMD | 8 |
|---|---|---|---|---|---|
| SPD | STR | MAT | RAT | DEF | ARM |
| 6 | 10 | 7 | 3 | 13 | 18 |

| LFT | FALCHION | | |
|---|---|---|---|
| | SPECIAL | POW | P+S |
| | Reach | 5 | 15 |

| RT | FALCHION | | |
|---|---|---|---|
| | SPECIAL | POW | P+S |
| | Reach | 5 | 15 |

| FURY | 4 |
|---|---|
| THRESHOLD | 11 |
| FIELD ALLOWANCE | C |
| VICTORY POINTS | 4 |
| POINT COST | 131 |
| BASE SIZE | LARGE |

Since that day Molik Karn has served Makeda and fought alongside her. Karn learned to respect and fear her, and even though he was enslaved he quickly demonstrated dominance over all other cyclopes in Makeda's army. The delight he has found in the warfare to the west suits his brutal appetites, and his cruelty has been amplified by the humiliation of the paingiver lash. The beast handlers are wary around him and keep their lashes ready to enforce obedience, but Karn rarely needs such encouragement. His nature makes him ideally suited to conquest and the subjugation of the weak. Makeda has said that if he were unchained and left to his own devices, he would soon carve his own savage empire, building his throne on the bones of the slain.

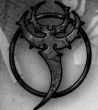

# Cyclops Shaman
## SKORNE CYCLOPS LIGHT WARBEAST

| CYCLOPS SHAMAN | | | CMD 7 | | |
|---|---|---|---|---|---|
| SPD | STR | MAT | RAT | DEF | ARM |
| 6 | 7 | 5 | 5 | 13 | 15 |

| HD | EVIL EYE | | | |
|---|---|---|---|---|
| | RNG | ROF | AOE | POW |
| | 8 | 1 | — | 12 |

| RT | BATTLE SPEAR | | |
|---|---|---|---|
| | SPECIAL | POW | P+S |
| | Multi | 4 | 11 |

| FURY | 3 |
|---|---|
| THRESHOLD | 9 |
| FIELD ALLOWANCE | U |
| VICTORY POINTS | 2 |
| POINT COST | 68 |
| BASE SIZE | MEDIUM |

*When that creature looked at me with its single terrible eye my heart seized with the certainty of imminent doom.*

—Stone Scribe Chronicler Kartol, as he lay dying

### Cyclops Shaman

**Beast Shaman** - When the Cyclops Shaman is forced to use an animus, reduce the fury cost by one.

**Precognitive Awareness** - The Cyclops Shaman gains +2 DEF against ranged and magic attacks. Once per turn, any time except during its activation, when an enemy model misses the Cyclops Shaman with a ranged or magic attack, the Cyclops Shaman may immediately move up to its current SPD in inches. If the attack has an AOE, the Cyclops Shaman moves before deviation for the AOE is resolved.

**Primal Magic** - The Cyclops Shaman may use the animus of any friendly Skorne warbeast within 8" of the Cyclops Shaman as if the animus were its own.

### Evil Eye

**Lingering Curse** - A model hit by Evil Eye suffers -2 on attack rolls for one round.

**Wraith Bane** - Evil Eye attacks may damage models only affected by magic attacks.

### Battle Spear

**Reach** - 2" melee range.

**Set Defense** - The Cyclops Shaman gains +2 DEF against charge and slam attacks originating from its front arc.

### TACTICAL TIP

**Beast Shaman** – This can reduce an animus cost to 0, but you still have to force the Cyclops Seer to use it, and you may force a warbeast for an animus only once per activation.

| ANIMUS | COST | RNG | AOE | POW | UP | OFF |
|---|---|---|---|---|---|---|
| **Spirit Blade** | 2 | 8 | - | - | | * |

Enemy upkeep spells and animi on target model/unit expire. When this animus targets an enemy model it is offensive.

Their intelligence combined with a resistance to the lash has made shamans tricky beasts to control. Beast handlers know that shamans are the most prone to treachery; they strike down those who would direct them if they think for even a moment that they can get away with it. Tyrants and dominars must keep a tight rein on them in battle to ensure their evil eyes always look toward the enemy.

Among the savage cyclopes are those of keener minds who use their unique perception and primitive rituals to evoke crude but effective primal magic. Skorne houses strong enough to capture and tame such shamans value their ability to curse their enemies, to harness the inner power of beasts, and to unravel enemy spells. The baleful eye of a cyclops shaman can boil the blood and rot the organs of any mortal who cannot evade its power, leaving them quivering in pain before death at last takes them.

Among the beast trade in the Skorne Empire, half-tamed shamans fetch a considerable price, worth two or even three times the more numerous savages and brutes. As with other specialties, skorne have been unable to cultivate shamans in captivity. They must seize them from tribes in the wild where the shamans learn their sorcerous tradition.

SKORNE

*A great leader comprises the center of his army no matter where he stands. He is the fulcrum of their gathered force.*

—From the *hoksune* code

Amid the Army of the Western Reaches, the ranking dominars rely heavily upon subordinate tyrants to dictate the flow of battle. They are the warlords whose efforts ultimately bring the skorne victory. The perfect synchronization of skorne armies and the fluid manner in which they shift to adapt to changing circumstances comes down to individual tyrants and their orders. Equal parts tactician and warrior, a tyrant stands alongside his men to lend his strength and battle prowess to their efforts. The mere presence of such a commander conveys renewed precision of movement to an army and allows each of its elements to march together as a seamless whole.

A standard bearer presenting the symbols of his house and his gathered cohort accompanies a tyrant commander at all times. The banner bears the legacy of all the honors his forces have earned in battle. This standard and the tyrant's own stoic disposition in the face of insurmountable odds remind skorne soldiers of the expectations of their ancestors. A tyrant must be ready to hold any position to the last warrior if the dominars ask such a sacrifice.

| TYRANT | | | | | CMD 9 |
|---|---|---|---|---|---|
| SPD | STR | MAT | RAT | DEF | ARM |
| 5 | 7 | 8 | 4 | 12 | 16 |

| STANDARD BEARER | | | | | CMD 7 |
|---|---|---|---|---|---|
| SPD | STR | MAT | RAT | DEF | ARM |
| 5 | 6 | 6 | 4 | 13 | 14 |

| HALBERD | | |
|---|---|---|
| SPECIAL | POW | P+S |
| Multi | 6 | 13 |

| SWORD | | |
|---|---|---|
| SPECIAL | POW | P+S |
| — | 3 | 9 |

| | |
|---|---|
| TYRANT'S DAMAGE | 8 |
| STANDARD BEARER'S DAMAGE | 5 |
| FIELD ALLOWANCE | 2 |
| VICTORY POINTS | 2 |
| POINT COST | 35 |
| TYRANT'S BASE SIZE | MEDIUM |
| STANDARD BEARER'S BASE SIZE | SMALL |

## Tyrant

**Battle Master** - The Tyrant may use one of the following abilities on one friendly Skorne unit in the Tyrant's command range any time during his unit's activation. These abilities last for one round. A friendly Skorne unit can only be affected by one Battle Master ability each turn.

• **Pathfinder** - During its activation, a model with Pathfinder ignores movement penalties from, and may charge across, rough terrain and obstacles.

• **Press Forward** - Models in affected unit advance at SPD +2".

• **Set Defense** - A model with Set Defense gains +2 DEF against charge and slam attacks originating from its front arc.

**Commander** - The Tyrant has a command range equal to his CMD in inches. Friendly Skorne models/units in his command range may use the Tyrant's CMD when making command checks. The Tyrant may rally and give orders to friendly Skorne models in his command range.

**Leader**

## Standard Bearer

**Attaché** - While the Standard Bearer is in base-to-base contact with the Tyrant, add +2" to the Tyrant's command range.

**Battle Standard** - Friendly Skorne models/units within 10" of the Standard Bearer never flee. Fleeing friendly Skorne models/units within 10" of the Standard Bearer immediately rally.

## Unit

**Fearless** - Models in this unit never flee.

## Halberd (Tyrant Only)

**Reach** - 2" melee range.

**Shared Defense** - This model and friendly warrior models in base-to-base contact with him gain +2 DEF against charge and slam attacks originating from his front arc.

## Sword (Standard Bearer Only)

## TACTICAL TIP

**Attaché** – This increases his command range, not his CMD stat.

# BLOODRUNNERS
## SKORNE PAINGIVER UNIT

| TORMENTOR | | | | | CMD 8 |
|---|---|---|---|---|---|
| SPD | STR | MAT | RAT | DEF | ARM |
| 7 | 5 | 8 | 4 | 14 | 11 |

| PAINGIVER | | | | | CMD 6 |
|---|---|---|---|---|---|
| SPD | STR | MAT | RAT | DEF | ARM |
| 7 | 5 | 7 | 4 | 14 | 11 |

| ASSASSIN WEAPONS | | | |
|---|---|---|---|
| | SPECIAL | POW | P+S |
| | — | 3 | 8 |

| FIELD ALLOWANCE | 2 |
|---|---|
| VICTORY POINTS | 2 |
| LEADER AND 5 TROOPS | 64 |
| BASE SIZE | SMALL |

*The darkness is merciful, for it obscures truths left for the light of day.*

—Lord Assassin Morghoul

### Tormentor
Leader

### Unit

**Advance Deployment** - Place the Bloodrunners after normal deployment, up to 12" beyond the established deployment zone.

**Anatomical Precision** - If a Bloodrunner's melee damage roll fails to exceed a living target's ARM, the target automatically suffers one damage point.

**Fearless** - A Bloodrunner never flees.

**Pathfinder** - During his activation, a Bloodrunner ignores movement penalties from, and may charge across, rough terrain and obstacles.

**Shadow Play** - When a Bloodrunner damages one or more enemy models during its combat action, at the end of its combat action one model in this unit may be placed anywhere within 1" of another model in this unit. Placing a model cannot cause another model in this unit to become out of formation.

**Stealth** - Attacks against a model with Stealth from greater than 5" away automatically miss. If a model with Stealth is greater than 5" away from an attacker, it does not count as an intervening model.

teachings and study anatomy to learn how to deliver precise killing blows and exploit the power of the final death to gain control over shadow.

Traditionally Bloodrunners hired out in small groups to perform surgical strikes in house wars. They were particularly valued when one house desired to conquer another without destroying the bulk of the enemy's internal assets. While some disdained this approach, the more cunning archdominars favored the absorption of an enemy house with its warriors intact. An open clash of arms would leave both houses weaker, but the work of the Bloodrunners allowed the victorious house to emerge from its conflict stronger than ever.

Since taking charge of the Bloodrunners, Morghoul has refined them into something new. He has encouraged an increase in their numbers and is using them as his personal servants, informants, and executioners. He deploys Bloodrunners to kill those he deems to be a threat to the new skorne solidarity, excising them like cancerous tissue.

Bloodrunners have turned killing into an art and walk the narrow divide between assassin and warrior. They practice rites and rituals that were drawn from the paingiver traditions but have evolved into a distinct power. The final release of death empowers them to flicker through shadows like phantoms. Working in tandem, a team of Bloodrunners scything through the enemy ranks looks like the macabre dance of a single entity: it becomes impossible to discern where one killer ends and another begins. They exploit the smallest gaps to deliver the killing thrust.

Bloodrunners have existed for centuries, counted as the closest of the paingivers to the warrior caste. However, they do not follow the *hoksune* code and see no shame in catching the enemy unaware from the shadows. Bloodrunners follow the core essentials of Morkaash's

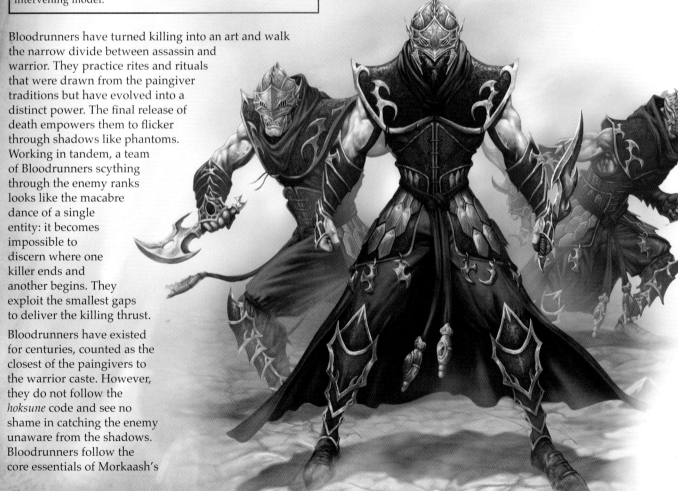

# BLOODRUNNER MASTER TORMENTOR
## SKORNE PAINGIVER SOLO

*Learn to draw strength from your vanquished foe in that moment of death, and forever after the fear of extinction will have no claim on you.*

—From the teachings of Morkaash, the first paingiver

A Bloodrunner master tormentor stalks the battlefields as a killer without rival. Even the smallest motion or step she takes conveys the potential for imminent death. The shadows find her wherever she strides, and those trying to track her motions amid the darkness discover their eyes are deceiving them. One moment a master tormentor stands in the distance, her serrated lash lazily describing a gentle arc, and the next she erupts into the midst of her enemies, cutting through joints to send limbs flying while bloodstreams writhe and twist like living serpents. The sight of a Bloodrunner master tormentor approaching means not only that the end is near but that those final seconds will be agonizing.

Master tormentors are not so proud that they must claim each kill personally. A master tormentor must be mindful of her role not only as an assassin but also as a leader and mentor in the Bloodrunner arts. It is her duty to assist in bringing each of her subordinates into perfect execution of the form.

The razor lash is the signature weapon of a master tormentor and requires formidable skill to employ. It can deliver a swift kill with the weighty blade at its tail, but

## Master Tormentor

**Acrobatics** - The Master Tormentor may move through other models if she has enough movement to move completely past the models' bases. The Master Tormentor cannot be targeted by free strikes. The Master Tormentor ignores intervening models when declaring a charge.

**Advance Deployment** - Place the Master Tormentor after normal deployment, up to 12" beyond the established deployment zone.

**Anatomical Precision** - If the Master Tormentor's melee damage roll fails to exceed a living target's ARM, the target automatically suffers one damage point.

**Coordinated Attack** - When attacking enemy models within melee range of the Master Tormentor, other friendly Bloodrunner models gain +2 to melee attack rolls and roll an additional die on their melee damage rolls.

**Fearless** - The Master Tormentor never flees.

**Pathfinder** - During her activation, the Master Tormentor ignores movement penalties from, and may charge across, rough terrain and obstacles.

**Perfect Balance** - The Master Tormentor cannot be targeted by combined melee attacks, combined ranged attacks, or free strikes. Perfect Balance negates back strike bonuses against the Master Tormentor. When knocked down, the Master Tormentor may stand up during her activation without forfeiting her movement or action.

**Stealth** - Attacks against the Master Tormentor from greater than 5" away automatically miss. If the Master Tormentor is greater than 5" away from an attacker, she does not count as an intervening model.

**Swordmaster** - The Master Tormentor may make one additional melee attack.

**Vanish** - When the Master Tormentor damages one or more enemy models during her activation, at the end of her activation her controller may place her anywhere completely within 7" of her current location.

### Razor Lash

**Reach** - 2" melee range.

its serrated bone blades unleash an excruciating wave of torment if the wielder wishes. Drawing on specialized mortitheurgy, a master tormentor can ride this unleashed wave of pain to grant herself unsurpassed mobility. Senior Bloodrunners savor the jolt of energy provided by these painful deaths like a fine wine.

SKORNE

# EXTOLLER SOULWARD
## SKORNE SOLO

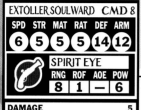

| EXTOLLER SOULWARD | | | | CMD 8 | |
|---|---|---|---|---|---|
| SPD | STR | MAT | RAT | DEF | ARM |
| 6 | 5 | 5 | 5 | 14 | 12 |

| SPIRIT EYE | | | |
|---|---|---|---|
| RNG | ROF | AOE | POW |
| 8 | 1 | — | 6 |

| DAMAGE | 5 |
|---|---|
| FIELD ALLOWANCE | 2 |
| VICTORY POINTS | 1 |
| POINT COST | 26 |
| BASE SIZE | SMALL |

*You will learn to see as I do. Look past the flesh and observe the spirit.*

—Narelka of House Kophar

### Extoller Soulward

**Fearless** - The Extoller Soulward never flees.

**Ghost Sight** - The Extoller Soulward ignores intervening models, terrain, and cloud effects when determining LOS. The Extoller Soulward ignores Camouflage, cloud effects, concealment, Invisibility, and Stealth when making attacks.

**Spirit Bank** - When a friendly living Skorne model is destroyed within 8" of the Extoller Soulward, the Extoller Soulward gains a soul token. The Extoller Soulward may have up to three soul tokens at any time. A friendly Ancestral Guardian within a number of inches of the Extoller Soulward equal to the Extoller Soulward's current CMD may spend soul tokens on the Extoller Soulward as if they were on the Ancestral Guardian.

### Magic Ability

The Extoller Soulward may cast one of the following spells as a special action. These abilities last for one round.

- **Forced Manifestation (★Action)** - Enemy models currently within 8" of the Extoller Soulward lose Incorporeal.

- **Ghost Shield (★Action)** - The Extoller Soulward gains +1 DEF and ARM for each soul token on her.

- **Guidance (★Action)** - Target friendly Skorne model/unit within 8" of the Extoller Soulward gains Ghost Sight.

### Spirit Eye

**Annihilating Gaze** - When a living model is hit by the Spirit Eye, add the target's current STR to the damage roll.

**Spectral Attack** - The Extoller Soulward ignores cover, screening, and Stealth when making Spirit Eye attacks. Spirit Eye attacks may damage models only affected by magic attacks.

Exacting procedures must be undertaken when awakening the eldest and greatest of ancestors. Senior extollers sometimes hear phantom voices not truly there, like echoes of alien thoughts intruding upon their own. A soulward must have an iron will to push past these distractions and invoke the true guidance, wisdom, and protection of the exalted.

An extoller's unique vision allows her not only to see spiritual energy but also to seize it and rend it. She can literally kill with a look, reaching past barriers to tear the soul within his enemies to tatters.

Their enemies call the skorne godless, and it is true they pay homage to no divinity. Instead they praise their ancestors, preserved eternally by exaltation in sacral stones. Extollers attend to the sacred tradition by selecting the greatest heroes of the battlefield for preservation and guiding spirits to ancestral guardians so they might escape the Void. Accordingly even the privileged warrior castes treat soulwards with deference and respect.

The rites by which a mortitheurge cleanses his or her soul for this sacred office carry a deadly risk. To learn the secrets of the extoller caste, a mortitheurge must pluck out an eye and replace it with a crystal that is reactive to spiritual energy. A number of them die from the shock and agony of the process. Those who survive gain special insight and learn to communicate with the exalted. Speaking to the ancients is neither simple nor easy, for their advice is cryptic and the touch of their minds can sometimes lead to madness.

SKORNE

# VOID SPIRIT
## SKORNE SOLO

*They are an unclean reminder of the Void, but in this desperate hour I will refuse no weapon, however vile.*

—Supreme Archdomina Makeda

Void spirits are the disembodied specters of departed skorne souls that, through some unnatural compulsion, have come back into the world to plague the living. Even short exposure to horrors beyond death's veil causes irreversible damage to the skorne spirit's psyche, ripping away former memories and leaving a thirst to lash out and kill. Antithetical to life, the touch of a void spirit siphons vitality away in a single painful moment and leaves nothing but an empty and shriveled husk. Void spirits jealously clutch at the souls of those killed around them, seeking to subject others to the pain they have endured. They are never entirely at ease on Caen and thus flicker from one place to another as they fight, making them difficult to pin down.

| VOID SPIRIT | | | | | CMD 8 |
|---|---|---|---|---|---|
| SPD | STR | MAT | RAT | DEF | ARM |
| 6 | 6 | 7 | 3 | 14 | 12 |

| KILLING TOUCH | | |
|---|---|---|
| SPECIAL | POW | P+S |
| Void Walk | 6 | 12 |

| DAMAGE | 5 |
|---|---|
| FIELD ALLOWANCE | 2 |
| VICTORY POINTS | 1 |
| POINT COST | 24 |
| BASE SIZE | SMALL |

## Void Spirit

**Annihilator** - Living models destroyed within 3" of the Void Spirit never provide a soul token.

**Death Spirit** - The Void Spirit gains an additional die on its melee damage rolls against living models.

**Incorporeal** - While Incorporeal, the Void Spirit ignores movement penalties from rough terrain and obstacles. It can move through obstructions and other models if it has enough movement to move completely past the obstruction or model's base. A model may move through the Void Spirit if it has enough movement to move completely past the Void Spirit's base. The Void Spirit does not count as an intervening model. The Void Spirit cannot engage models or be engaged. The Void Spirit suffers damage and effects only from magic attacks, animi, spells, and feats and is not affected by continuous effects. Continuous effects on an Incorporeal model expire during its controller's Maintenance Phase. The Void Spirit cannot be charged, slammed, or pushed. Slammed and thrown models move through the Void Spirit without effect. When the Void Spirit makes an attack it loses the Incorporeal ability for one round.

**Poltergeist** - When the Void Spirit is missed by an attack made by an enemy model, immediately after the attack has been resolved the Void Spirit's controller may choose to have the attacking model pushed d3" directly away from the Void Spirit.

**Terror** - Enemy models/units in melee range of the Void Spirit and enemy models/units with the Void Spirit in their melee range must pass a command check or flee.

**Undead** - The Void Spirit is not a living model and never flees.

**Void Leap (★Action)** - Center a 3" AOE cloud effect on the Void Spirit. The AOE remains in place even if the Void Spirit moves or is placed. While within the AOE, living models suffer -2 ARM. Void Leap lasts for one round.

## Killing Touch

**Void Walk** - When the Void Spirit destroys a living enemy model with a melee attack, its controller may place it anywhere completely within 10" of its current location. There must be room for the Void Spirit's base.

The skorne may fear the Void, but they know it is unnatural for spirits of the dead to return. Ordinarily they would destroy these abominations immediately. The supreme archdomina's decree authorizing the use of these spirits has caused some understandable strain among the ranks, particularly among the extollers.

Void spirits represent a rare phenomenon, but incidents of their appearance have escalated since the arrival of Void Seer Mordikaar, who has proven he can call them to task. He has instructed mortitheurges and extollers in the means by which they can control these entities.

# Tyrant Rhadeim
## SKORNE PRAETORIAN FEROX CHARACTER DRAGOON SOLO

*The cruelty of a ferox is not rooted in malice but in an awareness of having the power of life or death over its prey.*

—Tyrant Rhadeim

Astride his ferocious steed, Tyrant Rhadeim leads the Praetorian Ferox of the Army of the Western Reaches. The maneuvers he executes in the midst of battle have left enemy commanders bewildered and disordered as ferox and riders flow through their lines, leaving scattered corpses before they disengage. By the time the enemy has regrouped to stand against him, Rhadeim has already moved to strike elsewhere in the line, disintegrating poorly defended flanks and spreading confusion through the ranks.

He rose to fame through a combination of daring tactical ingenuity and a willingness to seize the initiative. He will adapt to any combat circumstance with apparent disregard for his standing orders or personal safety. He brings an element of unpredictability to the regimented and disciplined Army of the Western Reaches which is otherwise sorely lacking. That Makeda values his

unconventional approach to command is clear, although some might say her willingness to send him on risky missions could be a means of punishing rather than honoring him. Nonetheless, his long string of victories has only added to his legend. Other cavalry officers admire Rhadeim and are willing to follow him to any lengths since they know he will lead them to glory. Those same officers, however, are quick to instruct their subordinates not to follow his example too closely. A well disciplined army can only handle a few warriors such as he.

Rhadeim was raised as the heir to House Bashek, a rightfully proud and ancient lineage that has long been associated with mastering the difficult ferox. According to their ancestral legends, the Bashek were among the first skorne on the Plains of Sortaan to subjugate the great cats and turn them into half-wild and reluctant steeds. Breeding and riding them is a rite of passage in the house. The Bashek rely relatively little on paingiver beast handlers to tame their ferox, considering it vital that these beasts

retain their wild ferocity so long as they learn to obey their riders. House Bashek eventually came under the dominion of Archdominar Vaactesh of House Balaash, Makeda's legendary grandfather. Since that time they have served as one of the more influential subordinate houses owing direct fealty to Makeda's line.

Rhadeim took to the ferox from a very young age, proving his blood ran true. He fearlessly walked among them as if daring the cats to take a swipe at him. The cat handlers used to say young Rhadeim had the stare of a basilisk. He could stop a ferox with a single look and pin it there as he reached out to touch its oversized fangs. He began to train as a Praetorian ferox rider as soon as he was old enough to sit in the saddle. He served alongside Makeda during the difficult years when Balaash was isolated from its peers and later earned glories warring against other houses during the Second Unification.

In time he earned the Lance of Bashek, a relic of his ancestors. It contains a shard of the sacral stone of the founder of their house, and in a long-held tradition the extollers confirmed that the ancestral spirit within the lance approved of its next bearer. This weapon is reputedly capable of mortally wounding any foe when wielded by a skorne bearing the blessings of the house founder.

During the Second Unification Rhadeim proved the merits of his unconventional tactics to Makeda, gathering the house cavalry and organizing them into several smaller cohorts. Makeda was at first discomfited by his willingness to throw aside her most meticulous plans in favor of his own instincts, but she soon learned to trust the cavalry to his hands. They served as both reconnaissance and as a rapid strike force to confound the enemy. Several times Rhadeim took it upon himself to travel far from the main army on raids, diverting cohorts to cut off supply lines deep within enemy territory. More than once, his plunder brought invaluable stores of food and equipment back to Makeda's beleaguered army, allowing them to maintain forward momentum. While some dominars and tyrants bristle at his disregard of protocol, Makeda came to rely on his ability to adapt to any situation. Too many other tyrants let singular opportunities slip by with the excuse that they had not received orders.

Rhadeim has brought that same attitude to the Army of the Western Reaches, where Makeda has put him to work organizing an even larger contingent of Praetorian Ferox. Given the great distances involved in the still fledgling territories carved out of the Bloodstone Marches, the speed of the cavalry has been invaluable. Rhadeim has shown an uncanny knack for predicting the needs of his supreme archdomina and her immediate subordinates. He has a reputation for arriving on his own prerogative at key battles at just the right time to tip the balance.

In combat he seems similarly prescient, anticipating where enemy lines are about to falter and where lapses in command will leave an opening. As soon as he perceives a weakness, he drives his steed forward into the breach to strike for the kill. His subordinates describe him in awe as half ferox, his eyes as cold as the beast he rides and his predatory instincts as finely honed. In meetings with his peers few can long hold his stare, as if the gathered weight of centuries of cavalry tyrants is felt through his eyes.

# SPECIAL RULES

## Rhadeim

**Cohort** - Praetorian Ferox in a horde with Rhadeim gain Evasion. An affected Praetorian Ferox cannot end the Evasion movement out of formation or cause another model in their unit to become out of formation.

**Commander** - Rhadeim has a command range equal to his CMD in inches. Friendly Skorne models/units in his command range may use Rhadeim's CMD when making command checks. Rhadeim may rally and give orders to friendly Skorne models in his command range

**Dragoon** - While mounted, Rhadeim has base SPD 8 and base ARM 17. Dismounted, Rhadeim has base SPD 6 and base ARM 15.

**Evasion** - After resolving an enemy attack that misses mounted Rhadeim, he may immediately move up to 5". During this movement, Rhadeim may move through other models if he has enough movement to move completely past their bases, cannot be targeted by free strikes, and ignores rough terrain, obstacles, and other movement penalties and effects.

**Fearless** - Rhadeim never flees.

**Grace** - While mounted, Rhadeim cannot be knocked down.

**Relentless Charge** - While mounted, Rhadeim may charge across rough terrain and obstacles without penalty.

**Unpredictable Movement** - While mounted, Rhadeim may move up to 5" during his controller's Maintenance Phase. During this movement, he may move over other models if he has enough movement to move completely past their bases, cannot be targeted by free strikes, and ignores rough terrain, obstacles, and other movement penalties and effects.

## Lance of Bashek

**Pierce** - Targets with medium-sized or larger bases have their base ARM stats halved when calculating damage from a charge attack. Rhadeim gains +2 on charge attack damage rolls against models with small bases.

**Reach** - 2" melee range.

## Bite

**Ferox** - The Bite attack cannot be used to make charge attacks. Do not add Rhadeim's STR to the POW of the Bite attack. When dismounted Rhadeim loses this weapon.

| RHADEIM | | | | | CMD 9 | |
|---|---|---|---|---|---|---|
| SPD | STR | MAT | RAT | DEF | ARM | |
| 8/6 | 7 | 8 | 4 | 14 | 17/15 | |

| LANCE OF BASHEK | | |
|---|---|---|
| SPECIAL | POW | P+S |
| Multi | 7 | 14 |

| BITE | | |
|---|---|---|
| SPECIAL | POW | P+S |
| Ferox | 12 | — |

| MOUNT | | |
|---|---|---|
| SPECIAL | POW | P+S |
| — | 10 | — |

| MOUNTED RHADEIM'S DAMAGE | 8 |
|---|---|
| DISMOUNTED RHADEIM'S DAMAGE | 5 |
| FIELD ALLOWANCE | C |
| VICTORY POINTS | 2 |
| POINT COST | 72 |
| MOUNTED BASE SIZE | LARGE |
| DISMOUNTED BASE SIZE | SMALL |

Skorne

## SUPREME ARCHDOMINA MAKEDA
### EPIC WARLOCK

## LORD ASSASSIN MORGHOUL
### EPIC WARLOCK

## VOID SEER MORDIKAAR
### WARLOCK

**CYCLOPS SHAMAN**
LIGHT WARBEAST

**VOID SPIRIT**
SOLO

**EXTOLLER SOULWARD**
SOLO

**MOLIK KARN**
UNIQUE HEAVY WARBEAST

# Painting Skorne

## SKORNE SKIN TONES

The vast Skorne Empire stretches over hundreds of miles of torturous terrain, and as a result their skin color varies much like in humans. Skin tones can differ from house to house, so here are two options for how to paint skorne skin. Zaal's skin technique involves a stark contrasting skin tone utilizing quickly washed shadows while the Extoller's skin technique takes more time and care to balance softer and warmer shadows.

**Colors used:**

- ● Skorne Red
- ● Battlefield Brown
- ○ 'Jack Bone
- ○ Menoth White Highlight
- ● Thamar Black
- ○ Mixing Medium

**1** Basecoat with 'Jack Bone. Then wash the skin with a mix of Battlefield Brown, water, and Mixing Medium.

**2** After the wash is dry, go back and highlight with 'Jack Bone.

**3** Mix some Menoth White Highlight in with the 'Jack Bone and continue highlighting.

**4** Apply Menoth White Highlight on the uppermost edges as the final highlight.

**5** Paint a little Skorne Red mixed with Battlefield Brown under the eyes. Black out the sockets, mouth, and lips with Thamar Black.

**6** Paint the teeth with the Skorne Red / Battlefield Brown mixture from step 5, and paint the eye with Menoth White Highlight.

## SKORNE ARMOR

When painting a Skorne horde it is important to understand how to paint the red and gold armor cleanly. Here we show how the Privateer Press studio does it, but feel free to experiment to fashion your own process. Note that the trick to vibrant reds is using ink glazes. Remember that glazes need to be thin and applied conservatively with multiple coats.

**Colors used:**

- ● Skorne Red
- ● Ember Orange
- ○ Heartfire
- ● Exile Blue
- ● Coal Black
- ● Umbral Umber
- ● Thamar Black
- ◐ Radiant Platinum
- ◐ Rhulic Gold
- ○ Solid Gold
- ● Red Ink
- ○ Yellow Ink
- ● Brown Ink

Basecoat the red parts of the armor with Skorne Red. Begin shading with a mix of Umbral Umber and Exile Blue. Finish the deeper shading by adding Coal Black to the shading mix.

**1**

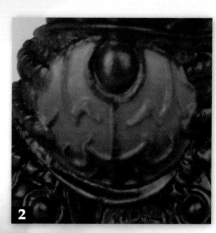

Begin highlighting with a mix of Skorne Red and Ember Orange. Add more Ember Orange and Heartfire to the mix and continue highlighting.

**2**

Skorne

# EXTOLLER

**7** Paint the teeth with Menoth White Highlight (MWH). For the lips, first paint a line of Thamar Black mixed with MWH on the lower lip. Then add more MWH to the mix to create an off-white, and dot onto the lip.

**1** Basecoat the Extoller with a mix of 'Jack Bone and Menoth White Highlight.

**2** Mix Gun Corps Brown, Bloodstone, and some of the basecoat color and blend it into the shadows and recesses.

**3** Add more Gun Corps Brown and Bloodstone to the mix and blend this color deeper into the shadows.

**4** For the final shadow, blend with a mix of Gun Corps Brown and Bloodstone.

**5** Go back with the basecoat color and touch up any overspills, mistakes, and zealous shadowing.

**6** Highlight the skin with a mix of Menoth White Highlight and the basecoat color.

**7** Blacken the eye sockets and lips with Thamar Black.

**8** Paint Beaten Purple onto the lips, and color the eyes with Menoth White Highlight.

**9** Add Menoth White Highlight to Beaten Purple and use it to highlight the lips. Then add more Menoth White Highlight to the mix and make the final dot.

## Colors used:

- ● Beaten Purple
- ◐ Bloodstone
- ◑ Gun Corps Brown
- ○ 'Jack Bone
- ○ Menoth White Highlight
- ● Thamar Black

**3** Highlight higher with Ember Orange.

**4** For the final highlight paint a line across the top with a mix of Ember Orange and Heartfire.

**5** Glaze the area with Red Ink mixed with a touch of Yellow Ink. Around five coats will do the trick. Finish the red with a final glaze of Red Ink.

**6** Reclaim the trim with Thamar Black, then basecoat the gold trim with Rhulic Gold thinned with a touch of Yellow Ink and Brown Ink. Shade the gold with a mix of Brown Ink and Yellow Ink.

**7** Begin highlighting the gold with a mix of Rhulic Gold and Solid Gold. Continue highlighting with a mix of Solid Gold and Radiant Platinum on the higher points.

**8** Give the gold a series of final highlight points on the upper tips with Radiant Platinum.

# MUTAGENESIS

Traversing the deep and convoluted passages far beneath Ios turned out to be far more difficult and tedious than any of them had anticipated. These passages were in much worse condition than the ones the Legion had used to bypass parts of the Thornwood and the Cygnaran border fortresses. It had been long centuries since Everblight had made use of them, and enormous differences in physiology tainted the usefulness of the dragon's recollections.

Small crevasses easily crossed by a dragon proved impassable for Vayl, Saeryn, Thagrosh, and the few spawn accompanying them. In that ancient era, Everblight had liberally bored through sections of solid rock to connect one cave to another with little regard for structural stability. This had resulted in several entirely collapsed sections. The teraphim proved their worth tunneling through these, but the route was winding and treacherous.

One other obstacle was no less significant: Thagrosh was still experiencing the pain and confusion of the absorption of Pyromalfic's athanc. The process was taking longer than he had anticipated and occupied the bulk of Everblight's consciousness. Vayl and Saeryn were the most distant from it—what they could sense on the fringes of their minds was only a fraction of their master's tremendous effort—and even they could feel the strain. It seemed as if Everblight's mind clenched tight around itself in an effort to seal itself off from outside distractions.

They understood without discussing it that the dragon's divided athanc likely made the process more difficult. He was absorbing Pyromalfic with only a portion of his original essence. Both Vayl and Saeryn half expected Everblight to ask them to return their shards to strengthen him, and the thought terrified them. Fortunately that had not come to pass as yet, but the possibility lurked in their minds.

Everblight gave them little direct guidance on their course, only the occasional eruption of memories and impatient commands to follow a certain passage or to tunnel through a given wall of stone. At one especially large chasm the dragon suddenly manifested strongly in their minds, vividly remembering times long past. An offshoot of this particular intersection would have taken them up to the old Fane of Ayisla below the ruins of Issyrah, the city where Everblight had lost his corporeal body in battle with the Iosans. That was a route Everblight adamantly forbade them to follow. After a brief moment the dragon mind vanished once again to return to the slow digestion of its prey.

The small party made slow progress, but each step had its price. They had no sense of how far they were beneath the surface, and at times the weight of so much stone above them seemed to press down with stifling intensity. Vayl in particular showed the strain. She was too proud to complain, but discomfort marred her usually serene expression between bouts of intense claustrophobia. She had first realized her loathing of these tight spaces during their briefer trek in caverns below the Thornwood while evading Cygnaran border defenders. Until then she had lived her life under the open sky and had never felt trapped beneath the earth. The longer they marched the harder it became to ignore the pressure lurking behind her eyes, a sensation similar to panic. She clamped down on it by sheer force of will, refusing to show weakness to either Thagrosh or Saeryn.

Their athanc shards extended the limits of mortal flesh, but although they could endure without food or water, it became increasingly uncomfortable. They felt all the pangs of starvation and desiccation even while their bodies survived. Infrequently they came across an underground stream and could assuage the worst of it, but hunger remained a constant companion.

The dragon's distraction diminished the usual mental intimacy shared by the warlocks, particularly those who were not with them. While Vayl and Saeryn could still sense one another unimpeded, both of them felt removed from Thagrosh due to his shared isolation with the dragon mind. The others on the surface seemed a world away. This intimacy shared between the two women was not a comfortable one, as they had never been particularly close. There was an undeniable rivalry between them amplified by their forced proximity.

Because of their own useless eyes they remained linked almost constantly to the senses of their teraphim. Not only did this carry a mental strain, but such an indirect method of vision also was not always sufficient to prevent them from tripping over unexpected obstacles from time to time. Even worse, after long hours bound to the minds of spawn it was difficult to pull loose and accept the sensation of warm blood coursing through their own hearts and limbs.

Vayl could feel Saeryn's additional distress as she coped with the absence of her twin. It was a sensation not entirely dissimilar to the loss of an arm or leg, even though she knew the separation was temporary. If Saeryn focused her will and reached hard enough she could feel Rhyas out in the world, running and killing beneath the open sky. Her sister's freedom fed a dark jealousy within her that bled across to Vayl's awareness despite Saeryn's attempts to keep her thoughts private. This lack of self control was unusual for Saeryn, giving Vayl a rare glimpse into her rival's mind.

Both Vayl and Saeryn kept these minor troubles to themselves. Nothing could compare to what Thagrosh was experiencing. Periodically they had to halt so that they could focus their sorcery entirely on siphoning the blighted energies bathing him like an endless tide. Surge upon surge of intense pain wracked his body as each cell screamed through its death throes and was reignited by the unnatural spark of blighted power. Early in the passage his entire skin had sloughed off, exposing bloody muscles and tendons while he howled in agony. Its rapid regrowth had been almost as painful.

Muscle seizures occasionally overcame the ogrun, and each time his body looked different afterward. Already he was taller than before, his torso considerably thicker. The muscles of his legs had grown and hardened, and the bones themselves lengthened in one agonizing night. As yet unfinished growths protruded from his back. At times his breathing became labored and strained, as if his lungs were insufficient to support his new bulk. The bones of his skull shifted and changed layer by layer, tearing his skin apart each time. When awake he often thrashed out at them without recognition. Once he left a trail of deep gashes across Vayl's chest before the light of awareness came back to his eyes.

The dragon's voice connected directly to him. Words escaped his lips he didn't seem to realize he uttered, dead languages and guttural pronunciations that held no meaning for either of the Nyss without the dragon's consciousness to translate them. Sometimes he spoke as Everblight himself to hurl taunts and invective at Pyromalfic in the struggle to complete the other dragon's absorption.

What neither Vayl nor Saeryn comprehended was that for a time Thagrosh connected not just to Everblight but also to the vanquished Pyromalfic. The alien mind felt like a seething and cancerous growth of incomprehensibility to Thagrosh despite his merged consciousness with Everblight. Nothing of his immersion in Everblight's essence and the maze of his memories prepared him for the blazing malevolence that invaded him as the foreign athanc fought for its existence. It latched onto him after sensing weakness in his mortal flesh and sank barbed claws straight into his cerebrum to rage across the shattered nerves of his inadequate ogrun brain.

---

## "You are nothing but an inadequate vessel. Everblight will discard you as soon as he can. Your mortal shell is weak! Can you see how it strains him?"

---

In all his millennia of existence Everblight had never consumed another dragon. He had no comparison for this process, but he knew he was succeeding, and that filled him with a burning pride. More importantly, he was doing it without even being completely whole. Never had one dragon tried to absorb the athanc of another without access to its full strength. Buried inside the dragon's mind, Thagrosh reveled in Everblight's growing pride as if it were his own.

As the process raged on, Thagrosh struggled with his own inner fear that his body could not withstand it and that it would leave him annihilated. Pyromalfic's voice would emerge at his times of doubt, insidiously, more intimate than the closest whisper. "You are nothing but an inadequate vessel. Everblight will discard you as soon as he can. Your mortal shell is weak! Can you see how it strains him? He longs to return to his natural flesh. You can adapt only so much. You are at your limit. How can this satisfy him? My end will seem merciful in comparison to yours."

He could not escape the sense that there was something fundamentally flawed in the vanquished dragon. More

disturbing than the actual words was a feeling beneath them related to a distant memory Pyromalfic had kept buried. For decades beyond counting, Pyromalfic had lain recovering from an injury that healed only bit by bit. The slow recuperation was similar to Everblight's after suffering at the claws of Toruk, but Pyromalfic had not had such an encounter. The injuries should not have persisted. The dragon had become convinced something weakened its regenerative capacity—perhaps even something intrinsic to its athanc. Was such a thing possible? This had clearly weighed on Pyromalfic's mind for years before the arrival of the Legion brought all such musings to an end.

Thagrosh received no reassurance from Everblight. The dragon knew that by the end of this process his strength would multiply, and he focused entirely on that goal and his plans to follow. This was only the first step. He would consume others, fusing enough athancs to loom over even Toruk and laugh at the pitiful creature calling itself the Dragon Father. He dreamed of taking his creator's neck in his own jaws and savoring the primal flesh. In that moment all athancs would become one, united by his will and perfected into the latticed pattern of consciousness identifying itself as Everblight.

The scrap of thought was gone as Thagrosh was overtaken by the excruciating pain of another convulsion of blight-induced tissue death and replacement. He could feel Vayl's and Saeryn's hands upon him drawing the blighted inferno away. Blight-fire flickered like black flames across their skin, pouring violet radiance into the darkness.

Eventually they began to tunnel their way upward at an angle to reach the surface. The warlocks separated to take shifts with one attending to Thagrosh while the other assisted with the excavation. When Vayl returned to the ogrun after one of Saeryn's turns with him she saw a peculiar sight through the senses of her teraph. Saeryn knelt by Thagrosh's reclining form with her head bowed in concentration. She extended her hand with her fingers stretched above Thagrosh's head. She wore a strange smile, and her expression gave Vayl pause.

Saeryn suddenly lowered her hand, opening her mind slightly in silent greeting as she became aware of Vayl's approach. "Is it my turn?"

Vayl's tone was sharp as she asked, "Do you have need of my assistance?" She could see there was no flood of blight overtaking Thagrosh. He seemed to be sleeping, as he did in short bouts when opportunity allowed. A trace of blighted radiance lingered in the area from an earlier convulsion, but that was all.

"I was seeking communion." Saeryn responded to the question Vayl had not asked. "Sometimes when he is sleeping, I can hear Everblight better. I thought to see how the integration proceeds."

Something about this troubled Vayl, but she kept her surface thoughts smooth. "Did you learn anything?"

Communicating this way in spoken words felt awkward, but at this moment of suspicion each of their minds had closed to the other. Nonverbal cues were difficult to interpret through the disembodied blight-sight of a spawn. Saeryn and Vayl were looking at each other in the absolute darkness, yet neither saw with her eyes. Blighted senses had not evolved to discern subtleties of expression. Each warlock sensed the surface ripples of thoughts before the other spoke actual words. Ordinarily this served as an accurate gauge between warlocks, but with Saeryn it was different. Vayl knew Saeryn was skilled at controlling these mental ripples—more skilled than she was herself. Speaking to Saeryn sometimes felt like speaking to a mirror, so little did she betray her inner thoughts.

Saeryn replied after a pause. "Everblight is trying to delay the final stage of his transformation until we are above ground. Thagrosh is suffering. Everblight pushes him. There is . . . something Thagrosh must try to accomplish, once we emerge."

"What does it involve?" Vayl asked.

"I can't say. And Everblight will not answer me." Saeryn turned back to Thagrosh with a look that seemed, at least in Vayl's opinion, vaguely predatory.

As they neared the surface they detected a persistent tapping and grinding in the stone. Some deliberate exertion was taking place nearby, but it was difficult to tell more. Vayl suspected Everblight knew, but the dragon kept his thoughts to himself. When they finally broke into the lower layer of a long vertical shaft filled with signs of industry, she comprehended what she had heard.

This was a mine; she had never been inside such a structure before, but she had no doubt. It had not existed when Everblight had emerged here centuries ago. The obscured sound of voices trickled down from far above. Their deprived eyes caught glimmers of distant lanterns, the first real light they had seen in countless days.

Thagrosh had pushed himself hard these last few stages, going without rest to fight through the pain that wracked him. Vayl turned to him. "We should go another way. We risk drawing attention." She barely spoke the words, letting their deeper connection carry the meaning instead of sound.

"No." Thagrosh's louder voice was almost a growl. "No time. We must emerge now." There was excitement in his posture in addition to strain. The teraphim mirrored him, peering upward with their eyeless faces. The process was almost over. Blighted energy surged through Thagrosh with increasing regularity now, enough that Vayl and Saeryn were having difficulty controlling it. Already new scaled growths had erupted along the hands and arms of both Nyss warlocks from diverting the tremendous energies. Vayl's left hand was almost paralyzed; several bones in her left wrist had fused, and the outer skin layers had hardened painfully. She felt she could reverse these effects, if they did not go much further.

There was no way to climb up from the depths silently. Soon the voices above them raised in alarm, and lanterns shone down toward them. From the language of the shouts they knew they were in a Rhulic mine—the voices were

definitely dwarven. Vayl knew they had no time to lose, as the Rhulfolk could be dangerous in numbers. She sent a teraph springing forward to let loose a blast of draconic fire that burned several miners to ash even as it melted flesh and bone. The other teraphim quickly clambered upward, sinking clawed feet into stone and leaping off thick wooden support beams.

Saeryn gave a pleased laugh and took hold of a nearby winch cable to clamber nimbly up, sending her sorcerous power to accompany the spawn in reaping death. She leapt off to the main side passage and drew several of her deathspurs, clearly eager to shed blood. Thagrosh followed behind the teraphim, his movements considerably more awkward, as his body had not yet settled properly. It was clear he was still in pain.

Vayl came last, climbing at a more reserved pace. She felt no particular need to participate in the meaningless slaughter beyond directing the teraphim, for the dwarves' deaths were inevitable. Thagrosh was a larger concern. She hoped another bout of seizures would not overtake him while he climbed. It was a long way to the bottom of the shaft, and a fall right now would likely be fatal.

She recognized a rumbling sound above as one or more steam engines approached, likely Rhulic mining 'jacks. Knowing her allies were fatigued from their difficult journey and depleted of all but a few spawn, she took nothing for granted. She let the floating Oraculus soar upward ahead of her, seeing through it and preparing to use its spiked barbs as a conduit for her magic.

When Vayl reached the main occupied passage she saw the battle was well in hand. Dwarf bodies lay scattered near their mining implements, several with deathspurs protruding from their skulls. Piles of ash attested to the fates of several others. A large Rhulic 'jack equipped with a powerful drill had gotten only partially into the passage before being blasted by teraph fire and set upon by Thagrosh. He had quickly reduced it to a vortex of ash.

Another of these smoke-belching contraptions followed the first, lumbering through the smoke toward Thagrosh. A Rhulic miner shouted encouragement at the thing from behind. The mining 'jack looked almost comical as it lurched forward on its awkward legs, but it latched an enormous clamp-like appendage onto Thagrosh's shoulder and squeezed. The transformed ogrun howled in pain as bones popped beneath the inescapable pressure of hydraulic strength. Holding him tight in its grasp, it brought its enormous spinning drill to bear and began to churn a bloody hole through his abdomen.

Thagrosh gritted his teeth against both rage and pain but obstinately refused to send the injury to any nearby spawn. He hammered the metal thing several times with Rapture, eventually tearing off its grappling mechanism. One of the teraphs sprang forward to join the attack, and Vayl extended her will to send a raw winter blast through the beast. Freezing air flooded the passage, its sharpest bite focused on the mining 'jack and the dwarf goading it. Chunks of ice formed on both of them as the 'jack came to a halt and the dwarf breathed one last rattling breath. Thagrosh grunted and kicked the frozen machine away even as he drew energy from the spawn and expended that power to close his wounds and knit his bones.

Saeryn took a moment to gather back her deathspurs. She then walked to the only injured teraphim and pulled a mining pick loose from its hide. The injury healed almost instantly at her touch, and she tossed the hefty tool aside. A quick glance between members of the party showed none of them were worse for the brief encounter, although Thagrosh's temper was elevated at the indignity of suffering an injury from such an unworthy contraption.

Through the extremely sensitive tremor-sense of the teraphim Vayl heard scrambling noises above them. Likely other dwarves fleeing to spread the alarm. She had a feeling they had not heard the last of the Rhulfolk. It had been a sloppy exit, all things considered, but with Thagrosh already in a foul mood and his bloodlust awakened, she decided to hold her tongue and save her criticisms for later.

They emerged from the mines to a startling blue sky, with sunlight striking the white surface of recently fallen snow. This blinded their unprepared eyes for several long seconds. Vayl felt a sense of homecoming even though these southern Rhulic mountains were very different from the remote Shard Spires six hundred miles northwest. Just the smell of the fresh mountain air was enough. The temperature was almost balmy, particularly after the cold of the caves—far better than the arid climes of the Bloodstone Marches. The soft snow was quickly melting into the earth as they watched. After their journey deep below the earth, the sight of these mellow hills and even the sad snowfall was an unexpected delight.

Vayl's concerns that they might emerge to a Rhulic firing squad proved unwarranted. The mine was relatively remote and isolated, which made sense given they were barely within Rhul's southern perimeter. Other than a single mine track winding sharply around the rocks to the northwest and an empty camp of nearby tents there was no immediate evidence of a settlement.

There was an almost ecstatic anticipation from Everblight, no longer able to contain his emotions as he neared the final steps of the athanc's absorption. The dragon's force of will seized their minds, and they turned to witness what he had anticipated for so long.

Thagrosh fell to the snow in front of them with an anguished grunt and a sound like the cracking of bones. His hands twitched spasmodically and yet with a certain deliberate purpose. They saw him tear at his chest with his oversized claw, ripping the flesh open with a spray of brackish blood lit by the glowing athanc within. Vayl gripped Oraculus tightly enough to slice through her hand and clenched the orb to her own chest in sympathetic pain. Since the day her own athanc shard had been inserted she had never been forced to part with it, but she had witnessed Thagrosh pull his from his body several times. So far he had done this only on the occasion of inducting a new warlock. She could not fathom what he was doing now.

Thagrosh's oversized right hand was thick with blood as he wrestled forth the noticeably larger athanc. He did not extract it fully, as his flesh latched onto it and fought with

him to yank it back to its resting place within his ribcage. His gaping chest wound exposed the anatomy of his inner organs through the distorted ribs. His lungs and heart had clearly been pushed aside to make room for this intrusive piece of crystalline matter.

Blood flowed freely from the wound. It pooled sizzling on the ground, devouring the snow and spreading with black and shimmering power. The blood rippled and lurched as a testament to the blighted force animating it. Thagrosh's blood was different from the blood of the other warlocks, and Vayl felt the fluid in her own veins was almost watery in comparison. She could smell the blighted potency. Its unique sulfuric tang and fire-laden reek was closer to true dragon vitae than to blood.

The athanc did not look the same. Its colors and shape seemed distorted from what she recalled. The soaked blood along its crystal length did not entirely account for this strangeness; there was a deeper reddish glow with the usual cold blue. This red was flickering and fading. It seemed isolated to a smaller portion of the crystal at the outward edge where the sharper crystal faces seemed to fold away and smooth before her eyes.

Thagrosh's other hand, the one with his ogrun fingers, fumbled hastily at Rapture's hilt and lifted the massive weapon to set its edge against the athanc. Vayl's teeth clenched as a keening noise erupted from the crystal together with a rippling distortion of blighted energy. Effort set Thagrosh's entire left arm trembling, and at last a small chip of the crystal fractured off. It pulsed blue and red in sequence, and the frequency accelerated as the shard fell toward the large pool of thickening dragon's blood. A tentacle of the liquid reached up to seize the falling fragment and pull it down into the blood pool.

Suddenly everything erupted into gory chaos. Everblight's will surged outward with almost overpowering intensity as he watched through all their eyes at once. Vayl's consciousness tried to retreat into her mind to hide. Thagrosh seemed almost to explode as his skin was flayed from his flesh as if by some invisible force. What they had seen happen early in the caverns now seemed mild. Many of his muscles fell loose of their tendons to flop into the bloodied pool, followed shortly by a slippery length of his intestines. For a time Thagrosh's upper torso looked more skeletal than alive.

Suddenly the bloody pool erupted in an explosion of growth. It was the full miracle of draconic generation at its most advanced and accelerated. A creature unlike any other they had ever seen began to emerge. Thick strands of blood fused and calcified into draconic bones while other strands became ropy tendons to string together a skeletal configuration. Tissues pulsed into muscular strips layering the skeletal base before scaled flesh sheathed and sealed them.

Vayl saw three fang-filled skulls solidify and wondered at seeing three spawns created at once until she saw their necks join to a single hideous torso. The spawn was clearly nowhere near its full size, but even at this stage she sensed a singular vitality. Her blight awareness felt the tiny new sliver of Everblight's athanc resting at the core of its body emitting pulses of blighted magic in layered patterns too complex for her to follow. With each blight pulse the flesh rippled in counterpoint as its final form solidified. When she reached out with her mind to connect to the spawn she was surprised to sense no trace of Everblight. Instead some other intelligence welcomed her touch and filled her with a sense of ravenous hunger. It wanted to feed. As one they heard Everblight gift this creature with the name "Typhon."

A strangely metallic whine distracted her. At last she realized this sound came from Rapture, lying where Thagrosh had dropped it amid the bloody pool. A section of his shed skin had fallen over its length, and beneath the flesh the blade vibrated with a rising hum. Finally, with an ear-splitting noise it shattered. Vayl released Oraculus and clapped both hands over her ears too late to stop the spike of sound from driving into her mind. She watched in disbelief as Thagrosh's flesh and blood seeped between the pieces of the ancient weapon and pulled them back together. Rapture had reformed as a living weapon, its metal pieces now connected by tendons and muscle that flexed and moved. It seemed to drink of the blood in which it lay.

She looked up to see Thagrosh's body undergoing its final convulsions as new muscles rapidly spread across the exposed and lengthened bones. At last skin and scales emerged to cover him. He stood to his feet in a fully triumphant posture and let the growths from his back extend, revealing themselves to be the webbed membranes of sizable wings. He reached down to recover Rapture and raised it to the sky, letting loose a draconic roar no mortal throat should have been able to produce.

Overcome with awe at his singular majesty, Vayl and Saeryn felt compelled to kneel even as Typhon raised its triple heads to answer.

Everblight was back among them in full presence with an overpowering sense of manic triumph. Tightly bound into the dragon's mind, Thagrosh reveled in the power of his transformed flesh. He showed no signs he remembered any of his earlier pain. Instead, he radiated a sense of invincibility despite the horrendous blood loss he had endured. Vayl recognized this attitude as dangerous even as she had to concentrate not to blindly join in on the emotion.

At Everblight's imperative they ordered the teraphim to haul dwarven bodies from the mine to offer to Typhon. The creature fed with voracious enthusiasm, growing before their eyes as its multiple jaws tore through every scrap of meat and marrow-filled bone. Distracted by the recent wonders, Vayl had momentarily forgotten the dwarves she had heard running away before their exodus. She brought the matter to Everblight's attention now.

The dragon's reaction was more decisive than she had expected. Thagrosh looked sharply in the direction she indicated. "Come, let us see what Typhon can do." Even his voice sounded different, deeper and more resonant. He spread his wings and leapt from the nearest rocky crag to look past the peak blocking their view of the mining cart track. Typhon immediately followed along the rails. Vayl and Saeryn shared a look and rushed to catch up, bringing the teraphim with them.

Thagrosh glided ahead of them, savoring his newfound freedom of motion. His enthusiasm and bloodlust were infectious as he caught sight of a Rhulic community nestled in the valley beyond the next rise. It was a small but prospering mining town with numerous rugged buildings pouring smoke from stout chimneys. The cold air allowed for startling clarity, and they could clearly see tiny figures like dots on the snowy ground rushing toward the town. It was too late to catch up with the fleeing miners before they sounded the alarm.

Vayl said to Thagrosh, "Let's seek refuge elsewhere. This will be a poor place for us to recover our strength if swarmed with armed Rhulfolk."

---

**She looked up to see Thagrosh's body undergoing its final convulsions as new muscles rapidly spread across the exposed and lengthened bones.**

---

Thagrosh turned to regard her with a fiendish grin made all the more fearsome by his new size and the bulk of his horned skull. His mental voice returned to her, "I disagree. There is no place better." He waved an oversized clawed hand toward the valley. "A single Rhulic town far to the periphery. Who will notice it is gone? How long will it take for the ever-cautious and argumentative Rhulic Moot to agree to investigate?" She realized it was Everblight rather than Thagrosh speaking, and his desire to destroy burned in the transformed ogrun's eyes. "Here we will find all we need. Mines, weapons, forges, a defensible position, flesh to feed spawn. Absylonia will join us soon. Rhyas and Lylyth can guide our foot soldiers here in good time. This will be a fine place to muster our strength before we move again." He turned back to the Rhulic town as the sound of tolling alarm bells reached them. "Yes, this pleases me . . ."

With a sweep of his wings he launched himself forward off the trail and soared down the steep slope with Rapture in hand. Typhon hissed and gave triple shrieking cries as it hurried after with the other spawn. Vayl's vision shimmered, and for a moment it was not Thagrosh she saw gliding awkwardly down to the lower soil but the long serpentine grace of Everblight in all his draconic glory. In his heart was a restless eagerness to breathe fire and see the world turned to ash. Already in his mind the exquisite sound of screaming and slaughter had begun.

# Thagrosh, the Messiah
## LEGION OF EVERBLIGHT BLIGHTED OGRUN EPIC WARLOCK CHARACTER

*Even this most lowly vessel is made godlike in my image.*

—Everblight, speaking through Thagrosh

Everblight did not warn Thagrosh of the tremendously painful transmutation that would follow the consumption of Pyromalfic's athanc. Indeed, it is doubtful the dragon knew what to expect, even if inclined to inform his host. From the first moments after the triumph at the Castle of the Keys, Thagrosh experienced a blend of agony and ecstasy as blighted energies suffused his being. The process of sublimating Pyromalfic's essence into Everblight's divided consciousness was slower than anticipated and brought a host of confusing memories, sensations, and physiological changes. He has endured, however, and reaped the rewards of

| SPELL | COST | RNG | AOE | POW | UP | OFF |
|---|---|---|---|---|---|---|
| BLACK CHASM | 4 | 8 | 4 | 14 | | X |

Models damaged by Black Chasm are knocked down.

| DRAGON'S BLOOD | 2 | 6 | - | - | | X |

Target friendly non-warlock Legion model/unit gains +2 ARM. When an affected model is destroyed by a melee attack, roll a d6. On the roll of 5 or 6, the attacker suffers one damage point.

| FLESH EATER | 3 | 10 | - | 13 | | X |

When a living model is destroyed by Flesh Eater, it is removed from play and Thagrosh or a friendly Legion warbeast in his control area removes d3 damage points.

| GLORY OF EVERBLIGHT | 3 | SELF | CTRL | - | | |

Thagrosh and friendly Legion warbeasts currently in his control area roll an additional die on attack and damage rolls this turn. Discard the lowest die in each roll.

| UNNATURAL AGGRESSION | 2 | 6 | - | - | | X |

Any time other than during its activation that target friendly non-trooper Legion model suffers damage from an enemy attack but is not destroyed, after the attack has been resolved, the affected model may immediately move up to its current SPD in inches directly toward the attacking model if the affected model is not stationary.

his suffering. Though still recovering from the ordeal, Thagrosh has become something the world has never seen. He is no longer ogrun. His form is closer to and yet distinct from the dragons themselves. He has become Everblight's true avatar.

Even after the change, Thagrosh did not immediately feel comfortable with his new flesh. He still feels his skin, bones, and sinew shifting, as if an even more painful metamorphosis could come upon him at any time. This discomfort vanishes in battle as he revels in his new strength and the effortless evocation of blighted power. Some part of him understands that his mortal flesh will ultimately prove incapable of containing the might of dragons, but when combat is upon him he relishes the godlike sensation. Doubts for his future creep into the corners of his mind only later in the silence when he stands vigil over his protean army as it licks its wounds and gathers its strength for the next engagement.

These changes came when Thagrosh had just begun to separate his identity from that of Everblight. In the weeks before the Castle of the Keys he had reached an unspoken accord with his master and put forth a distinct voice as leader of the Legion. Since he consumed Pyromalfic's athanc, Everblight's presence is even stronger, a raging tornado of intelligence filled with its own arrogant sense of superiority. It is as though Everblight is shifting uncomfortably just behind the top layer of his thoughts, a vast alien presence impatiently looking through his eyes and speaking with his tongue. Sometimes for long hours Thagrosh loses himself entirely, subsumed into the mind of the dragon. Into this drowning sensation glimmers of Pyromalfic's shattered consciousness intrude like phantoms. Each time Thagrosh rises from the depths it is harder to ignore the next pull.

The draconic temper increasingly dominates Thagrosh's mood more than anything else. As the dragon spreads his mind and grows in power, it becomes more difficult for Thagrosh to restrain the impulse to let loose his full strength. Thagrosh feels this fury as a brand of searing iron which ignites the pure dragon blood pumping

# SPECIAL RULES

## Feat: Dragon Storm

*Mortal flesh should not bear the weight of a hidden god. With an ear-rending howl Thagrosh expels a fraction of that power to ignite the blood of all draconic horrors blessed of Everblight. Boiling over with fury and strength, they surge forward to strike and rend. Each beast becomes a separate claw or fang of the dragon.*

After all friendly models have completed their activations this turn, friendly Legion warbeasts currently in Thagrosh's control area may move up to their current SPD in inches and make one normal attack. Completely resolve each model's move and attack before moving on to the next.

## Thagrosh

**Abomination** - Models/units—friendly or enemy—within 3" of Thagrosh must pass a command check or flee.

**Athanc** - After leaching, Thagrosh automatically gains one fury point if he has fewer fury points than his FURY.

**Blood Spawn** - Once per game, when Thagrosh suffers five or more damage points from an enemy attack that is not transferred, Thagrosh's controller may place a non-unique lesser warbeast in play anywhere completely within 3" of Thagrosh. There must be room for the warbeast's base. The warbeast cannot activate this turn.

**Hubris** - When Thagrosh begins his normal movement with an enemy model in his melee range, he cannot end his movement farther from that model than he began.

**Wings** - Thagrosh ignores movement penalties from rough terrain and obstacles. Thagrosh may move through another model if he has enough movement to move completely past the model's base. Thagrosh may charge across rough terrain, over obstacles, or through other models. Thagrosh cannot be targeted by free strikes.

## Blight Fire

**Critical Frost** - On a critical hit, the model hit suffers Frost. A model suffering Frost must forfeit its movement during its next activation.

**Fire** - Models hit suffer Fire. A model on fire suffers a POW 12 damage roll each turn during its controller's Maintenance Phase until the fire expires on a d6 roll of 1 or 2. Fire effects are alchemical substances or magical in nature and are not affected by water.

## Rapture

**Eruption of Ash** - If target model is destroyed by Rapture, center a 3" AOE cloud effect on it and then remove the model from play. The cloud effect remains on the table for one round. Enemy models in the AOE at the time it is put in play suffer a POW 12 damage roll. Enemy models entering into or ending their activation in the cloud suffer a POW 12 damage roll. Eruption of Ash damage rolls cannot be boosted.

**Reach** - 2" melee range.

| THAGROSH | | | | CMD 10 | |
|---|---|---|---|---|---|
| SPD | STR | MAT | RAT | DEF | ARM |
| 5 | 11 | 7 | 5 | 13 | 17 |

| BLIGHT FIRE | | | |
|---|---|---|---|
| RNG | ROF | AOE | POW |
| SP | 1 | — | 12 |

| RAPTURE | | |
|---|---|---|
| SPECIAL | POW | P+S |
| Multi | 7 | 18 |

| CLAW | | |
|---|---|---|
| SPECIAL | POW | P+S |
| — | 3 | 14 |

| FURY | 7 |
|---|---|
| DAMAGE | 20 |
| FIELD ALLOWANCE | C |
| VICTORY POINTS | 5 |
| POINT COST | 98 |
| BASE SIZE | LARGE |

through his veins. It is not enough to be victorious; he must personally crush each foe, humiliating them utterly before finally annihilating them. During the awkward early weeks in the midst of his transformation, this battle lust put his survival in peril. Now he seeks any excuse to prove why the Legion's ultimate dominion is not just inevitable but imminent.

# Lylyth, Shadow of Everblight
## LEGION OF EVERBLIGHT BLIGHTED NYSS EPIC WARLOCK CHARACTER

*Where she strides, His shadow falls.*
—Thagrosh, the Messiah

| SPELL | COST | RNG | AOE | POW | UP | OFF |
|---|---|---|---|---|---|---|
| PIN CUSHION | 2 | 10 | - | - | X | X |

When a friendly Legion model makes a ranged attack against target enemy model/unit, roll an additional die on attack and damage rolls. Discard the lowest die in each roll.

| SHADOW PACK | 2 | 6 | - | - | | |
|---|---|---|---|---|---|---|

Target friendly Legion model gains Stealth. While in base-to-base contact with the affected model, friendly Legion models also gain Stealth. Attacks against a model with Stealth from greater than 5" away automatically miss. If a model with Stealth is greater than 5" away from an attacker, it does not count as an intervening model. Shadow Pack lasts for one round.

| SNARE | 2 | 10 | - | 10 | | X |
|---|---|---|---|---|---|---|

A model damaged by Snare must forfeit its movement during its next activation. Snare lasts for one round.

Lylyth has been born anew in the dragon's radiance. She is the Shadow of Everblight, and where his Legions march she moves like death itself. While Thagrosh rebuilds his shattered army, he has sent Lylyth to fall upon the enemies of Everblight to buy time for the whole of the Legion. The arrows of her minions have consumed entire towns and villages. Her memories are drenched in blood, but each murder eases the ghosts of her past.

Lylyth faced certain death and abandonment by Everblight while investigating the Castle of the Keys, but the Omen and Sigil saved her in that last desperate hour. Her reunion with her dragon master, intensified by the destruction of Pyromalfic, was like a dark rebirth that strengthened her resolve and uncovered newfound power.

Though Lylyth has put aside the thoughts of her brush with death, the experience left its mark. She now hurls herself tirelessly into battle after battle to prove her worth to Everblight. In the core of her being lies a dark well of dread she dares not face. This links to the memory of Everblight discarding her as useless flesh and to awareness that her shard of his athanc is more important to Everblight than the rest of her being. With the dragon's mind tightly bound to her own, she has been able to forget the faces of kinsmen she killed and the guilt of her father's accusations, which haunted her in those isolated moments.

Since the destruction of Pyromalfic, Lylyth's senses and reflexes have sharpened beyond human reckoning. She can hear the faintest sounds and see with a vision beyond sight. Her arrows fall like black rain and strike with inhuman accuracy. At times her lethal senses are infectious, elevating those who follow her into reflections of her murderous intuition. No longer reliant on the charms and enchantments of others, Lylyth has fashioned Whisper, a weapon of flawless simplicity. In her hands it is as much a manifestation of her will as the warbeasts who follow her.

Her amplified senses and renewed awareness come at a cost, however. Lylyth has found it difficult to endure crowded places and is inclined to shun even the presence of her own kind. She prefers to keep constantly on the move and avoids all but the smallest Legion camps except when duty requires her presence. Her kinship is reserved

## SPECIAL RULES

### Feat: Decimation

*Lylyth can invoke Everblight's blessing to convey her own perfect awareness of the battlefield to her followers, allowing them to experience how it feels to be the perfect hunter. Fired from countless bows, arrows rise to eclipse the sun before falling in a piercing rain to leave nothing but the sounds of the dead and dying.*

Increase the RNG of range weapons of friendly Legion models/units currently in Lylyth's control area by 4". When a friendly Legion model/unit currently in Lylyth's control area directly hits one or more enemy models with an initial melee or ranged attack during its activation, immediately after that attack is resolved the affected model may make one additional attack with the same weapon without spending fury, being forced, and regardless of the weapon's ROF. Decimation lasts for one turn.

### Lylyth

**Arcane Archer** - When making magic attacks, Lylyth may use her RAT instead of her FURY.

**Elite Cadre** - Striders included in an army with Lylyth, gain +1 MAT, RAT, CMD, and Hunter.

**Evasive** - Lylyth cannot be targeted by free strikes. When an enemy ranged attack misses Lylyth, immediately after the attack has been resolved she can move up to 2".

**Game Hunter** - When Lylyth damages a living warbeast with a ranged attack, that warbeast loses its animus and cannot be healed for one round.

**Hunter** - Lylyth's LOS is never blocked by forests. When making a ranged attack, Lylyth ignores Camouflage, concealment, and Prowl.

**Pathfinder** - During her activation, Lylyth ignores movement penalties from, and may charge across, rough terrain and obstacles.

**Rapid Shot** - When Lylyth hits an enemy model with a ranged attack during her activation, after this attack has been resolved she may make an additional ranged attack. Attacks gained from this ability cannot generate further additional attacks from this ability. Attack's gained from Rapid Shot do not count against a weapon's ROF.

**Swift Hunter** - When Lylyth destroys an enemy model with a ranged attack, immediately after the attack has been resolved she may move up to 2".

| LYLYTH | | | | CMD 8 | |
|---|---|---|---|---|---|
| SPD | STR | MAT | RAT | DEF | ARM |
| 7 | 4 | 5 | 8 | 16 | 14 |

| WHISPER | | | |
|---|---|---|---|
| RNG | ROF | AOE | POW |
| 12 | 2 | - | 12 |

| FURY | 5 |
|---|---|
| DAMAGE | 15 |
| FIELD ALLOWANCE | C |
| VICTORY POINTS | 5 |
| POINT COST | 70 |
| BASE SIZE | SMALL |

only for the striders and archers comprising the hunters of Everblight's army. Her hatred of humanity in particular has grown to intolerable levels.

She now leads her dedicated followers in a private war against the enemies of Everblight. That she has done so without any requests for support or supplies impresses even Everblight. She carefully selects targets large enough to demoralize yet small enough to fall quickly to the arrows of her hand-selected force. Her striders perform meticulous reconnaissance before she gives the command to attack, coordinating her underlings with a keen-minded attention to detail enabled by her draconic awareness.

# Absylonia, Terror of Everblight
## LEGION OF EVERBLIGHT BLIGHTED NYSS WARLOCK CHARACTER

*If Everblight's blessing puts shape to the killer within us, what is at the heart of Absylonia?*

—Saeryn, the Omen of Everblight

The gift of a fragment of Everblight's athanc generally brings subtle changes in Nyss, whose essence the dragon has studied exhaustively. Absylonia is different. Her blighted transformation continues to reshape her flesh, and there is no sign that she will ever settle into a stable form. She is a unique embodiment of Everblight, a creature who can adapt her flesh and bones to suit her needs. Her mind and body have been changed irrevocably and now bear little resemblance to what she was. The blood flowing through her veins surges in sympathetic harmony with the spawn she brings to battle. Most would call Absylonia a horror, but among the Legion she represents uniquely draconic perfection.

For most of Everblight's chosen the real change happens deep within. They must open their minds to control blighted energies and assume a leadership role in the Legion while offering absolute obedience to the dragon. Each of the chosen must adapt to the watchful presence and guiding voice of Everblight. Absylonia's twisted form may have resulted from an initial resistance to this change. She has little memory of those early days except as a hazy

Legion of Everblight

| SPELL | COST | RNG | AOE | POW | UP | OFF |
|---|---|---|---|---|---|---|
| ARTERIAL SPRAY | 3 | 8 | - | 14 | | X |

When Absylonia destroys a living enemy model with Arterial Spray, remove the model from play. Before the model is removed from the table her controller may make a magic spray attack using that model as the spell's point of origin. That model is considered the attacker for purposes of determining LOS for the attack. Determine eligible targets and measure the spray from that model. Absylonia does not suffer the target in melee attack roll penalty against models that are in melee with the destroyed model. Models hit by the spray suffer a POW 10 damage roll.

| BLIGHT FIELD | 2 | CTRL | 4 | | | - |
|---|---|---|---|---|---|---|

Place the Blight Field AOE anywhere completely in Absylonia's control area. While in the AOE, enemy models cannot be forced or allocated focus. The Blight Field AOE remains in play for one round. This spell may be cast once per round.

| PLAYING GOD | 2 | 6 | - | | | X |
|---|---|---|---|---|---|---|

Target friendly Legion warbeast gains Reach on its melee weapons and Terror. A weapon with reach has a 2" melee range. Additionally, the affected warbeast can perform headlock/weapon lock and throw power attacks and can make power attacks and charge without being forced.

| TENDRILS | 2 | 8 | - | | | X |
|---|---|---|---|---|---|---|

Target enemy small- or medium-based model hit by Tendrils is pushed any number of inches directly toward this spell's point of origin.

recollection of pain and confusion and remembers even less of her former life as a Nyss. This almost blank mental slate is pleasing to Everblight, who finds her consciousness easy to inhabit and influence with none of the background static of residual memories. In many ways Everblight has treated Absylonia with particular patience, as if she were a favored child. He spends considerable time retraining her animalistic instincts and nurturing her for the work ahead.

Within days of her transformation Absylonia proved to be entirely devoted to the dragon's will. While lacking both memories of her former existence and, initially, the language of her former people, she demonstrated an inhuman cunning backed by the powers imbued from her transformation. She possesses intuitive control over the spawn around her, and those generated from her blood grow with surprising alacrity—an ability which transcends the other warlocks to rival Thagrosh himself. She can restore her own body or even the worst mutilated spawn to wholeness with a single outpouring of blighted power.

Accordingly, Everblight chose to leave Absylonia behind when he sent Thagrosh and the bulk of his army to confront Pyromalfic at the Castle of the Keys. She was kept back so not all of Everblight's athanc pieces would be endangered and so she could continue creating new spawn. Though she did not know it at the time, her extensive work would enable Everblight to replace nearly half the spawn devastated in the destruction of Pyromalfic. Now she has answered her master's call to rejoin the Legion, bringing both her reserve force and an enthusiasm for bloodshed.

Even at her most human Absylonia resembles an abomination more than a Nyss. Her mutable form and the resiliency of her spawn have terrified those who oppose her. They realize the futility of their resistance the instant

# SPECIAL RULES

## Feat: Panacea

*The imperishable flesh of a dragon is able to mend with an alacrity that mocks lesser creatures. By sending forth an invigorating feast of blighted power, Absylonia erases her own injuries and devours the wounds of the dragonspawn near her. Each arises in perfect wholeness as Absylonia accepts trivial reminders of each wound on her own skin.*

Remove all damage from Absylonia. After removing the damage, Absylonia may take one or more points of damage. For each damage point she takes remove all damage from one friendly living Legion warbeast currently in her control area.

## Absylonia

**Terror** - Enemy models/units in melee range of Absylonia and enemy models/units with Absylonia in their melee range must pass a command check or flee.

## Spontaneous Mutation

During her activation Absylonia may spend one or more fury points to mutate spontaneously. For each fury point spent she gains one of the following abilities for one round. She can gain each mutation once per activation.

- **Barbed Hooks** - Absylonia's Blight Claws have a 2" melee range. When Absylonia hits an enemy living or undead model with a melee attack, before damage is rolled she may move any distance directly toward the model hit. Absylonia cannot be targeted by free strikes during this movement.

- **Brutal Damage** - Roll an additional die on Blight Claw damage rolls.

- **Eyeless Sight** - Absylonia ignores Camouflage, cloud effects, concealment, forests, Invisibility, and Stealth when declaring charges or making attacks.

- **Glide** - When Absylonia charges, she charges at SPD +5" and may move through models other than her target if she has enough movement to move completely past the models' bases. Absylonia cannot be targeted by free strikes during this movement.

## Blight Claws

**Spirit Eater** - Absylonia may reave the fury points from enemy warbeasts she destroys with a Blight Claw attack if she is closer to the warbeast when it is destroyed than other warlocks that could reave its fury.

**Waster** - Models hit by a Blight Claw attack lose Tough and cannot regenerate for one round.

| ABSYLONIA | | | | | CMD 7 |
|---|---|---|---|---|---|
| SPD | STR | MAT | RAT | DEF | ARM |
| 6 | 7 | 6 | 3 | 15 | 16 |

| BLIGHT CLAW | | |
|---|---|---|
| SPECIAL | POW | P+S |
| Multi | 6 | 13 |

| BLIGHT CLAW | | |
|---|---|---|
| SPECIAL | POW | P+S |
| Multi | 6 | 13 |

| FURY | 6 |
|---|---|
| DAMAGE | 16 |
| FIELD ALLOWANCE | C |
| VICTORY POINTS | 5 |
| POINT COST | 66 |
| BASE SIZE | SMALL |

she sweeps away the injuries of her army with a single blighted outpouring. She glides swiftly across the field of battle on sleek membranes grown just seconds before, extending from between her fingers and arms. Her limbs and appendages can lengthen in moments, the bones thickening and stretching with a sickening sound. Random chitinous barbs and spikes extrude through her flesh and shift unpredictably in battle, leaving gruesome wounds where she strikes. These shifts happen instinctively and without forethought. In time she may learn to refine control over her form even more, bringing forth new draconic gifts and advantages with which to rend her enemies.

# Typhon
## LEGION OF EVERBLIGHT UNIQUE HEAVY WARBEAST

*Men die. Empires crumble. Only the power of dragons is eternal.*

—Everblight to Thagrosh

Even those accustomed to horrors and numb to violence find the sight of Typhon terrifying. This truly monstrous creature bears little resemblance to any beast in nature. It is the organic consequence of a malevolent intelligence bent on creating weapons spawned of its own blood, flesh, and bone. Its three heads writhe sinuously on lengthy necks as it pulls its heavy bulk forward with its claws, each head shrieking cries in a dissonant cacophony. All three move of their own accord, seeking victims to rip apart with their powerful jaws or breathing out concentrated streams of superheated ash to melt metal and flesh. Even more formidable is the creature's resilience; Typhon's wounds seem to close as quickly as it receives them.

Typhon is unlike Everblight's ancient spawn, which had their genesis in the long-forgotten times during the reign of Morrdh. It is a new triumph, created in the aftermath of the battle at the Castle of the Keys. Typhon's origins go back considerably further, however, and are connected to the more esoteric theories derived by the dragon during its disembodied exile. While those who

| ANIMUS | COST | RNG | AOE | POW | UP | OFF |
|---|---|---|---|---|---|---|
| **Excessive Healing** | 2 | Self | - | - | | |

When the model using this animus is damaged by an enemy attack, after resolving the attack the affected model removes d3 damage points. Excessive Healing lasts for one round.

## SPECIAL RULES

### Typhon

**Affinity (Thagrosh): Symbiotic Regeneration** - When Typhon is forced to regenerate while in Thagrosh's control area, instead of rolling for Regeneration Typhon and Thagrosh may each remove up to three damage points.

**Blood Creation** - Typhon never attacks friendly Legion warlocks. When Typhon frenzies, it never selects a friendly Legion warlock to attack.

**Eyeless Sight** - Typhon ignores Camouflage, cloud effects, concealment, forests, Invisibility, and Stealth when declaring charges or slams or making attacks.

**Regeneration [d6]** - Typhon may be forced to remove d6 damage points from anywhere on its life spiral once per activation. Typhon cannot regenerate during an activation it runs.

**Multiple Heads** - Typhon's front arc extends 360°. Typhon can make three initial attacks each combat action, using any combination of Blight Breath and Jaw attacks. Typhon can make ranged attacks while in melee. Typhon does not suffer the target in melee attack roll penalty against models that it is in melee with. Blight Breath attacks made against a model Typhon is in melee with cannot hit another combatant if they miss their intended targets. Typhon does not gain an aiming bonus on attack rolls made against models it is in melee with. Typhon loses one initial attack for each aspect it has lost. Typhon cannot be forced to make additional Blight Breath attacks.

### Jaw

**Fling** - When Typhon hits an enemy model with a Jaw attack, before damage is rolled, Typhon may be forced to throw its target rather than make a normal damage roll. The target is thrown d6" with the same effect as a throw power attack and suffers a damage roll equal to Typhon's current STR plus the POW of the Jaw. Do not make a deviation roll when determining the thrown model's point of impact. If the thrown model collides with another model with an equal or smaller-sized base, that model suffers a collateral damage roll equal to Typhon's current STR.

**Reach** - 2" melee range.

| TYPHON | | | | | CMD 7 |
|---|---|---|---|---|---|
| SPD | STR | MAT | RAT | DEF | ARM |
| 6 | 11 | 7 | 5 | 13 | 17 |

| HD | BLIGHT BREATH | | | |
|---|---|---|---|---|
| | RNG | ROF | AOE | POW |
| | SP | 1 | — | 13 |

| HD | JAW | | |
|---|---|---|---|
| | SPECIAL | POW | P+S |
| | Multi | 4 | 15 |

| FURY | 4 |
|---|---|
| THRESHOLD | 10 |
| FIELD ALLOWANCE | C |
| VICTORY POINTS | 4 |
| POINT COST | 143 |
| BASE SIZE | LARGE |

observe Everblight's "art" would find the concept alien and incomprehensible, Everblight sees himself first and foremost as a creator. The dragon is proud of his studies into form and function, of the keen understanding he has gained over draconic forms, and of the deliberate application of blighted energies. Everblight is never satisfied and feels driven to improve on what has come before. Typhon represents the culmination of centuries of careful planning, plotting, and scheming, the first of a terrible new breed.

Everblight has long sought to consume the athanc of another dragon. When one dragon devours the heart of another, the two athancs fuse together, granting the victor the strength of the vanquished. For Everblight, the prospect of destroying another dragon brings not only increased power but also unique generative opportunities. The process of destruction is rooted in a type of birth—the reversal of Toruk's ancient division of his own athanc. All athancs feel the undeniable urge to rejoin and become whole again. There is a period of struggle and adjustment before complete synthesis occurs, and it was during this vital time that Everblight conceived of a special experiment. Spawn are ephemeral creatures that draw their life force from borrowed dragon's blood infused with the blighted energy of an athanc. This essence contains only a fraction of the blighted intensity of the dragon. Everblight has long considered a means of providing a spawn with a true essence.

Accordingly, after the destruction of Pyromalfic, Everblight set this experiment in motion. He compelled Thagrosh to carve the smallest possible piece of his athanc. As the disparate crystals of two dragons fought for alignment, Thagrosh cut loose a tiny fragment and dropped it into a sizable quantity of his own spilled blood.

The goal was to create something from nothing, a unique genesis possible only during this transitory state. The timing was tricky, as Everblight knew he could not risk weakening Thagrosh further through exsanguination lest he endanger the warlock's escape from the minions of the Circle now stalking him. The resulting spawn is a part of Everblight and yet separate and distinct. It feels compelled by harmonic pressure to obey Everblight but is not a part of Everblight's divided consciousness.

Typhon is a purely draconic creature possessing a fragmentary soul of its own. Its athanc shard ties it intimately to Thagrosh, but it can generate its own blighted blood and think and act with more independence than the regular spawn anchored directly to the will of the warlocks serving Everblight. It is from this small crystal that Typhon has gained its sense of self, crude and bestial though it may be.

Typhon's most important power is that it shares a dragon's immortality. As long as its dissociated athanc fragment exists, Typhon can grow again from almost nothing. At last Everblight created a spawn as invulnerable as the

dragons themselves, capable of rising from its own ashes to become whole once more. Adding further to its value is the strong inherent connection between Typhon and Thagrosh himself, as the warlock whose blood spawned it. This unanticipated side effect enables both Typhon and Thagrosh to recover much more rapidly from injuries when in close proximity to one another.

In time Everblight hopes he will gain other opportunities to feast on athancs, bringing more of Toruk's divided essence into his grasp. With each victory, Everblight plans to exploit the process once again, adding even more perfect weapons to his arsenal. It remains to be seen if Typhon's sense of self and will have any unintended consequences as the creature matures.

# Nephilim Protector
## LEGION OF EVERBLIGHT LIGHT WARBEAST

| | |
|---|---|
| **FURY** | 3 |
| **THRESHOLD** | 9 |
| **FIELD ALLOWANCE** | U |
| **VICTORY POINTS** | 2 |
| **POINT COST** | 75 |
| **BASE SIZE** | MEDIUM |

*They are the product of our spilled blood; now let them shed blood in our stead.*

— Vayl, Disciple of Everblight

### Nephilim Protector

**Bodyguard** - Once per round, when a friendly Legion warlock is directly hit by a ranged attack during an opponent's turn, the Nephilim Protector may move to intercept the attack. To use this ability, the Nephilim Protector must be within 2" of the friendly warlock. When this ability is used, the Nephilim Protector immediately moves up to its current SPD in inches and must position itself as an intervening model between the warlock and the attacker. The Nephilim Protector is then hit automatically by the attack, suffering the damage and effects instead of the warlock. The Nephilim Protector cannot use Bodyguard again for one round. If the Nephilim Protector is Incorporeal or denied its full movement, it cannot use Bodyguard.

**Empathic Transference** - A friendly Legion warlock may transfer damage to the Nephilim Protector even if the Nephilim Protector has a number of fury points equal to its current FURY.

**Eyeless Sight** - The Nephilim Protector ignores Camouflage, cloud effects, concealment, forests, Invisibility, and Stealth when declaring charges or slams or making attacks

### Halberd

**Powerful Charge** - When making a charge attack with the Halberd, the Nephilim Protector gains +2 to its attack roll.

**Reach** - 2" melee range.

### TACTICAL TIP

**Heightened Reflexes** – Notice that this says hit, not directly hit. Remember this when the AOEs start landing.

| ANIMUS | COST | RNG | AOE | POW | UP | OFF |
|---|---|---|---|---|---|---|
| **Heightened Reflexes** | 2 | 6 | - | - | | |

When knocked down, target friendly Legion model may stand up during its activation without forfeiting its movement or action. When hit by an enemy ranged attack outside the affected model's activation, after the attack has been resolved the affected model may move up to its current SPD in inches. Heightened Reflexes lasts for one round.

Dividing his athanc among multiple generals enhances his own chances of survival only as long as they endure. The dragon developed the Protectors to ensure their safety.

Protectors have an instinctive preset imperative to guard Everblight's generals and are ready to dive into harm's way with no concern for their individual lives. They also serve as ideal sacrifices for warlocks to shunt grave wounds to, bred as they are to accept these injuries even when other spawn are incapable. Protectors are ever wary of their surroundings and require no rest. Incapable of mental fatigue, they are able to stand at high alert interminably as they have no other natural state.

Nephilim continue to evolve under Everblight's watchful eye, proving themselves an efficient breed. Their ability to wield weapons while retaining the assets of draconic blood makes them ideal soldiers. Everblight has refined the process of their creation, now able to sustain Nyss incubators through several births. In time, Everblight hopes to develop spawning vats to replicate nephilim in even greater numbers. For now, he is content to expand their function and exploit their adaptable nature. Enter the Nephilim Protectors, shaped from birth to guard Everblight's warlocks from harm.

Since the Battle of the Castle of the Keys, the priority of spawning these creatures has only increased. While the gains were clearly worth the risk, exposing so many of his warlocks to potential destruction has troubled Everblight.

## LEGION OF EVERBLIGHT BLIGHTED OGRUN UNIT

*It is a wonder which is more horrible, the broken remains of their victims or their joyous howls upon each kill.*

—Garkarsh Martovin, Wolf of Orboros Huntsman

Only in comparison to the deranged warmongers would the warspears be described as anything except violent savages. The blight has twisted their minds as well as their flesh, addicting them to the joy of bloodlust. The force with which they can deliver their massive spears is enough to pierce iron and impale a man at thirty paces.

Out of some twisted sense of sport, ogrun warspears enjoy the opportunity to test their might against more formidable adversaries. Though killing humans provides minor amusement, it is no challenge. They prefer combatants like trolls, warpwolves, cyclopes, and warjacks. As they rush their victims, they add their momentum to their hurled spears to deadly effect. If their enemies are not killed outright, the tremendous lengths of wood dangling from the creatures' vitals can trip them up long enough for the blighted ogrun to close and finish the job.

Despite these gruesome entertainments, warspears are sane and clever compared to the twisted warmongers. The two breeds often fight side by side, though rivalries are inevitable. Warspears occupy a precarious middle ground between the warmongers and the chiefs of the collective blighted ogrun, passing orders to the vassals leading individual bands.

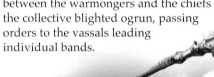

### Vassal

**Ambuscade (Order)** - Each Warspear who receives this order may advance up to its current SPD +3" directly toward a target model, throwing its war spear as it closes. The target model must be an eligible target for ranged attacks. After all models in the unit have completed their movement, each Warspear participating in the Ambuscade makes a Thrown War Spear ranged attack against its target, gaining +2 to the attack roll. Warspears are not considered to be in melee when making the Thrown War Spear ranged attacks, nor are their targets considered to be in melee with the Warspears. Warspears that move at least 3" gain boosted damage on successful Thrown War Spear ranged attacks. A Warspear cannot target a model with which he was in melee at the start of his activation with the Ambuscade ranged attack. When an ambuscading model performs its combat action, if the intended target of the attack is no longer in play, as is the case when another model in the unit destroys the intended target, the ambuscading model may make attacks against other eligible targets but does not make an ambuscade attack.

### Leader

#### Unit

**Fearless** - A Warspear never flees.

**Terror** - Enemy models/units in melee range of a Warspear and enemy models/units with a Warspear in their melee range must pass a command check or flee.

#### Thrown War Spear

**Critical Puncture** - On a critical hit, the model hit suffers -2 SPD and DEF, cannot run, and must forfeit its action during its next activation. Critical Puncture lasts for one round.

**Thrown** - Add the Warspear's current STR to the POW of his Thrown War Spear ranged attacks.

#### War Spear

**Reach** - 2" melee range.

**Set Defense** - A Warspear gains +2 DEF against charge and slam attacks originating from its front arc.

| VASSAL | | | | | CMD 8 |
|---|---|---|---|---|---|
| SPD | STR | MAT | RAT | DEF | ARM |
| 6 | 9 | 7 | 6 | 12 | 15 |
| SPEARMAN | | | | | CMD 6 |
| SPD | STR | MAT | RAT | DEF | ARM |
| 6 | 9 | 6 | 5 | 12 | 15 |

| THROWN WAR SPEAR | | | |
|---|---|---|---|
| RNG | ROF | AOE | POW |
| 8 | 1 | — | 4 |

| WAR SPEAR | | |
|---|---|---|
| SPECIAL | POW | P+S |
| Multi | 4 | 13 |

| | |
|---|---|
| VASSAL'S DAMAGE | 8 |
| SPEARMAN'S DAMAGE | 5 |
| FIELD ALLOWANCE | 2 |
| VICTORY POINTS | 3 |
| LEADER AND 2 TROOPS | 65 |
| UP TO 2 ADDITIONAL TROOPS | 19 ea |
| BASE SIZE | MEDIUM |

# Blighted Swordsmen Abbot & Champion
## LEGION OF EVERBLIGHT BLIGHTED NYSS SWORDSMEN UNIT ATTACHMENT

| ABBOT | | | | | CMD 9 |
|---|---|---|---|---|---|
| SPD | STR | MAT | RAT | DEF | ARM |
| 6 | 6 | 8 | 4 | 14 | 13 |

| CHAMPION | | | | | CMD 8 |
|---|---|---|---|---|---|
| SPD | STR | MAT | RAT | DEF | ARM |
| 6 | 6 | 8 | 4 | 14 | 13 |

| NYSS CLAYMORE | | |
|---|---|---|
| SPECIAL | POW | P+S |
| — | 4 | 10 |

| SECOND NYSS CLAYMORE | | |
|---|---|---|
| SPECIAL | POW | P+S |
| — | 4 | 10 |

| ABBOT'S DAMAGE | 5 |
|---|---|
| CHAMPION'S DAMAGE | 5 |
| FIELD ALLOWANCE | 1 |
| VICTORY POINTS | +1 |
| POINT COST | 29 |
| BASE SIZE | SMALL |

*Behind the blade you may hear its shimmering wail. That is the song of a weapon which thirsts for the taste of flesh.*

—Swordsman Abbot Syryth Laryssar

## Abbot

**Blight's Blessing** - While the Abbot is in play, models in this unit gain +2 DEF against magic attacks.

**Dark Prayers** - The Abbot may recite one of the following prayers at any time during his unit's activation. Every model in the unit, including himself, gains the listed ability for one round.

• **Cleave** - Once each activation, after resolving a melee attack in which a model in this unit destroys an enemy model, the attacking model may immediately make an additional melee attack against a model in its melee range.

• **Relentless Charge** - Models in this unit may charge across rough terrain and obstacles without penalty.

• **Wraith Bane** - Attacks made by models in this unit may damage models only affected by magic attacks. A model in this unit may charge incorporeal models.

**Officer** - The Abbot is the unit leader.

**Unit Abilities** - The Abbot has Blighted Swordsman unit abilities.

## Champion

**Combo Strike (★Attack)** - The Champion may make Nyss Claymore attacks separately, or he can make a special attack to strike with both Nyss Claymores simultaneously. Make one attack roll for the Combo Strike. Add the Champion's STR once and the POW of both Nyss Claymores to the damage roll.

**Preemptive Strike** - The Champion may immediately make one normal melee attack against an enemy model ending its normal movement in the Champion's melee range. If the Champion makes a Preemptive Strike, he cannot make another until after his controller's next turn.

**Unit Abilities** - The Champion has Blighted Swordsman unit abilities.

### Second Nyss Claymore (Champion Only)

the meditative discipline of sword mastery, allowing them to evade the horror of their actions by concentrating solely on their skill. They turned emptiness itself into a form of spirituality, seeking to embrace an emotional void to achieve absolute perfection with the blade.

Those who fully embraced this new philosophy and learned to kill as a form of meditation have since become the greatest blade masters of their race. These are the abbots, both feared and respected within the Legion for the absolute calm with which they can skillfully execute any form of atrocity.

The abbots have achieved something akin to a new state of enlightenment, a recognized ability to fight with utter dispassion and grace. The monks of the blade have attracted devotees from the most skilled and disciplined swordsmen. Abbots and their students are devoted not to a god but to the abstraction of the blight and the refinement it brings to their flesh. Abbots focus on the sword to manifest the blight within them, achieving subtle but powerful blessings in the process. Their best students are called champions, and some have learned to focus so completely on the swordsman's art that they can perform the supremely difficult task of fighting with two claymores in tandem.

Among the Nyss corrupted by the dragon's blight, the swordsmen were the first to answer Everblight's call. Many lost their sense of self, unable to comprehend what compelled them to hack apart their kinsmen. The hollowness they felt aligned naturally with

# Strider Officer & Musician

## LEGION OF EVERBLIGHT BLIGHTED NYSS STRIDER UNIT ATTACHMENT

*The striders are both hunter and hound. That horn calls them to chase and sets their prey to flight.*

—Kaya the Moonhunter

Strider deacons are tremendously efficient hunters and killers. Their skill with the bow derives from a unique mix of inherent Nyss ability and the blight-based enhancement to their bodies. They have quickly risen to leadership positions within the newly evolving blighted Nyss society, earned by shrewdly anticipating the needs of Everblight's warlocks. Deacons must operate with autonomy, instantly learning the lay of the land in new regions and standing ready to utilize that knowledge in the ever-changing plans of the Legion.

In time deacons become living repositories of battle tactics and artisans of ambush. In movement a deacon seems like an animal, possessed of keen instincts and endless stamina. Indeed, the last step to becoming a deacon involves a test of this stamina. The trial begins with a swim through icy waters, continues with a moonlight race, and culminates in a climb up a sheer rocky incline. At the summit, the candidate must defeat veteran striders waiting in ambush. The final task is to hunt down and execute a target designated by the candidate's peers. From the start of the trial, he may neither eat nor drink: he must return with feathers dipped in the blood of his final kill before he is allowed sustenance. Those who complete the task have earned their right to lead.

The horn bearers who follow them into battle communicate a deacon's will across the most desolate landscapes. By their sound, deacons call striders to assemble or unleash them upon the enemies of Everblight. Nyss have used such horns

| DEACON | | | | | CMD 9 | |
|--------|-----|-----|-----|-----|-----|---|
| SPD | STR | MAT | RAT | DEF | ARM | |
| 7 | 6 | 7 | 8 | 15 | 11 | |

| MUSICIAN | | | | | CMD 6 | |
|----------|-----|-----|-----|-----|-----|---|
| SPD | STR | MAT | RAT | DEF | ARM | |
| 7 | 6 | 5 | 6 | 15 | 11 | |

| NYSS LONG BOW | | | |
|-----|-----|-----|-----|
| RNG | ROF | AOE | POW |
| 12 | 1 | — | 10 |

| SWORD | | |
|-------|-----|-----|
| SPECIAL | POW | P+S |
| — | 3 | 9 |

| DEACON'S DAMAGE | 5 |
|-----------------|---|
| FIELD ALLOWANCE | 1 |
| VICTORY POINTS | +1 |
| POINT COST | 28 |
| BASE SIZE | SMALL |

## Deacon

**Officer** - The Deacon is the unit leader.

**Tactics: Bushwhack** - Models in this unit gain Bushwhack. A model with Bushwhack may make ranged attacks before moving. After all models in this unit have completed attacking, models in this unit may advance normally but can take no additional actions.

**Tactics: Rapid Shot** - Models in this unit gain Rapid Shot. When a model with Rapid Shot hits an enemy model with a ranged attack during its activation, immediately after this attack has been resolved, it may make one additional ranged attack. Attacks gained from this ability cannot generate further additional attacks from this ability. Attacks gained from Rapid Shot do not count against a weapon's ROF.

**Unit Abilities** - The Deacon has Strider unit abilities.

## Musician

**Combat Coordination** - While the Musician is in play, models in this unit may make combined ranged attacks in skirmish formation groups rather than open formation groups.

**Musician** - While the Musician is in play, models in this unit never flee.

**Trumpet of Doom** - Once per game during his unit's activation, the Musician may use Trumpet of Doom. Enemy models/units currently within 10" of the Musician cannot give or receive orders for one round.

**Unit Abilities** - The Musician has Strider unit abilities.

since ancient times to rapidly convey information across great distances, particularly in times of strife. Combined with the deacons' silence of motion, the sudden sounding of these horns followed by a wave of deadly accurate arrows has terrified the humans of northern mountain towns. The musicians accompanying a deacon can convey a rich variety of information in subtle shifts of tone and length of note. In battle, they can also belt out a mournful wail that drowns out all other sound and sends an instinctive chill straight to the bones of their enemies.

Legion of Everblight

# Warmonger War Chief

## LEGION OF EVERBLIGHT BLIGHTED OGRUN SOLO

| WAR CHIEF | | | | | CMD 9 |
|---|---|---|---|---|---|
| SPD | STR | MAT | RAT | DEF | ARM |
| 5 | 9 | 8 | 3 | 12 | 17 |

| WAR CLEAVER | | | |
|---|---|---|---|
| | SPECIAL | POW | P+S |
| | Reach | 5 | 14 |

| WAR CHIEF'S DAMAGE | 10 |
|---|---|
| FIELD ALLOWANCE | 2 |
| VICTORY POINTS | 1 |
| POINT COST | 39 |
| BASE SIZE | MEDIUM |

*Brutal and stupid though they may be, ogrun will heed leaders strong enough to terrify even them.*

—Vayl, Disciple of Everblight

### War Chief

**Abomination** - Models/units – friendly or enemy – within 3" of the War Chief must pass a command check or flee.

**Berserk** - Every time the War Chief destroys another model with a melee attack, he must immediately make one melee attack against another model in his melee range, friendly or enemy.

**Blood-Quenched** - The War Chief gains a cumulative +1 STR and ARM for each living enemy model he destroys with a melee attack during his activation. This bonus lasts for one turn.

**Fearless** - The War Chief never flees.

**Field Officer** - An additional Warmonger or Warspear unit may be fielded over normal Field Allowance limitations for each War Chief included in the army.

**Flesh Glutton** - Immediately after resolving an attack in which the War Chief destroys a living model with a melee attack, the War Chief may stop making attacks gained from Berserk and remove d3 damage points.

**Veteran Leader** - Friendly Blighted Ogrun troopers gain +2 MAT and RAT while the War Chief is within their LOS.

**Warmonger Commander** - The War Chief has a command range equal to his CMD in inches. Friendly Warmonger models/units in his command range may use the Warmonger War Chief's CMD when making command checks. The War Chief may give orders to friendly Warmonger models in his command range. While in the War Chief's command range, friendly Warmongers cannot attack other models in their unit.

### War Cleaver

**Reach** - 2" melee range.

leader, someone worthy of being called *korune*. The blight has not changed the fact that some ogrun are born to follow and others to lead. The instinct to heed one's *korune* is so powerful that it can partially override a warmonger's berserker frenzy.

A war chief has proven his right to dominion over multiple vassals just as those vassals might have proven theirs to small bands of warmongers or warspears. Wary of his strength and cowed by the sheer terror of his presence, vassals heed a chief and cooperate. War chiefs look to Thagrosh as the embodiment of the dragon that has enthralled their twisted minds. When Thagrosh stands before his ogrun, they become united of purpose and stronger than any other force in the Legion.

Though all warmongers can propel themselves into a killing frenzy, only a few are willful enough to lead the corrupted tribes as war chiefs. Blight transforms each of these horrors into murderous fiends overcome by hunger. The very scent of blood lends the war chief strength, and he will sometimes pause amid his bloodletting to gorge on fresh kills. A war chief's skin becomes quenched steel when washed by the blood of the fallen, allowing the ogrun to shrug off blades and arrows as if they were minor irritations. Yet for all their bloodthirsty gluttony, war chiefs are the only leaders who can keep the blighted ogrun in line.

Even though the blight has transformed both flesh and mind, some essential core of the ogrun remains. Ogrun feel it is their purpose in life to follow a great

# Strider Deathstalker

## LEGION OF EVERBLIGHT BLIGHTED NYSS SOLO

*Though unquestionably the pinnacle of some malign evolution, such fiends have no place in nature.*

—Morvahna the Autumnblade

| DEATHSTALKER | | | | CMD | 8 |
|---|---|---|---|---|---|
| SPD | STR | MAT | RAT | DEF | ARM |
| 7 | 6 | 7 | 8 | 15 | 11 |

| NYSS LONG BOW | | | |
|---|---|---|---|
| RNG | ROF | AOE | POW |
| 12 | 1 | — | 10 |

| SWORD | | |
|---|---|---|
| SPECIAL | POW | P+S |
| — | 3 | 9 |

| | |
|---|---|
| DAMAGE | 5 |
| FIELD ALLOWANCE | 2 |
| VICTORY POINTS | 1 |
| POINT COST | 30 |
| BASE SIZE | SMALL |

Some few striders rise above the ranks of all their peers as precision instruments of death. These creatures seem divorced from their old species, barely recognizable as Nyss. A Deathstalker blends into her surroundings and can sit silently for hours without complaint to avoid giving away her position. The patience of a Deathstalker is unnerving even to other striders, and through a silent stare they can convey much information to those versed in their odd mannerisms. By the way they tilt their heads and stare unblinkingly, Deathstalkers bear more resemblance to ravens or falcons than to those who were once their kin.

Deathstalkers consider it their reward to exult in slaughter. Still, they plan for these attacks in meticulous detail, gathering as much information as possible before they strike. They are a breed of silent death striking from the shadows. Their assaults terrorize their prey, who desperately try to spot and evade the killers stalking them. The attacks of a single Deathstalker have convinced enemies that an entire force of archers besieged them. Deathstalkers toy with their victims dispassionately, like predatory animals, yet their games are far more intricate and deliberately cruel. After provoking the enemy to foolish action, they stand poised and wait, arrow at the ready, as long as it takes for a target to make a mistake.

## Deathstalker

**Advance Deployment** - Place the Deathstalker after normal deployment, up to 12" beyond the established deployment zone.

**Camouflage** - The Deathstalker gains an additional +2 DEF when benefiting from concealment or cover.

**Hunter** - The Deathstalker's LOS is never blocked by forests. When making a ranged attack, the Deathstalker ignores Camouflage, concealment, and Prowl.

**Pathfinder** - During her activation, the Deathstalker ignores movement penalties from, and may charge across, rough terrain and obstacles.

**Rapid Shot** - When the Deathstalker hits an enemy model with a ranged attack during her activation, after this attack has been resolved she may make an additional ranged attack. Attacks gained from this ability cannot generate further additional attacks from this ability. Attack's gained from Rapid Shot do not count against a weapon's ROF.

**Sniper** - When damaging a warjack with a ranged attack, the Deathstalker's controller chooses which column takes damage. When damaging a warbeast with a ranged attack, the Deathstalker's controller chooses which branch takes damage. After a successful ranged attack, the Deathstalker may automatically inflict one damage point instead of making a damage roll.

**Stealth** - Attacks against the Deathstalker from greater than 5" away automatically miss. If the Deathstalker is greater than 5" away from an attacker, she does not count as an intervening model.

**Tactical Coordination** - When the Deathstalker destroys an enemy model with an attack, friendly Strider models within a number of inches of the Deathstalker equal to her current CMD may move up to 1" immediately after the attack has been resolved. A model cannot end this movement out of formation or cause other models that are in formation to no longer be in formation.

Deathstalkers enjoy an unspoken place among the Legion and demand obeisance from fellow Nyss by virtue of their piercing intelligence and the obvious favor of Everblight. Whatever arrogance Deathstalkers possess is justified by their intelligence, skill, and ruthlessness. Legion warlocks trust them to execute long and complex missions while giving them considerable leeway when commanding subordinate striders. Coordinating their less-skilled brethren with the barest glances and gestures, they move effortlessly to encircle and entrap their quarry. Even as they guide their peers to victory, Deathstalkers ensure the choicest kills are theirs alone.

# Blighted Nyss Sorceress & Hellion
## LEGION OF EVERBLIGHT BLIGHTED NYSS CAVALRY SOLO

*By His grace we will split the sky asunder and let hell rain down on those who would stand against us.*

—Nyss Sorceress Nyleth

Sweeping out of the frozen skies, hellions fall upon their land-bound enemies and deliver their masters to the heart of battle. The half-mad sorceresses who ride them must be agile enough to stand precariously atop their steeds without saddles or harnesses. When rider responds in tandem with steed, the two move together with a shared consciousness. Hellions whip across the battlefield at dizzying speeds while their riders unleash powerful magic wherever the need is most pressing. With little more than a shouted word and a pointing finger, a sorceress can summon a knot of howling wind to rip a distant victim limb from limb.

In the conquered Nyss, Everblight inherited a rich sorcerous tradition. Sorcery has a distinguished history among the Nyss: it was initially connected to their religious practices. Certain bloodlines have given rise to a greater number of these intuitive evokers, prompting Nyss priests to nurture and train them to unlock their full potential. Since joining the Legion these bloodlines have risen to new prominence, as Everblight's energies have awakened the power even in siblings who had not previously manifested it. Sorcerers train to retain a solid mix of martial skill and arcane potential that makes them exceptionally valuable to the Legion.

Even as the Legion's blighted culture has evolved, Everblight's warlocks have refined the manner in which these inheritors of Nyss sorcery can best serve the Legion. They represent a uniquely versatile asset that Everblight is eager to exploit. As the most literate of the Nyss, they assist the ranking officers in organization efforts amid the chaos of constantly shifting war camps. Athough Everblight and his warlocks enjoy instantaneous communication across any distance, the rest of the Nyss must rely on more mundane means to convey orders. Sorceresses have played a key role in this, using their swift flying steeds to great advantage.

Everblight has also begun to explore the way the runic text of the Nyss language can augment certain arcane enhancements when empowered by blighted energies. Sorceresses aid in the crafting of the spawning vessels and have begun to expand that art by pushing the power of their blighted runecrafting in new directions. When they are not flying atop their steeds in battle, the sorceresses attend to these essential tasks, ensuring the Legion armies can keep up with Everblight's sometimes mercurial plans.

In battle, sorceress and hellion represent the perfect blend of Nyss prowess and the unique assets brought by the dragonspawn of Everblight. Historically, several bloodlines of battle sorcerers were known to ride ulk steeds into battle alongside the Nyss hunters. Instead the blighted sorcerers were given hellions, the swift steeds that once ushered the warlords of Morrdh to battle. These creatures originated from Everblight's first experiments in the creation of flying spawn.

The experiment proved an immediate success and hellions have become a common sight, often sent ahead to provide direction to the other flying elements of the Legion. One of Everblight's favored techniques is to send several hellions

# SPECIAL RULES

| SORCERESS | | | | | CMD 8 |
|---|---|---|---|---|---|
| SPD | STR | MAT | RAT | DEF | ARM |
| 8 | 5 | 6 | 4 | 14 | 16 |

| SPEAR | | |
|---|---|---|
| | SPECIAL | POW | P+S |
| Reach | 4 | 9 |

| TAIL | | |
|---|---|---|
| | SPECIAL | POW | P+S |
| Hellion | 12 | — |

| MOUNT | | |
|---|---|---|
| | SPECIAL | POW | P+S |
| — | 10 | — |

| DAMAGE | 8 |
|---|---|
| FIELD ALLOWANCE | 2 |
| VICTORY POINTS | 1 |
| POINT COST | 45 |
| BASE SIZE | LARGE |

## Sorceress

**Wings** - The Sorceress ignores movement penalties from rough terrain and obstacles. The Sorceress may move through another model if she has enough movement to move completely past the model's base. The Sorceress may charge across rough terrain, over obstacles, or through other models. The Sorceress cannot be targeted by free strikes.

## Magic Ability

As a special attack or action, the Sorceress may cast one of the following spells during her activation. Determine the success of magic attacks by rolling 2d6 and adding the Sorceress' Magic Ability score of 7. The Sorceress cannot make additional attacks after making a magic attack.

- **Aerial Coordination (★Action)** - While within 8" of the Sorceress, friendly Legion warbeasts with the Wings ability may charge without being forced and gain +2 on melee attack rolls. Aerial Coordination lasts for one turn.

- **Blight Storm (★Action)** - Place a 5" AOE anywhere completely within 8" of the Sorceress. When an enemy model in the AOE is directly hit by an attack and the damage roll fails to exceed its ARM, the enemy model automatically suffers one damage point. Blight Storm lasts for one round.

- **Storm Howler (★Attack)** - Storm Howler is a RNG 10, POW 13 magic attack. Models damaged by Storm Howler cannot cast spells for one round.

- **Wind Ravager (★Action)** - While within 8" of the Sorceress, enemy models cannot make ranged attacks. Wind Ravager lasts for one round.

## Spear

**Reach** - 2" melee range.

## Tail

**Hellion** - The Tail attack cannot be used to make charge attacks. Do not add the Sorceress' STR to the POW of the Tail attack.

screaming down behind enemy lines to disrupt ranks of venators, archers, or riflemen. From there, the sorceresses can summon powerful windstorms to kill the enemy without risk of retaliation. Entire companies have been on the receiving end of this tactic, buffeted by swirling dust and gale-force winds as Legion archers and raptors close the gap to rain down arrows on the confused army. Sorcerers are similarly adept at using their height and the coordinating power of their magic to bolster harriers or angelii.

Of all the dragons, Everblight alone has fully exploited the power of flight. Thus far the enemy has been slow to adapt, and Everblight hopes to keep them continually off their balance. Victory often rests in hitting the enemy from unexpected directions before converging for the kill.

## THAGROSH, THE MESSIAH
### EPIC WARLOCK

## LYLYTH, SHADOW OF EVERBLIGHT
### EPIC WARLOCK

## ABSYLONIA, TERROR OF EVERBLIGHT
### WARLOCK

## STRIDER OFFICER & MUSICIAN
### STRIDER UNIT ATTACHMENT

## STRIDER DEATHSTALKER
### SOLO

## WARMONGER WAR CHIEF
### SOLO

## TYPHON
### UNIQUE HEAVY WARBEAST

# Painting Legion of Everblight

## THE 12 STEPS TO EVERBLIGHT

Painting the beasts of Everblight can be accomplished in 12 easy steps. These steps include the flesh, chitin, and teeth. This is the way we paint them in the studio—with Everblight's approval, of course.

### Colors used:

- Sanguine Base
- Skorne Red
- Khador Red Base
- Exile Blue
- Murderous Magenta
- Carnal Pink
- Frostbite
- Battlefield Brown
- Umbral Umber
- Hammerfall Khaki
- Gun Corps Brown
- 'Jack Bone
- Menoth White Highlight
- Morrow White
- Thamar Black
- Red Ink
- Brown Ink
- Mixing Medium

**1** Begin by basecoating the flesh with Frostbite mixed with a touch of Exile Blue and a touch of Skorne Red.

**2** Add more Exile Blue and Skorne Red to the basecoat for the shading.

**3** Highlight the flesh by adding Morrow White to the basecoat.

**4** Wash the desired flesh areas with a mix of Khador Red Base, Carnal Pink, Murderous Magenta, Mixing Medium, and water.

## BLOOD SPLATTER TECHNIQUES

Many of the Legion models incorporate ripped skin and flesh that show the ravages of dragon blight. Adding gory details to these models emphasizes their character and increases realism. There are two techniques we use in the studio to create these effects: the "blow" technique and the "flick" technique. Let's look at how each works, the differences in the results, and some common mistakes.

### Colors used:

- Red Ink
- Brown Ink

**1** **Blow Setup:** The paint mixture I use to simulate blood is a mixture of two parts Brown Ink and one part Red Ink. Load a fine hobby brush with ink. Wipe some of it off on a paper towel, but make sure your brush retains a point. Position your brush about half an inch away from the target area.

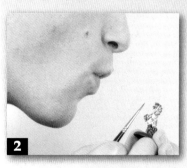

**2** **Blow Action:** Next just blow a very hard, short burst of air on the brush to spatter the paint. Be sure to have a second, slightly damp brush handy to soak up any overspray. It's best to practice this on something else before committing to a miniature.

**5**

Shade the washed areas with a mix of Khador Red Base and Murderous Magenta.

**6**

Reclaim any flesh areas with Morrow White and chitin areas with Thamar Black.

**7**

Basecoat the teeth with 'Jack Bone.

**8**

Shade the teeth with a mix of Umbral Umber and Sanguine Base.

**9**

Highlight the teeth with Menoth White Highlight.

**10**

Basecoat the chitin with a mix of Battlefield Brown, Umbral Umber, and Gun Corps Brown.

**11**

Shade the chitin with a mix of Thamar Black, Brown Ink, and Red Ink.

**12**

Highlight the chitin with a mix of Battlefield Brown and Hammerfall Khaki.

**3**

**Blow Results:** The blow technique is great for precise, focused spattering. Because it is easy to control and yields a random pattern this is the technique I use most often.

**4**

**Blow Overkill:** The most common mistake when using this technique is to oversaturate an area by overloading your brush or layering too many spatters on top of each other. Try to keep the spatters concentrated on one part of the model and remember: a little goes long way.

**5**

**Flick Setup:** For this technique use a work or base hobby brush. Load up your brush and wipe a little off, maintaining a point on the brush tip. Then position the brush about half an inch away from the target area. Pull the tip of your brush back as far as it will go and let fly!

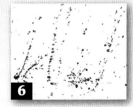

**6**

**Flick Results:** The flick technique creates swaths of spatters so is great for simulating blood flung up in the heat of combat. Remember to have a second brush ready to clean up immediately after each fling, as this technique is not very accurate.

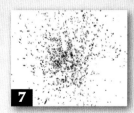

**7**

**Flick Wrong Brush:** One common flicking error is to use a brush that does not come to a fine point, such as a flat or dry brush. Another is to forget to point your brush tip between each flick. The result of these mistakes is the same: an entirely random spray pattern, like when a toothbrush is used to spatter paint.

**8**

**Combined Technique:** Using blowing and flicking together can create some especially nice blood-spatter effects. You can also use these techniques to paint spattered mud and create texture on stone surfaces.

"By all means, please come in. Make yourself at home." Professor Viktor Pendrake spoke over his shoulder as he paused in applying his quill to a page half-filled with hasty but legible script. Similar pages littered the table where he wrote, including some bearing impressive sketches of various wild beasts and monstrous creatures.

Scout General Bolden Rebald approached the desk, coughing once into his hand. Pendrake smiled to himself, knowing Cygnar's spymaster had a habit of trying to put people off their guard by catching them unawares. "My apologies, Professor. A bad professional habit. I've become a bit too accustomed to entering rooms quietly. I'm glad to know your ears are as sharp as ever."

"They compensate for my eyes, which have become increasingly unreliable," Pendrake said with good humor. This made light of the fact that one of his eyes was nonfunctional, a milky blind orb. A thick white scar above and below the socket suggested an old injury he never mentioned.

"Have you enjoyed your time with your peers at the Royal Cygnaran University?" Rebald glanced at the adjoining table and saw several packed bags. "I guess that answers that."

"They have been kind and I have appreciated the tour, but I am anxious to get back. I must admit I've never felt comfortable in Caspia. Too many people, too many towering walls, too far from the wilderness. For all its problems, I prefer Corvis. It may be a while before I come here again, barring another royal summons." Pendrake hastened to add, "Not that I haven't appreciated the hospitality. I wouldn't want the king to consider me ungrateful."

Rebald smiled and shook his head. "Perfectly understandable, Professor. Indeed I suspect His Majesty would prefer to spend more time abroad himself if he had the luxury." Cygnar's spymaster frowned apologetically. "I wanted to catch you before you left. I have need of your services rather earlier than I expected."

Pendrake put his quill aside and gave Rebald his full attention. "Of course. I am glad to do my part. Tell me how I may be of service." He raised a finger and smiled. "But remember I am not a spy, Sir Rebald, just a scholar."

"Never *just* a scholar, Professor," Rebald protested wryly. He sighed. "We have new trouble brewing in the north. No, not the kind in red uniforms. A 4th Army garrison at Stonebridge could benefit from your expertise on the topic of trollkin. They may resist the idea of taking you on, but I will insist. Not that I expect them to heed your advice, but with you there maybe I can gain a better understanding of the situation."

"Trollkin?" Pendrake asked, looking troubled. "That's a surprise. I thought you required me related to the skorne."

"We likely will, soon enough. But we have recent word of a general withdrawal of skorne soldiers along the border. They are not gone for good, I'm sure, but clearly their failed attack on Fort Falk cost them. We have a short reprieve. Of more immediate concern is a plan underway by the 4th Army to 'handle' our trollkin uprising at Crael Valley."

Pendrake shifted uncomfortably. "I do not believe attacking the trollkin settled there is wise, despite their unlawful status. I thought King Leto had decided this already?"

"Yes, he had. However, the violence has escalated and the political climate has changed. King Leto has done all he can to prevent bloodshed. If he were to do more our northern nobles would not stand for it. They see an urgent need to protect their lands. The 4th Army has taken it into their heads to use this opportunity to show their mettle."

"I have spent time among the trollkin, and I can tell you they are formidable, doubly so if defending themselves." The professor's expression was an admonishment. "As I insisted to the caretakers of the royal census, estimates of trollkin populations in the Wyrmwall and the Gnarls are too conservative. There are far more trollkin in our interior than anyone will acknowledge, and they are increasingly finding unity of purpose. Violence against Crael Valley could spark a widespread uprising."

Rebald nodded. "I know. I have read your reports, and I agree with your assessment. However, events may have gone too far already. That is why I need you there. I am convinced there is more behind this escalation than meets the eye."

"Oh?"

"The 4th Army is corrupt, Professor. It has served as a useful outlet for many of our worst elements. For years we have shifted problem personnel there, knowing they could do little harm along the peaceful Ordic border. Their commanding general is in the pocket of Duke Dergeral, who has never been a friend of the crown. Given Ceryl's remote location this has not been a major concern."

Pendrake observed with a chuckle, "Even when I served, the 4th was not staffed by Cygnar's finest."

The scout general continued, "The 4th Army has come forward offering to defend the Dragon's Tongue River. They are vital reinforcements in our time of need, so the Warmaster is happy. But this sudden enthusiasm to support the war is as sincere as a whore's flattery. Duke Dergeral is a smart man when it comes to finance and bribery, but he is not subtle. He stands to gain something, and I need to know what. Right now I can't see the shape of things."

"I told you, I am not a spy," Pendrake insisted. "It may not be easy for me to stay detached. I serve Cygnar first and foremost, but do not put me in a position to choose between my corrupt countrymen and trollkin who have saved my life on numerous occasions."

"I'm sorry, Professor, but that is precisely where I need you," Rebald answered firmly. "I am not asking you to fight these trollkin. You can stay outside of the conflict. But I need you with the 4th Army to find out what is happening. I will make sure you have considerable leeway. No 4th Army officers will have authority over you, and you will be free to come and go as you please. Just keep me apprised."

Pendrake did not hesitate long; he was not by nature an indecisive man. "Very well." He shook Rebald's extended hand. "I will be on the first train north at dawn. I will see what I can do, but I make no promises."

Travel across the Bloodstone Desert was a trying endeavor even for one well accustomed to its rigors. Saxon Orrik had likely made the trip more times than any other living being, and each time he brought a lengthy mental list of tasks requiring his attention. His value to his master was in his ability to adopt whatever personas were required to juggle seemingly contradictory tasks and agendas. Unlike some who practiced similar trades, he was not adept at disguises. Nonetheless he was different things to different people, each of whom knew him only as a weather-beaten and tanned old ranger versed in the Marches. Particularly in recent years he had found age itself to be an excellent cover. People were prone to underestimating him or ignoring him entirely—habits he used to his advantage.

This time back into the west Orrik knew his routine would be different. For the last decade he had been a creature of the desert, only occasionally dipping his toes in human civilization. He had become more skorne than human, he sometimes reflected when looking in the mirror. He knew the skorne mind, their culture, and their language. It had been his task to guide them across the trackless wastes, to blend in among them. They never forgot what he was, but sometimes they did forget he was even there.

Orrik knew he would be taking far greater risks in the days ahead. He was here for a longer haul. He had no idea how long it would be before he saw his master again or even where his master would be. By now Vinter would have left the Abyssal Fortress. Orrik knew he must mentally divorce himself from his old tasks. His mind was a series of carefully crafted compartments, each with its own instructions. He must befriend those who would happily slit his throat if they knew what he was really doing and convince others who had seen him at the Conqueror's side that he was a free agent. It would take time, and any mistake would be fatal.

It was a daunting task, but Orrik looked forward to it. The desert sands and unrelenting sun had become such constant companions that they bored him now. He would still serve as a Marches guide to those who needed one. This was the simplest cover for him to adopt, but the intrigues ahead interested him more.

It was with these thoughts that Orrik stepped into Ternon Crag. He had already spent a short time at the nearest skorne fortress. There subordinates of Archdomina Makeda had cajoled him into conveying a message to Asheth Magnus. Orrik was generally comfortable in the role of messenger, but this one prompted misgivings.

The skorne had tortured Magnus near to death, and now they wished to offer the mercenary warcaster the news that he had passed their tests and could work for their coin again. It was not an apology. The situation would have been laughable if Orrik did not know the skorne so well. They were utterly sincere. To them torture was not a personal affront, simply a process for determining truth. An officer among their ranks would never take umbrage at being tortured to test his loyalty. They did not understand the human mind, particularly Asheth Magnus'. Orrik had a feeling *that* man would take things more personally.

Either way, Orrik had his own reasons for finding Magnus. He was hoping to gain the warcaster's trust and convince him that he too had fallen out of favor with Vinter IV. This might take some doing, but Orrik had his orders and even long roads had to begin somewhere.

The Crag looked lively when he passed through, despite its unclear status. It had recovered from the oppressed quiet it had suffered under the boot of the skorne, but they could likely recapture it at their leisure. The trollkin who had "liberated" it had long since vanished across the Black River to the west after recruiting their local kinfolk. Meanwhile, though, its remaining citizens enjoyed their tenuous freedom profiteering on fringe trades related to wars abroad. The mercenary business was booming, as Ternon Crag had made its name as a neutral place to hire sell-swords.

The Ternon Crag Steelhead branch was particularly active, with dozens of men in various stages of gearing up or packing. It was obvious before he heard any of their talk that they had just landed a lucrative contract. He managed to arrange a meeting with the local branch commander, a veteran campaigner named Stannis Brocker, who appeared less than thrilled to see him.

The large warrior sighed in exaggerated commiseration from behind his desk when Orrik asked after the warcaster. "Sorry, friend, I haven't seen or heard from Magnus in two months. Can't say I blame him. The locals took to giving him a bad name after that skorne occupation. No one can prove he was involved, but that doesn't matter to rumors. His estate has been empty, but no one's dared make a claim on it."

Orrik scowled across the table but only to convey urgency. He knew he would not get anywhere trying to intimidate Brocker. The man was tough as old boot leather. "It is no secret you work for him periodically. He reserves all his big contracts for you. I need to find him. It's important."

Brocker leaned forward conspiratorially, "Just betwixt you and me, this current job has nothing to do with him. He'd probably be livid with me if he even knew. Given I haven't heard a peep from him I can't be worrying about that. A commander has to pay his men, and that takes work, so I'm taking what work I can get." The warrior's defensive tone told Orrik that Brocker's contract must be working for Cygnar. Nothing else would have the potential to agitate Magnus.

Orrik gave a weary smile. "I know how that is, trust me. I have had several occasions to work both sides of various wars in my day. Always tiresome." Orrik hid it well, but Brocker's apparent sincerity troubled him. The man was not a good liar, which meant he really had not seen Magnus.

MINIONS

What in Urcaen was the warcaster doing? Orrik continued casually, "What was the last work you did for him?"

Brocker spread his hands apologetically. "Now you know I can't tell you things like that."

This was a familiar routine, as Brocker knew no ultimate loyalty besides coin. He could be discreet if necessary, but he was always willing to sell a certain amount of information for additional income. Orrik passed a weighty pouch containing raw gold ore across the desk. "Perhaps this will help cover some of your operational costs."

A lieutenant had been standing at ease near the office door in case his commander needed him, but Brocker waved him off now. The man closed the door behind him. With this privacy, Brocker leaned forward and said in a quieter tone, "Magnus hired us for an odd operation down at Eastwall while the Menites were running amok in Caspia. You heard about that mess?" Orrik nodded once, and Brocker continued. "Magnus didn't want any Eastwall reinforcements moving to help Caspia. I have a feeling he was stirring things up so he could get into the city. Pretty sure he managed to slip inside with a few handpicked men to watch his back. Don't think he stayed long. Last I saw of him."

"Well, that's interesting," Orrik mused. Such a move was bold; even he himself would not have risked walking into the City of Walls. "Must have been important." He dropped a second pouch on Brocker's desk. He was overpaying, but it was all part of a longer term investment.

The pouch disappeared as soon as it landed. Brocker continued, "I have no idea why he was there. But if I was a betting man, I'd put money on that odd Midwinter mage fella having some part in it. Heard of him? Can't recall his first name. Anyhow, haven't seen Magnus since. The best part is, those cronies covering his back in the city? Two of 'em vanished, and a third was fished out of the sewer with his neck slit. Make of that what you will." He paused with a conspiratorial smile. "Looking into Magnus right now might not be so good for your health. You're safe with me, of course, but I'd advise not asking too many questions."

"I appreciate the warning," Orrik noted, steepling his fingers. "You've heard nothing regarding Magnus since? From anyone? Isn't that unusual?"

"A bit. But he's got a lot of irons in the fire. Never know what he's about. Any other man, I'd expect he was dead by now, but this is Magnus. He's too damned mean and stubborn to get himself killed. Although Caspia *would* be the place to do it, I reckon."

"Ah well, I suppose it will just have to wait until later." Orrik shrugged as he rose from his seat. "I have other business, to the west." He had heard enough here to indicate there was a good chance he was being hired on the opposite side of the contract Brocker's men were preparing for just outside. It was the polite course among mercenaries not to dwell on those times when one hired gun would soon be pointing a rifle at another amid the inevitable vagaries of battle.

Curiosity played across Brocker's face, but he was an old hand and knew better than to indulge it. "Good luck. Stop back by next time you're through the Crag. Meanwhile, any message I should give to Magnus if I see him?"

Orrik pretended to weigh the option but shook his head. "No, I'd better wait to deliver this one in person. Thank you, Brocker. You've been most helpful."

As Orrik left the Steelheads he had mixed thoughts. He was quite curious to know what Magnus was doing or if the man was even alive. But he had other pressing matters to attend to, issues of greater importance to his master's plans. He was eager to start his next job, for it offered the singular opportunity to shoot Cygnaran Army officers. Orrik looked forward to that as another man might anticipate a furlough.

Alten Ashley took a long deep swallow from the oversized clay jar, draining it completely, then slid it back across the table to Grissel Bloodsong. "Well, thanks for the drink, but I'd better be getting back to the Crag. Too cool here, not enough sand; I feel out of place. Just wanted you to know it looks like the Steelheads are taking that contract. The bounties I saw were pretty high, so tell Grim to watch his back too. Sorry I missed him." He staggered slightly as he stood. "Ech, that stuff has some kick."

> ## "Looking into Magnus right now might not be so good for your health. You're safe with me, of course, but I'd advise not asking too many questions."

The fell caller had been drinking far more but showed no sign of it. She had reverted to speaking Cygnaran as was her habit with the monster hunter. She asked, "Why don't you stick around? We could pay you, and I could use another rifle. I can offer half again your usual rate. This is easy work. The entire situation could blow over without a fight."

"I hope it does. Maybe they're bluffin'—who knows? But all the same, I can't get caught up in shooting Cygnaran Army folk right now. That's not my kind of fight. Not that I don't sympathize. I'll do what I can, but I don't want to be here for the showdown."

"If you're worried about your name getting out, we can keep you hidden away in a firing blind with some pygs. No one would see you." She sighed. "We might have bitten off more than we can handle. And we haven't heard from either Madrak or Doomshaper."

"I'm flattered. But what's one more rifle going to do? I'm a hunter. Good at taking down the big game." He squinted and pantomimed pulling the trigger. "That don't include things like Ironclads. 'Sides, I already saw you brought on some other hired gun." He winked, "I'd think you were replacing me if that fella by the campfire wasn't old enough to be my grandpa. Who is he? Gave me a funny look as I walked by, like he was itching for a fight."

"Who? Oh, that's Heron. An old desert ranger I've known for years. Used to trade with us along the Hawksmire River. Would hire on as a guide for kith east of the Black. Quiet, keeps to himself, good with a blade and rifle. Has some old grudge against Cygnar, which is fine by me."

"Name's familiar, and I can almost place his face. Maybe run into him in the Crag." He grinned. "Likely I stole his woman, which is why he was glaring at me. Happens all the time."

## "My master knows his worth, but this trollkin situation could undo everything you have worked for."

Grissel chuckled and shook her head. "Don't pick any fights while you're here, but think on my offer. I'd appreciate having you around; we could use all the help we can get. Still, if you'd rather stay out of this one, I'll understand. Where's that ogrun you were with last time? I wouldn't mind having him here."

"Gudrun? No idea where he is. Probably drunk in a gutter somewhere." Alten snapped his fingers. "Hey, I know where Rorsh is holed up, him and that giant boar of his. That farrow owes me a favor. Want me to track him down and see if he'd be interested? He's always up for a good scrap. And I figure he's smarter than he lets on."

Grissel frowned. "Bit of a wild card, but maybe we could find a place for him. Problem is feeding that boar and making sure the trolls don't eat it in return." She shrugged. "Send him my way if you see him."

Alten offered a mock salute and took his leave, picking up Bucking Jenny by the door as he left. He decided to swing back by the campfire and get a better look at the old rifleman, but when he walked by there the man was already gone.

Saxon Orrik slipped away from the trollkin encampment without drawing attention. The sentries knew him by sight, but he was careful to evade their notice and took precautions to ensure he was not followed. It had been a long while since he had stepped this far inside Cygnaran soil, and he felt an almost unexpected thrill at the sensation. In some respects his inordinate caution was perhaps unnecessary—the chances of anyone actually recognizing him after so many years away were extremely slim—but he knew better than to make assumptions. In his mind a clock was ticking; he had far too many things to accomplish in too little time.

Major Liam Boylan was late to the rendezvous site, and Orrik was starting to consider it a botched meeting when the disheveled man finally arrived. Boylan offered a small smile and clasped his hand by way of apology. They each spent a few minutes silently scanning their surroundings, checking to be sure neither had been followed. Even when they were mutually satisfied they spoke in low tones. Orrik began, "I can't stay long, and we will not be in communication again until the next phase."

"Of course. You should know. There have been certain . . . complications. The capture of Doomshaper did not go as hoped. We have moved on to the messier contingency."

"Yes, I'm aware of that," Orrik snapped, his disapproval clear. "This complicates matters considerably. The last thing we need right now is for the 4th Army to be tied down battling the trollkin kriels."

"We have no intent of this becoming a long-term situation. Our scouts assess the trollkin strength as considerably diminished. All reports indicate we should be able to pull this off with acceptable losses. Particularly with Madrak gone, they should—"

Orrik interrupted with a snarl, "Your scouts are idiots, and your reports are wrong. The army hasn't even completed its transition east. If you attack that compound with a light probing force you'll just be throwing men away. Men we need for the next phase, which is coming soon."

Boylan's eyes widened. "How soon? I thought we still had considerable time."

"Things have changed. We need all your men east as quickly as possible. What we don't need is you tied up here. These soldiers need to be tucked in nice and safe in their reserve garrisons, waiting for their orders."

"There are protocols we have to follow if we are to avoid drawing even more scrutiny," the major argued. "An army can't be shifted at the snap of our fingers. But rest assured we are moving as swiftly as possible. The next large group is already underway and should arrive soon."

"Not soon enough." Orrik's jaw clenched, but then he sighed. "But I know the constraints upon you. Can I convince you to delay your reprisal attacks?"

"The general would require an order from the duke, who would require a direct order from you-know-who." Boylan shrugged. "We have made promises. If we fail to deliver, it will critically undermine the goodwill we've built up in the region. I understand your concerns, believe me. I share them. But if we succeed here it will be worth the losses. If we restore those farmlands to their previous owners and demonstrate to the northern nobles we are a viable solution to their problems, we will be in a far stronger position. I know you are less involved with the politics, but there are several nobles in the north whose loyalties are at a tipping point. We can provide the nudge to send them over. We have already exhausted Ceryl's grain stores to replenish local food supplies after the draught. The duke has invested the bulk of his assets on this gamble."

"He will be rewarded accordingly, rest assured. My master knows his worth," Orrik insisted, "but this trollkin situation could undo everything you have worked for."

"You are working from the inside, correct? Can you manage things from there?"

Orrik snorted, "You forget my cover. I am just an old guide, a hired gun—I have little sway." He paused in thought, rubbing his sun-weathered chin. "This could actually work to our advantage if handled correctly. We might turn this into an opportunity, with the aid of your general."

"How so?"

"I'm certain there are a number of officers whose reliability and dubious loyalty to our cause make them a liability—companies or even entire regiments we might anticipate being likely to cause problems further down the road once it becomes clear what we are doing."

"We have plans in place for that, but it is a sticky problem."

Orrik continued, "Why not allow such men to receive heroic deaths in the line of fire against the trollkin? Arrange with General Deckley to be sure those sent first into Crael Valley are the most disposable and least essential to us: the overly optimistic, the idealists, and those otherwise not acquainted with proper pragmatic sensibilities or amenable to bribes. He may already have been thinking in this direction, but push it further. It should not be difficult to cull a large portion of the bad apples. Your numbers will be diminished, but the overall strength and solidarity of your force will be increased, at least for our purposes. Meanwhile the 4th Army will have begun to change its reputation in the eyes of the populace. Nothing tugs at the heart like noble sacrifice."

"An intriguing idea," Boylan admitted. "I like it. I'm not certain how feasible it will be in this short of a time frame, but perhaps . . . . I will speak to General Deckley. One of his most trusted subordinates is at Stonebridge and can likely help to implement such a plan."

"I will do what I can from here regarding the trollkin, but remember my influence is severely limited. Just be sure your men allow them to withdraw if they choose to do so. Do not corner them." He leveled his gaze on the soldier. "I cannot linger in this region. I may be gone by the time you make your move."

"You can't possibly believe anyone is still alive who remembers your face, let alone your crimes."

Orrik smiled grimly. "There are a few. When you've lived through what I have, you learn not to take chances."

Viktor Pendrake knew it was slightly irresponsible to take a detour, but his conscience would not allow him to meet with his 4th Army liaison without seeing the situation at Crael Valley with his own eyes. Otherwise all he had to go on were the oft-unreliable accounts from various Cygnaran newspapers, most of which were notorious for reporting hearsay and even fabricating stories to suit their readers. He was reasonably confident no officials noticed him arrive at the Bainsmarket station, and he was certain he could come up with a feasible excuse for being a few days late.

Approaching a highly militant, well armed, and rather tense trollkin encampment without previously established arrangements was not generally a good idea, particularly in the darker hours. For that reason he had created a rustic and well camouflaged shelter for the night at a fairly safe distance. Over the decades he had created countless such concealments to watch wilderness creatures undetected. Accordingly, this shelter blended easily into the shadowy landscape. It might not have held up quite so well in the full light of day, but for now Pendrake felt all but invisible hunkered down and trying to settle in to sleep.

When he had left the train station it had seemed a brilliant idea to get back to nature. He had thought to have wearied of soft Caspian beds, but now he discovered his old discipline had faded more quickly than expected. Lying beneath bug-ridden twigs and leaves with rocks and more twigs poking into his back was rather less romantic than his memory suggested. Perhaps Caspian beds had their merits after all. He wondered if he was getting too old for this.

He froze as he heard quiet movement outside. He hoped he had not attracted a trollkin patrol. When he carefully peeked out, he was startled to see what looked to be a human making his solitary way toward Crael Valley, clearly endeavoring to keep a low profile. The man passed within ten yards of Pendrake's position, and just then chance happened to draw the clouds away from the moon to give a clear glimpse of his face. Pendrake lay frozen and disbelieving, wondering if his mind had finally cracked. He was almost positive the man he had just seen was none other than his old mentor Saxon Orrik: Cygnaran outlaw, henchman to Vinter Raelthorne IV, and a man he had last seen at the Abyssal Fortress a thousand miles away.

Pendrake tried to convince himself that his eye had deceived him, that it must be some other man who only bore a resemblance. No. The posture, the movement, the slung rifle, the blade at his waist—all provided a degree of certainty. "Isn't that interesting?" Pendrake whispered to himself, wondering what this occurrence might portend. Whatever it was, he was certain it was bad for Cygnar and likely bad for the trollkin also.

He gave up the idea of sleep and stole from the shelter. As he looked after Saxon, he felt torn between the impulse to follow and the more practical action of sending a warning to the scout general. The man had likely not become any less dangerous or vigilant in a decade among the skorne, however, and pride was a luxury of youth. Rather than risk his own premature death spying on a master hunter, he opted for discretion. He sighed, knowing he would not be able to visit the trollkin and assess their situation as he had hoped. Turning back in the direction from which he had come, Pendrake mentally whispered a prayer for the continued safety of his blue-skinned friends.

# Brun Cragback
## RHULIC MINION MERCENARY CHARACTER SOLO

*The Glass Peaks are cold, unforgiving, and treacherous. Anyone who feels at home alone up there is liable to be the same.*

—Decklin Steelthunder, Searforge Commission officer

A rugged and fearless loner with intimate knowledge of every game trail and mountain pass in western Immoren, Brun Cragback first earned notoriety in the remote regions along the periphery of Rhul. He is a seasoned warrior who would rather kill a man than endure a lengthy conversation. When blood needs spilling, it is far better to have Brun as an ally than face him in battle. With his gun or axe in hand and Lug beside him, he fears no man or beast.

Before becoming a recluse, Brun Cragback served his small clan by patrolling the western peaks near the border with Khador. His kin were embroiled in a feud with Khadoran settlers of Skirov descent who were regularly trespassing in their territory. Given the nature of these twisting mountain passes, it was difficult to be sure where Khador ended and Rhul began. The problem had given rise to intermittent

| SPELL | COST | RNG | AOE | POW | UP | OFF |
|-------|------|-----|-----|-----|-----|-----|
| STONEHOLD | 2 | SELF | - | - | X | |

When Cragback is hit by an attack, roll one less damage die on the damage roll against him. Cragback and friendly models in base-to-base contact with him cannot be knocked down.

bloodshed for decades. Before Brun entered the picture most of these skirmishes were small and inconsequential, considered an almost respectable tradition by some.

Brun is not a dwarf who appreciates half measures. Hearing of the never-ending nature of this feud he took it upon himself to settle matters once and for all. Without consulting his kinfolk Brun waited for a moonless night and marched straight into the human camp with his axe in hand. His disdain for the humans only grew when he saw they had not even bothered to post sentries. The ensuing carnage was almost too easy, hardly a sporting test of his skill. When he returned to his kinsmen soaked in gore he was surprised to see horror on their faces. They protested that he had gone too far, fearful that their clan would bear the brunt of his impropriety if the Moot decided to get involved. There was talk of exiling him and stripping him of his clan name, but Brun refused to wait for their decision. Before they could ask him to leave he turned his back on them, eager to find his destiny alone amid the mountains.

The only activity Brun enjoys more than a good brawl is exploring unknown territory. Unlike most of his kin he has never felt the urge to settle in one specific place and set up a home. As soon as Brun feels he has mastered every nook and cranny of a given locale, he packs up his tent and travels on. He has made a vow never to own any more than he and his pack mule can carry, and in times of avalanche or other disasters he has sometimes abandoned even that. His memory of any location he has traveled remains perfect, as if each footstep inscribes the peaks and valleys he walks directly onto his mind.

This compulsion to venture into new territory has taken Brun to the frozen regions of Khador, northern Llael, and Cygnar's Wyrmwall Mountains. He has never lacked for work as a guide and battle-ready escort, providing assistance to those travelling from one place to another in hostile regions. He does not work regularly as a mercenary—not as often as those who earn their coin as seasonal soldiers—but he accepts periodic work with the Searforge Commission when his supplies or funds run low. His habit is to steer clear of sizable communities and he avoids cities like the plague, meaning Searforge agents sometimes have to work to track him down and arrange for his services. Given the difficulty in separating him from his oversized bear companion (and the scarcity of baths in the wild), Brun's avoidance of towns is likely appreciated.

# SPECIAL RULES

## Mercenary
Brun Cragback & Lug will work for the Searforge Commission.

## Minion
Brun Cragback & Lug will work for the Circle and Trollbloods.

## Cragback
**Fearless** - Cragback never flees.

**Flank** - When Cragback makes a melee attack against an enemy model that is within Lug's melee range, Cragback gains +2 to attack rolls and rolls an additional damage die.

**Lesser Warlock** - Cragback is not a warlock, although he has the following abilities: Damage Transference, Forcing, Healing, Fury Manipulation, and Spell Caster. Cragback can cast Lug's animus as a spell. Cragback's model type is solo, not warlock. Cragback's abilities that refer to "friendly faction warbeasts" work only with Lug. Other warlocks cannot use the listed warlock abilities with Lug.

**Lifebond** - While in base-to-base contact with Lug, Cragback may transfer damage to Lug without spending a fury point.

**Pathfinder** - During his activation, Cragback ignores movement penalties from, and may charge across, rough terrain and obstacles.

**Weapon Master** - Cragback rolls an additional die on his melee damage rolls.

| CRAGBACK | | | | CMD 9 | |
|------|------|------|------|------|------|
| SPD | STR | MAT | RAT | DEF | ARM |
| 5 | 6 | 7 | 5 | 13 | 15 |

| BLUNDERBUSS | | | |
|------|------|------|------|
| RNG | ROF | AOE | POW |
| 8 | 1 | — | 12 |

| AXE | | |
|------|------|------|
| SPECIAL | POW | P+S |
| — | 4 | 10 |

| FURY | 3 |
|------|------|
| DAMAGE | 10 |
| FIELD ALLOWANCE | C |
| VICTORY POINTS | 1 |
| BRUN CRAGBACK AND LUG | 113 |
| BASE SIZE | SMALL |

## TACTICAL TIP

**Lesser Warlock** – Brun Cragback's model type is solo, not warlock.

Brun has spent time among some of the northern trollkin kriels and has contacts with the human blackclads who call themselves the Circle. When he is in the vicinity and war erupts, he stands ready to leap into the fray with pragmatic efficiency. Accompanied by his gigantic bear Lug, he inflicts a heavy toll on any enemy he meets. He has fought Khadoran soldiers, Nyss both "with scales and without," and a wide assortment of bandits, outcasts, and bloodthirsty monsters. Nothing fazes Brun Cragback; whether it flies, slithers, or breathes fire, he will gladly shoot it, chop it down, or send Lug to crush it.

Brun earned a name for himself through his own skill with arms, but without question the enormous armored bear that tags along with him enhances his reputation tenfold. Together Brun and Lug walk into the path of gunfire, frenzying trolls, or charging pikemen with equally casual disregard. Brun brushes aside questions about Lug, claiming he has no idea why the "confounded animal" follows him. Whatever the reason, their raw destructive power is undeniable. Enduring Brun's sour disposition seems a small price to pay for any potential employer.

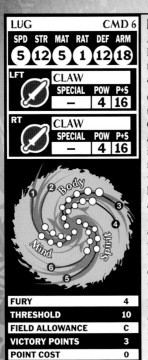

| LUG | | | | | CMD | 6 |
|---|---|---|---|---|---|---|
| SPD | STR | MAT | RAT | DEF | ARM | |
| 5 | 12 | 5 | 1 | 12 | 18 | |

| LFT | CLAW | | |
|---|---|---|---|
| | SPECIAL | POW | P+S |
| | – | 4 | 16 |

| RT | CLAW | | |
|---|---|---|---|
| | SPECIAL | POW | P+S |
| | – | 4 | 16 |

| FURY | 4 |
|---|---|
| THRESHOLD | 10 |
| FIELD ALLOWANCE | C |
| VICTORY POINTS | 3 |
| POINT COST | 0 |
| BASE SIZE | LARGE |

## Lug

**All Terrain** - During its activation, Lug ignores movement penalties from, and may charge and slam across, rough terrain and obstacles.

**Chain Attack: Chomp** - If Lug hits the same target with both of its initial Claw attacks in the same activation, after resolving the attacks it may immediately make an additional melee attack against the target without being forced. If the attack hits, the target immediately suffers a damage roll with a POW equal to Lug's current STR. When damaging a warjack, Lug's controller chooses which column takes this damage. When damaging a warbeast, Lug's controller chooses which branch takes this damage.

**Flank** - When Lug makes a melee attack against an enemy model that is within Cragback's melee range, Lug gains +2 to attack rolls and rolls an additional damage die.

**Tantrum** - When Cragback is destroyed or removed from play, instead of going wild Lug automatically frenzies during its controller's Control Phase every round.

**Warbeast Bond** - Lug is bonded to Cragback. While in Cragback's control area, Lug gains +2 THR. While Lug is within 3" of Cragback and is not stationary, Cragback cannot be targeted by free strikes, gains +2 DEF against melee attacks, and models attacking Cragback do not gain back strike bonuses.

| ANIMUS | COST | RNG | AOE | POW | UP | OFF |
|---|---|---|---|---|---|---|
| **Bear Hands** | 1 | Self | - | | - | - |

An enemy model damaged by a melee attack made by a model using this animus may be knocked down or pushed 2" directly away from the affected model. Bear Hands lasts for one round.

There are few things more terrifying than a twelve-foot-tall armored bear rearing up on its hind legs to let loose an ear-shattering roar before charging to attack. Those who face the mass of fur and muscle do not have time to reflect on its mood before claws rip them in half. What they fail to realize is that Lug is actually a generally good-natured beast who simply likes to play hard.

Brun Cragback did not need to coerce, train, or pressure Lug into fighting. Rather the bear takes delight in romping through masses of men and swatting everything within reach of his massive claws. Clearly the bear has no real sense of mortality, and to be fair Lug is just as oblivious to his own injuries in battle so long as he is given free reign to play. The only hint of sorrow and melancholy the bear demonstrates is after the fighting when the battle has gone quiet. Lug will paw at the fallen bodies as if trying to urge them to stand back up and play some more.

Brun says he has lost track of how long he and Lug have been together, but he reckons it to be less than a decade. While his memory of specific events in the intervening years is hazy Brun seems to relish the story of how he came by the bear. Apparently Brun encountered a white mountain bear while hunting near Nyss

territory in the Shard Spires. Eager to acquire a nice thick pelt of fur before the coming winter, Brun dispatched the ornery bear without a second thought. He was in the middle of the messy operation of skinning her when he heard the querulous roar of another bear and the sound of approaching paws. In a moment of desperate inspiration, Brun wrapped himself in the hide and stood to confront the newcomer.

Rounding the mountain pass was a half-grown but already dangerous adolescent bear—apparently the dead animal's spawn—which slid to a confused stop in front of him and sniffed the hide he was wearing while making suspicious noises. Apparently satisfied, the bear at last sat back on its haunches and tucked into some of Brun's food supplies. Ever since that moment, Lug has followed after Brun Cragback, accompanying him everywhere. Brun is convinced the stupid bear thinks he is its mother and has worn the improvised cloak ever since. Whether Lug would actually cease to recognize him without the hide seems unlikely, but the dwarf maintains he'd rather stay on the safe side.

Though Brun regularly hurls every foul epithet imaginable at his animal companion, the bond between them is obvious. Brun claims Lug is the stupidest bear ever born, but outsiders watching the beast have seen it demonstrate undeniable cunning. Belying his casual attitude, the dwarf has spent a sizable portion of his mercenary earnings

# MINION MERCENARY UNIQUE HEAVY WARBEAST

outfitting the bear for war, making special arrangements for the thick armor protecting Lug's girth. Brun purchased this special plated barding at no small expense from a master smith out of Skirov, and the bear seems to take pride in wearing it. Brun will generally hold off outfitting the bear for war unless he expects battle, and the beast becomes unaccountably excited as Brun straps each plate to his bulk. Those who have seen them after battle confirm that Brun always feeds Lug first, even when the dwarf goes hungry. Cragback claims this is simply a matter of self preservation and denies it is any sign of affection for the smelly beast.

*That b'ar is stupid deadly. Hard to tell when it's more dangerous: when it's hungry or when it wants to play.*

—Brun Cragback

# Dahlia Hallyr
## MINION MERCENARY CHARACTER SOLO

*There is a melody underlying every force, thought, and action. By playing the proper notes one can change the world.*

—Dahlia Hallyr

There is an undeniable aura of mystery that surrounds all elves, whatever their background, but even among those elusive people Dahlia Hallyr is an enigma. Although born in Ios, she has been an outsider to her own people for long decades, traveling abroad in western Immoren and refusing to settle permanently in any one place. She is a nomadic wanderer whose blood flows with the power of sorcery. She manifests this magical potential through a singular technique: her unearthly music. By the notes of her flute she entrances those who hear her.

| SPELL | COST | RNG | AOE | POW | UP | OFF |
|---|---|---|---|---|---|---|
| ENTRANCING RHYTHM | 2 | 10 | - | - | | X |

Target enemy warbeast suffers Torpor. Torpor is a continuous effect that reduces the warbeast's SPD to 1 and DEF to 7. Torpor expires in the model's controller's Maintenance Phase on a d6 roll of 1 or 2.

| | | | | | | |
|---|---|---|---|---|---|---|
| HAUNTING MELODY | 2 | SELF | CTRL | - | | X |

While in Dahlia Hallyr's control area, enemy models cannot give or receive orders and suffer -2 CMD.

The Hallyr line traces directly back to the lost Empire of Lyoss, before the split between those who would follow Aeric to become the Nyss and those who remained in Ios. Between both peoples the name has maintained its sorcerous mystique. Raised in the city of Iryss by affluent parents, Dahlia proved to be exceptional from a young age, not only for her talent but also for her stubborn refusal to heed the dictates of her elders. Her fascination with music was not atypical of her family, as their sorcery often went hand-in-hand with other artistic pursuits, but Dahlia confounded all tutors assigned to discipline her talents. She was prone to ignoring their instructions entirely, walking away in mid-lesson or conducting conversations with the empty air. Such behavior prompted rumors to circulate that she might have inherited the less esteemed legacy of the Hallyr line: a penchant for eccentricity verging on insanity.

A market for talented artists exists among the aristocracy living in Iryss and Shyrr. The more militant Iosans deem such circles to be decadently oblivious to the dangers facing their race, but some prefer to divert their minds through idle entertainment. Certainly Dahlia could have pursued a lucrative career helping them ignore their fate through sheer force of denial with her seductive musical notes. She confounded her family by eschewing elven society entirely and leaving Ios, determined to pursue her own destiny. Her goals since leaving her homeland are unknown. She keeps no council and claims few friends. The only constant in her life has been an inner compulsion to wander and perfect her music.

Western Immoren is a vast and terrifying place, and there was little in her upbringing to suggest Dahlia would so easily endure the wilds. Despite her apparent shortcomings she has proven to be a survivor of considerable skill. Certainly the sorcerous power of her music has played a large role in keeping her safe. There are some people touched by a special sort of madness that preserves them in the face of warfare and strife, and that seems to be true of Dahlia Hallyr.

She has shown no aversion to violence or warfare and indeed goes out of her way to seek it out sometimes. Despite this, she does not see herself as a warrior, but rather an observer. Everything she witnesses lends texture to her musical notes. At times it seems as though she does not interact with the world at all but only watches from

## SPECIAL RULES

### Mercenary
Dahlia Hallyr & Skarath will work for the Retribution.

### Minion
Dahlia Hallyr & Skarath will work for the Circle and Trollbloods.

### Hallyr
**Charmer** - When a friendly warbeast frenzies in Hallyr's control area, it may forfeit its activation.

**Fearless** - Hallyr never flees.

**Lesser Warlock** - Hallyr is not a warlock, although she has the following abilities: Damage Transference, Forcing, Healing, Fury Manipulation, and Spell Caster. Hallyr can cast Skarath's animus as a spell. Hallyr's model type is solo, not warlock. Hallyr's abilities that refer to "friendly faction warbeasts" work only with Skarath. Other warlocks cannot use the listed warlock abilities with Skarath.

| HALLYR | | | | CMD 8 | |
|---|---|---|---|---|---|
| SPD | STR | MAT | RAT | DEF | ARM |
| 6 | 4 | 5 | 4 | 16 | 11 |

| | |
|---|---|
| FURY | 4 |
| DAMAGE | 8 |
| FIELD ALLOWANCE | C |
| VICTORY POINTS | 1 |
| DAHLIA HALLYR AND SKARATH | 107 |
| BASE SIZE | SMALL |

the outside. For years she has relied on others to help deflect the many dangers of western Immoren.

Dahlia uses her entrancing music to gather guardians, and in recent years she has become particularly enamored of the tremendous tatzylwurms. These serpentine creatures possess singular grace and deadly prowess and respond as if born to heed the notes of her flute. Battle to her is akin to a dance, and she enjoys the interplay of blade and serpent as if each battle were a performance for her eyes alone. On witnessing her trancelike delight in these deadly engagements some have come away convinced of her mental instability, but she insists these fools simply do not understand her vision of the world.

In her travels Dahlia has made her services available to several groups, loaning her power and the killing prowess of Skarath to their battles. She appears to have made arrangements with members of the Circle Orboros and several large trollkin kriels, neither of whom interferes with her travels across their territories. She has visited individual Circle leaders and Trollblood elders in private consul. She claims to have no love for the urban centers of mankind and has expressed a strong loathing for the discordant hum of human magic, which strikes her ears like shattering glass. She has shown no moral qualms in fighting for causes that are not her own although she clearly prefers to let her serpentine companion do the dirty work. Whether her involvement in the wars that grip western Immoren is part of some more systematic plan or simply following the impulses of the moment is something only Dahlia knows. Certain arcanists serving the Retribution are convinced her latent power has not entirely awakened to its full strength, and it seems clear they hope to make use of her in the wars to come.

MINIONS

## SKARATH — CMD 6

| SPD | STR | MAT | RAT | DEF | ARM |
|-----|-----|-----|-----|-----|-----|
| 6 | 10 | 6 | 5 | 14 | 16 |

**HD — ACID SPRAY**

| RNG | ROF | AOE | POW |
|-----|-----|-----|-----|
| SP 1 | — | — | 13 |

**HD — JAW**

| SPECIAL | POW | P+S |
|---------|-----|-----|
| Multi | 6 | 16 |

| | |
|---|---|
| FURY | 4 |
| THRESHOLD | 10 |
| FIELD ALLOWANCE | C |
| VICTORY POINTS | 3 |
| POINT COST | 0 |
| BASE SIZE | LARGE |

## Skarath

**Bounding Leap** - After advancing but before performing an action, Skarath may be forced to move up to an additional 5". During this movement, Skarath may move through other models if it has enough movement to move completely past their bases. During this movement Skarath cannot be targeted by free strikes and ignores rough terrain, obstacles, and other movement penalties and effects. Any effects that prevent charging or slamming also prevent Skarath from using Bounding Leap. Skarath may use Bounding Leap once per activation.

**Serpentine** - Skarath cannot make slam or trample power attacks.

**Warbeast Bond** - Skarath is bonded to Hallyr. While in Hallyr's control area, Skarath gains +2 THR. When Skarath frenzies while in Hallyr's control range, her controller selects the model Skarath will attack.

### Acid Spray

**Corrosion** - A model hit by the Acid Spray suffers Corrosion. Corrosion is a continuous effect that slowly erodes its target. Corrosion does one damage point each turn to the affected model during its controller's Maintenance Phase until it expires on a d6 roll of 1 or 2.

### Jaw

**Critical Consume** - On a critical hit, small-based non-warlock/warcaster model hit is removed from play.

**Paralytic Venom** - A living model damaged by a Jaw attack must forfeit its movement during its next activation.

**Reach** - 2" melee range.

To its victims Skarath is a serpentine horror, and the last sight they see is the alien gape seconds before it consumes them whole. Skarath is a particularly large pale tatzylwurm, a refined specimen who perfectly embodies the cunning and savagery of this species. Tatzylwurms are one of the most frightening examples of monstrous predators in western Immoren, and Skarath lives up to this pedigree.

While all tatzylwurms are dangerous, the pale variety is the most aggressive—the most inclined to use its tremendous leaping ability to pounce on anything it deems to be a threat, even if not motivated by hunger. Otherwise fearless trolls steer clear of territories where the pale tatzylwurm hunts. Their acid can melt flesh and their poison will paralyze their chosen prey, allowing them to consume and digest their victims at leisure. Indeed pale tatzylwurms prefer to digest their prey while it is still alive, in a process which can take several long hours.

| ANIMUS | COST | RNG | AOE | POW | UP | OFF |
|--------|------|-----|-----|-----|-----|-----|
| **Serpent Strike** | 2 | 6 | - | - | | |

When target friendly model is missed by an enemy melee attack, it may immediately make a melee attack targeting the attacking model if it is within the affected model's melee range. Serpent Strike lasts for one round.

Dahlia Hallyr discovered long ago that tatzylwurms respond particularly well to her music and she has taken to utilizing members of this species exclusively as her chosen guardians. She has refined a broad repertoire of note sequences which provoke specific actions and postures from the tatzylwurms protecting her. Skarath has been with her for seven years and in that time the two have refined their connection to the point where they respond to one another in perfect harmony.

She clearly holds this particular guardian in special esteem, speaking to it in loving tones and sometimes performing her music just for the sake of observing its graceful and sinuous dance. She is an indulgent mistress at times and is not always inclined to restrain the serpent when it strikes at prey, even if that prey is an innocent passer-by. Indeed there have been times when Dahlia has urged the serpent to delay consuming its meal so that its paralyzed victim can serve as a captive audience to her latest musical innovations.

Perhaps because of Dahlia's travels Skarath has enjoyed a regular diet which may account for its tremendous size. Even by the standards of pale tatzylwurms Skarath is well beyond the norm, having reached a length comparable to the more docile painted variety of the breed. Its coloration is also of a more vibrant hue compared to the sometimes drab gray hide common to other specimens. Skarath's reflexes in battle are almost preternatural, likely enhanced by Dahlia's own awareness of her surroundings. One of the most surprising and deadly maneuvers common to tatzylwurms is their ability to convulse their muscled bodies in a single great wave allowing them to leap tremendous distances before attacking. While capable of moving swiftly even without this ability, the leaping strike gives them a range which catches many opponents off guard. Skarath has years of combat experience and demonstrates uncanny intelligence at exploiting his abilities to keep Dahlia safe from harm.

MINIONS

# Skarath

## MINION MERCENARY PALE TATZYLWURM UNIQUE HEAVY WARBEAST

> *Highly aggressive and territorial, these predators are utterly untamable. The pale tatzylwurm is a peerless hunter willing to devour anything that moves.*
>
> —Professor Coriandr Jagus

# Rorsh

## FARROW MINION CHARACTER SOLO

*This world is a heap of troubles. Best not wait for them to find you.*

—Rorsh, translated from the farrow

Rorsh and his gargantuan companion Brine wander the battlefields of western Immoren seeking sport and the opportunity for profit. The pair swaggers into the most desolate war encampments on the fringes of the Iron Kingdoms to offer their services at a reasonable price with no questions asked. A farrow of action, Rorsh is a cool professional unfazed by the horrors of war. He will calmly pause in battle, heedless of nearby dangers, to employ his favorite tool of distraction: a stick of dynamite lit with a foul-smelling cigar.

Though Rorsh claims to be a mercenary by trade, most civilized nations have branded him an outlaw. Only the desperate communities on the fringes of civilization are willing to pay his bill. As merchants and lawmen from the frozen wastes of Khador to the blazing sands of the Protectorate can attest, Rorsh and Brine are guilty of every form of opportunistic brigandage known to man (and some unknown to man).

He generally responds to his impressive list of crimes with a shrug and a grunt, as if to say he only did as survival required. Rorsh has participated in several train heists in northern Cygnar, the plundering of military blasting powder stores, and the robbery of several small town banks. Were he inclined to speak about such things Rorsh would admit to mixed luck in these exploits. While he has always managed to evade capture, fate has conspired to keep a truly profitable score from landing in his lap.

MINIONS

| SPELL | COST | RNG | AOE | POW | UP | OFF |
|---|---|---|---|---|---|---|
| PIGPEN | 2 | SELF | * | - | | X |

While within 3" of Rorsh, enemy models treat open terrain as rough terrain.

Rorsh also prefers not to advertise the rather large number of victims he has left in his wake. While he adopts the guise of a cheerful farrow with a knack for landing in trouble, his deeds say otherwise. It is no accident that the enormous boar following Rorsh into battle has developed a taste for human flesh. The beast has cleaned up a number of Rorsh's more messy entanglements with the local law. Rorsh appears to be of the mindset that once the body is gone a farrow can't rightly be guilty of murder. His preference for staying in lawless communities on the fringes of civilization has thus far proven this attitude to be surprisingly apt.

Rorsh keeps a tight lip. He understands several languages well enough, but he has trouble with human vocal inflections. Even words in the guttural farrow tongue rarely pass his lips—he prefers to communicate by posture, glares, and raw intimidation. He conveys his meaning by a single chop of his hand, a feral grin, or a simple nod when offered payments meet his standards. He has no particular affinity for his own species, fighting alongside them or not as suits the needs of his employers and forming no lasting friendships before moving on. Occasionally younger farrow try to follow after him hoping to learn from his example, but with the exception of Brine he does not abide hangers-on. Those who poke their noses into his business too persistently generally wind up disappearing.

Rorsh prefers areas that are dry, dusty, and windswept. He makes his way between small settlements along the edge of the Bloodstone Marches, Ternon Crag, the Dragon's Tongue, and the Hawksmire River. He steers clear of human mercenaries for reasons known only to him but likely related to his impressive roster of crimes. In the fringe regions Rorsh travels it is not uncommon for mercenary companies to serve as local law, and Rorsh has had more than a few unpleasant run-ins with such hired help. Otherwise the farrow brigand is not overly picky about his choice of employers.

His predilection for explosives has occasionally gotten him in trouble. There was the time he accidentally caught a warder of the Circle Orboros in a diversionary blast while attempting to stop Cygnaran rangers from flanking his position. He shrugged off this casualty but has been on the outs with the druids ever since. They seem to hold a grudge: he has had to evade several of their assassination attempts in payback for their fallen brother, which resulted only in a larger tally of deaths and likely an even more pronounced vendetta. They have refused all his attempts to offer financial recompense, but fortunately for Rorsh they must have bigger fish to fry than him. He has found that keeping on the move has kept him safe from the growing list of organizations and individuals who would like to see him locked away or dead. So long as Brine is at his side, Rorsh seems unconcerned that his list of friends has not grown with similar alacrity.

# SPECIAL RULES

## Minion
Rorsh & Brine will work for the Legion of Everblight, Skorne, and Trollbloods.

## Rorsh
**Diversionary Tactic (★Action)** - Center a 4" AOE on Rorsh. Models in the AOE other than Rorsh and Brine suffer a POW 6 blast damage roll. After Diversionary Tactic damage rolls have been resolved, Rorsh may move up to his current SPD in inches. If Brine was also in the AOE, it can move up to its current SPD in inches as well. During this movement, Rorsh and Brine cannot be targeted by free strikes.

**Fearless** - Rorsh never flees.

**Hog Wild** - Rorsh may make ranged attacks before his normal movement this activation. After resolving the ranged attack, Rorsh must advance and may make melee attacks during his combat action.

**Lesser Warlock** - Rorsh is not a warlock, although he has the following abilities: Damage Transference, Forcing, Healing, Fury Manipulation, and Spell Caster. Rorsh can cast Brine's animus as a spell. Rorsh's model type is solo, not warlock. Rorsh's warlock abilities that refer to "friendly faction warbeasts" work only with Brine. Other warlocks cannot use the listed abilities with Brine.

**Souie!** - If Brine is outside of Rorsh's control area at the start of Rorsh's controller's Control Phase, before Rorsh leaches fury, Brine may move up to its current SPD in inches. Brine must end this movement closer to Rorsh than it began.

## Dynamite
**Cumbersome** - Rorsh cannot make ranged attacks with Dynamite and the Lever Action Pig Iron during the same activation.

## Lever Action Pig Iron
**Rapid Shot** - When Rorsh hits an enemy model with a ranged attack during Rorsh's activation, immediately after this attack has been resolved, he may make one additional ranged attack. Attacks gained from this ability cannot generate further additional attacks from this ability. Attacks gained from Rapid Shot do not count against the Lever Action Pig Iron's ROF.

| RORSH | | | | | CMD 8 |
|---|---|---|---|---|---|
| SPD | STR | MAT | RAT | DEF | ARM |
| 5 | 7 | 7 | 5 | 13 | 15 |

| DYNAMITE | | | |
|---|---|---|---|
| RNG | ROF | AOE | POW |
| 6 | 1 | 4 | 12 |

| LEVER ACTION PIG IRON | | | |
|---|---|---|---|
| RNG | ROF | AOE | POW |
| 10 | 1 | — | 12 |

| CLEAVER | | |
|---|---|---|
| SPECIAL | POW | P+S |
| — | 4 | 11 |

| FURY | 3 |
|---|---|
| DAMAGE | 8 |
| FIELD ALLOWANCE | C |
| VICTORY POINTS | 1 |
| RORSH AND BRINE | 100 |
| BASE SIZE | SMALL |

| BRINE | | | | | CMD 6 |
|---|---|---|---|---|---|
| SPD | STR | MAT | RAT | DEF | ARM |
| 5 | 12 | 5 | 1 | 12 | 17 |

| HD | GORE | | |
|---|---|---|---|
| | SPECIAL | POW | P+S |
| | Critical | 5 | 17 |

| FURY | 4 |
|---|---|
| THRESHOLD | 9 |
| FIELD ALLOWANCE | C |
| VICTORY POINTS | 3 |
| POINT COST | 0 |
| BASE SIZE | LARGE |

## SPECIAL RULES

### Brine

**Bacon** - When Brine is destroyed, remove d6 damage points from each living warbeast in base-to-base contact with it.

**Pain Response** - While all of its aspects are damaged, Brine gains +2 to melee damage rolls.

**Pig Headed** - If Brine suffers sufficient damage to be destroyed, Brine remains in play for one round and cannot be destroyed during this time. During this time, Brine ignores the effects of lost aspects. After one round, Brine is destroyed.

**Relentless Charge** - Brine may charge across rough terrain and obstacles without penalty.

**Warbeast Bond** - Brine is bonded to Rorsh. While in Rorsh's control area, Brine gains +2 THR. During its activation, Brine may charge or slam an enemy model that was damaged by a melee or ranged attack made by Rorsh this turn without being forced.

### Gore

**Critical Knockdown** - On a critical hit, target model is knocked down.

| ANIMUS | COST | RNG | AOE | POW | UP | OFF |
|---|---|---|---|---|---|---|
| Pig Farm | 2 | Self | - | | - | |

The model using this animus gains an additional damage die on melee attacks against living models. When a living model is destroyed by a melee attack made by the affected model, the destroyed model is removed from play and the affected model removes d3 damage points. Pig Farm lasts for one turn.

Brine has all the temperamental traits of a wild boar, proving almost impossible to kill and becoming even more deadly when provoked by injury. Those who have fought the beast attest it can endure punishment that would kill any lesser creature. The more grievous its injuries, the more fearsome its relentless attacks become. Its maddened squeals while lashing out with its tusks are terrifying, and its weight and bulk can shatter anything in its path.

Rorsh may be taciturn about his past but the creature accompanying him, a bipedal boar named Brine, is the larger mystery. This monstrous beast bears no resemblance to any species even veteran monster hunters have seen before. In most regards it seems pig-like, particularly when rushing forward on all fours to gore a dire troll or split a man in half. At the same time Brine's forward appendages resemble hands and it prefers to walk erect on its hind legs when not charging into battle. Some have hazarded whether or not Brine might be a relative of Rorsh, like a peculiar and grotesque half-brother. Those with such opinions had best not voice them too loudly in Rorsh's company lest they earn a mouthful of pig iron.

A more likely theory describes Brine as a remnant of whatever unnatural process created the farrow in the first place. Others guess that Brine is just an oversized, half-witted, freakishly strong farrow akin to the giants of legend, which supposedly bear a human likeness. Given that the origins of the farrow are a mystery of their own, this enigma will likely persist. Regardless of Brine's origins or species, the resemblance to a wild boar is uncanny. Those on hand when it suffers fiery injury by Protectorate cleansers claim the smell of the burning flesh is disturbingly intoxicating, like a sizzling side of bacon.

Brine is never far from Rorsh and serves to amplify the threat represented by the already formidable farrow. The boar's presence has made Rorsh a singularly compelling hire for those willing to meet his demands. Rorsh may be deadly with a gun, handy with explosives, and wickedly efficient with his cleaver, but it's Brine who lets the duo comfortably stand toe-to-toe against larger threats like warjacks and warpwolves. The oversized pig has also been largely responsible for Rorsh's ability to evade the law. Even determined guardsmen, mercenaries, or soldiers cannot hope to stand against Brine.

# Brine

## MINION UNIQUE HEAVY WARBEAST

As to the relationship between Rorsh and Brine, that is anyone's guess. The two have been an inseparable pair for as long as anyone can remember, and some insist they are utterly reliant on one another for survival. Most disturbing are rumors that Brine savors human flesh, which Rorsh makes use of to eliminate the evidence of his crimes. Feeding the creature without the benefit of battle would certainly be a chore. It is entirely possible that keeping Brine supplied with fresh meat is why Rorsh applies himself so diligently both to seeking work for hire and indulging in the occasional crime spree.

*War is the cheapest way to feed him.*

—Rorsh

# WRONG EYE
## GATORMAN MINION CHARACTER SOLO

> *There be a power in that eye o' his, gleamin' in the darkness and invokin' all manner o' vile slithery unpleasantness.*
>
> —Therin, swampy elder of a bayou village off the Black River

There are things lurking deep in the swamps and forgotten waterways that man was not meant to know. Chief among them are the cunning gatormen, as hungry as their simpler counterparts but smart enough to shape tools and weapons. Some possess a keen insight into the spirit world, the energies of blood and death, and the forces that lurk unseen in the fetid darkness. Gatormen base their faith around the central notion of predation and the cycle of

hunger, hunting, and death. For one entity to be satiated it must consume another. These dark and foreboding ritual practices fuel the power of a great bokor known as Wrong Eye. All who live in the bayous of western Immoren know of his legend and hope to avoid his capricious wrath. Swampies insist that even dark gods can be appeased with sacrifices but it is best to avoid Wrong Eye entirely. Even his own kind are terrified of him.

The mind of the gatorman is not like the mind of man, something those dealing with this shaman must remember. Wrong Eye emerges from the humid damp like a reptilian oracle. Those who look him in the eye sense immediately that they face an entity whose thoughts are unfathomable. Darkness lingers around him, bringing a sense of malice and hunger. Any negotiation with Wrong

| SPELL | COST | RNG | AOE | POW | UP | OFF |
|---|---|---|---|---|---|---|
| CRAZY EYE | 2 | 8 | - | - | | X |

Target living enemy non-warcaster/warlock model immediately moves up to its current SPD in inches in a direction determined by the deviation template, ending this movement facing that direction. The affected model cannot be targeted by free strikes during this movement.

| SPELL | COST | RNG | AOE | POW | UP | OFF |
|---|---|---|---|---|---|---|
| VOODOO DOLL | 2 | 8 | - | - | | X |

Wrong Eye's controller chooses one of target warbeast's aspects. That aspect suffers the effects of being lost for one round. The warbeast is not destroyed as a result of Voodoo Doll.

Eye brings the possibility of bloodshed and feeding frenzy. Even hardened blackclads and trollkin champions sometimes lose their nerve and offer him more favorable terms than they might have initially intended.

Wrong Eye represents an element of dangerous unpredictability akin to the alligator lying in a shallow river. Even when it rests unmoving like a log, it is impossible to tell whether it has just eaten and is satiated or lies in wait ready to strike. Wrong Eye presents himself as amiable and polite in most cases, a sophisticated and keenly intelligent representative of his species. But tales persist of him suddenly erupting in a murderous rage at the slightest perceived insult. There is never any warning of the shift from one side of his personality to the other. Those who have dealt with him successfully insist the easiest way to maintain his more whimsical and friendly demeanor is to lavish him with a series of small baubles.

The outward accoutrements with which he adorns himself are the best clue as to the inner workings of Wrong Eye's enigmatic mind. Those ignorant of his legend might find his appearance comical, but such an impression quickly fades. Wrong Eye is a fiercely curious and acquisitive being whose shamanism draws on the concept of consuming the power of others. All that he kills becomes a part of his spiritual arsenal, and dark rumors insist he is a cannibal as well as a connoisseur of the flesh of other intelligent species. Devouring dim-witted beasts interests him not, but the creative impulse of mankind holds morbid fascination for Wrong Eye. He has adorned himself to imitate humanity for this reason, wearing attire either cobbled together in mimicry or stolen from those he has stalked and consumed.

Those few with the vision to see such manifestations can confirm that spirits of the dead linger near Wrong Eye, unable to leave his side even as they loathe him. The slightest hint of spiritual sensitivity allows one to hear their whispers when he is near, half coherent warnings or sudden sharp gasps of startled pain. Whether Wrong Eye enjoys this following or even notices them is unknown: his stare is cold and impassive, his toothy smile revealing nothing.

Even without murdering his quarry Wrong Eye can use the dolls he shapes to influence them by driving needles

## SPECIAL RULES

### Minion
Wrong Eye & Snapjaw will work for any faction.

### Wrong Eye
**Amphibian** - Wrong Eye can voluntarily enter deep water and does not suffer damage due to ending his activation in deep water. Wrong Eye can move through deep and shallow water without penalty and can run or charge. While within deep water, Wrong Eye cannot be targeted by ranged or magic attacks, his DEF is not reduced, he can give or receive orders, and he can make melee attacks against other models in deep water.

**Fearless** - Wrong Eye never flees.

**Lesser Warlock** - Wrong Eye is not a warlock, although he has the following abilities: Damage Transference, Forcing, Healing, Fury Manipulation, and Spell Caster. Wrong Eye can cast Snapjaw's animus as a spell. Wrong Eye's model type is solo, not warlock. Wrong Eye's warlock abilities that refer to "friendly faction warbeasts" work only with Snapjaw. Other warlocks cannot use the listed abilities with Snapjaw.

### Swamp Hook
**Reach** - 2" melee range.

**Reel 'em In** - If the Swamp Hook hits a target with a small or medium-sized base, that model may be moved up to 2" directly toward Wrong Eye, stopping short only if it contacts another model, an obstacle, or an obstruction. During this movement the model cannot be targeted by free strikes.

| WRONG EYE | | | | CMD 9 | |
|---|---|---|---|---|---|
| SPD | STR | MAT | RAT | DEF | ARM |
| 5 | 8 | 6 | 3 | 12 | 17 |

| BITE | | |
|---|---|---|
| | SPECIAL | POW | P+S |
| | — | 5 | 13 |

| SWAMP HOOK | | |
|---|---|---|
| | SPECIAL | POW | P+S |
| | Multi | 5 | 13 |

| | |
|---|---|
| FURY | 4 |
| DAMAGE | 10 |
| FIELD ALLOWANCE | C |
| VICTORY POINTS | 1 |
| WRONG EYE AND SNAPJAW | 103 |
| BASE SIZE | MEDIUM |

through their limbs to make his chosen victims suffer by proxy. He wears a vest of bones and other tokens as elements of his elaborate spiritual armor, warding him from danger. One could dismiss Wrong Eye's peculiar notions were it not for the actual power he demonstrates. With a single look of his oversized ocular, Wrong Eye compels weaker-willed creatures to caper and twitch.

When potential employers address him with proper formality and respect, they find their courtesies returned. Wrong Eye sees himself as a shrewd manipulator of the factions employing him and deems no mortal his superior. His arrogance in this regard is certainly part of his madness, but the true power brokers seem to find him amusing and useful enough to overlook his eccentricities. Certainly the tremendous alligator that guards him has helped to preserve him from easy retaliation. He may possess some glimmer of true prophetic insight: his survival instinct always seems to place him on the winning side.

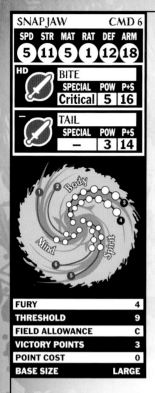

| SNAPJAW | | | | | CMD 6 |
|---|---|---|---|---|---|
| SPD | STR | MAT | RAT | DEF | ARM |
| 5 | 11 | 5 | 1 | 12 | 18 |

| HD | BITE | | |
|---|---|---|---|
| | SPECIAL | POW | P+S |
| | Critical | 5 | 16 |

| — | TAIL | | |
|---|---|---|---|
| | SPECIAL | POW | P+S |
| | — | 3 | 14 |

| FURY | 4 |
|---|---|
| THRESHOLD | 9 |
| FIELD ALLOWANCE | C |
| VICTORY POINTS | 3 |
| POINT COST | 0 |
| BASE SIZE | LARGE |

# SPECIAL RULES

## Snapjaw

**Amphibian** - Snapjaw can voluntarily enter deep water and does not suffer damage due to ending its activation in deep water. Snapjaw can move through deep and shallow water without penalty and can run or charge. While within deep water, Snapjaw cannot be targeted by ranged or magic attacks, his DEF is not reduced, and it can make melee attacks against other models in deep water.

**Hunger Motivated** - Snapjaw may charge living models that are already damaged without being forced. When Snapjaw charges a living model that is damaged, it charges at SPD +5".

**Man Eater** - Snapjaw may charge small- and medium-based living models without being forced.

**Warbeast Bond** - Snapjaw is bonded to Wrong Eye. While in Wrong Eye's control area, Snapjaw gains +2 THR. When Snapjaw destroys a living model with a melee attack while in Wrong Eye's control area, remove d3 damage points from either Snapjaw or Wrong Eye.

## Bite

**Critical Death Roll** - On a critical hit, the model hit is knocked down and Snapjaw gains an additional die on the damage roll.

| ANIMUS | COST | RNG | AOE | POW | UP | OFF |
|---|---|---|---|---|---|---|
| Submerge | 2 | Self | - | | - | |

The model using this animus cannot be targeted by ranged or magic attacks. Submerge lasts for one round.

longevity, and willful cunning quite unlike any natural alligator roaming the swamps.

In truth, Snapjaw arose from the swampy terrain of the Bloodsmeath in the Thornwood over seven decades ago and was a noted terror in the region long before Wrong Eye brought it into his service. Whatever brought them together, they are certainly a bonded pair now, as one is rarely far from the other. Villages along the various backwoods waterways have learned to be wary of the sound of heavy splashing in the darkness, huddling close to their feeble fires and locking their doors tight.

Though unimaginably fierce when goaded by Wrong Eye to battle or driven into a killing frenzy by the scent of blood, this beast is otherwise a lazy hunter content to steal easy pickings. Wayward children wallowing in streams too far from home are a preferred snack. It is equally content to eat any livestock or unfortunate pets that happen to cross its path.

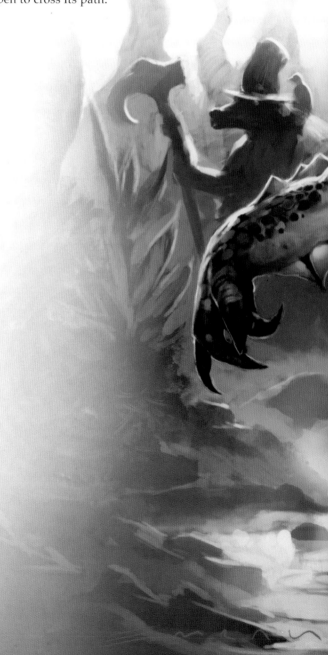

Anyone dealing with Wrong Eye must also endure the lurking threat of Snapjaw. This oversized alligator prefers to linger near its master submerged below the calm surface of a shallow pool or gently flowing river. It can stay in this posture serene and unmoving like a dead thing for hours, never so much as blinking or twitching its limbs. Yet the moment Wrong Eye compels it, the great beast leaps forward with blinding speed to attack, consuming men whole in its toothy maw or shattering boats to kindling with its muscled tail.

The two have been together as long as anyone can remember, and the legends of Wrong Eye always depict his guardian standing ready to strike. Bokors of the gatormen community describe Snapjaw in terms usually reserved for great spirits, not living beasts. They believe the creature to be a physical embodiment of Wrong Eye's inner nature, a manifestation of his great awakened power. Many bokors strive to emulate Wrong Eye's deeds and cast an envious eye on his hulking companion. Others have attracted lesser alligators and other simple beasts to their service, but none can boast a companion the equal of Snapjaw.

Swampy legends in the region speak of the "Bane of Bloodsmeath," describing an enormous hungry alligator that walks upright and preys on the unwary. A number of unlikely tall tales have surrounded this creature, including the supposition that it arose from some unnatural marriage between an insane swamp hermit and a female alligator that borrowed human form on nights of the new moon. It is unlikely any of these tales have any basis in fact, but Snapjaw demonstrates a posture,

# Snapjaw
## MINION UNIQUE HEAVY WARBEAST

Wrong Eye sometimes lets Snapjaw wander off into settled regions to see what it can find. The bokor takes grim amusement in following at a distance and watching as the creature stirs up the small human communities. The gatorman chortles as locals try to rally and drive the beast away. The feeble efforts of local militia armed with pitchforks and other crude farm implements have never done much more than scratch Snapjaw's thick scaled hide.

Once Snapjaw selects its prey its eyes never waver and it closes with absolute conviction while ignoring any injuries. The only instinct it feels is ancient primordial

*That's not a regular alligator, and I certainly don't like the way he's looking at me.*

—Professor Viktor Pendrake

hunger. It will continue to devour until it drowns that hunger in a tide of meat and blood. Wrong Eye likes to think he provides all of the brains required for the pair, but given his dubious sanity that is little comfort to anyone confronted by them.

# Saxon Orrik

## MINION MERCENARY CHARACTER SOLO

*Pendrake is a fool. There is no truth in nature that a man cannot find within himself. Nature exists to be conquered, not studied.*

—Saxon Orrik

Saxon Orrik's savage cruelty is as legendary as his mastery of the wilds. He has spent his life stalking wilderness regions where mankind finds no welcome. His experiences have long since toughened him to life's misfortunes and made him callous of pain and suffering. He sees mankind as no more deserving of special consideration than any animal caught in a trap or hunted to ground. Long years spent in the unforgiving desert with no company but the skorne have reinforced this attitude. Nature is cruel, and so is man.

Orrik began his military career as a Cygnaran scout during the last years of the reign of Vinter Raelthorne III, father to both Leto and the man whom the skorne would call the Conqueror. In those days every scout was left to his own compass and had tremendous leeway in his methods of patrolling the borders. Bloody skirmishes too numerous to count played out in contested regions between small, vicious companies of Khadorans and equally ruthless Cygnarans. Orrik's grim efficiency soon earned him the friendship of Cygnar's bloodthirsty heir, Prince Vinter IV. Orrik spent several long months serving as a ranger under Vinter along the northern border, and they discovered they shared both a number of common interests and a certain cold pragmatism.

Orrik's formal military career ended abruptly after he and mercenary irregulars under his command "made an

example" of several hundred Khadoran villagers who had settled too close to Cygnaran soil. At the time Orrik was mentoring a young scout named Viktor Pendrake, who observed this exercise with horror. Pendrake felt morally obligated to report Orrik's crimes to his superiors, and the incident quickly escalated into an embarrassment that the ranking scouts could not quietly sweep under the rug.

Though Vinter III was a harsh king to his subjects, he demanded strict adherence to the law, which explicitly forbade the deliberate slaughter of civilians. Such violence on the borders had previously gone unreported, but when word of this incident reached the king he felt obliged to act. As part of a larger series of reforms and investigations, Saxon Orrik was dishonorably discharged and sentenced to twenty years' hard time following a perfunctory military tribunal.

Orrik endured several difficult years locked away in military prisons. Eventually he escaped to survive on the run for several months before one of his associates betrayed him to the authorities. His subsequent imprisonment was far harsher than the first, and there was talk of sending him to Bloodshore Island. Orrik believed he was doomed to languish forgotten in confinement for the rest of his years.

The death of Vinter III and subsequent crowning of King Vinter IV bought Orrik a reprieve. No one was more surprised than he when the new king not only remembered him but ordered his release. Given his tarnished record, Saxon could not serve openly in the military, but Vinter IV made the former scout an agent of the budding Inquisition.

Saxon's gratitude cemented a loyalty to his master that outlasted the Lion's Coup. Without Vinter IV, he likely would have died on Bloodshore Island, and he has never forgotten that. He was among a number of Inquisitors who sought to free Vinter IV from his imprisonment while he awaited trial and execution following the coup. Vinter soon solved that problem for himself by making his now-famous escape. Word quickly reached Orrik that Vinter had drifted east on an airship across the impassable Bloodstone Marches.

For several long years Orrik survived on the fringes of civilization and kept his identity a secret before at last he received a coded message confirming that Vinter had conquered a previously unknown species across the desert. Vinter's instructions to Orrik were simple. After passing along a separate packet of coded instructions to Head Inquisitor Dexer Sirac, Orrik was to hurry east to rejoin his liege.

Vinter IV is famous for surviving his journey east, but Saxon Orrik repeated that feat without an airship to expedite his passage. This crossing proved to be a tremendous ordeal. He had to learn to hunt whatever slithering beasts he could for scraps of meat while finding increasingly inventive methods of procuring water and shelter. By the time he rejoined his king, Orrik had become a true master of the Bloodstone Desert. His crossing had forged him into the perfect man to guide the skorne back

## SPECIAL RULES

### Mercenary
Saxon Orrik will work for Cryx, Khador, the Protectorate, and Magnus' Agenda.

### Minion
Saxon Orrik will work for the Circle, Skorne, and Trollbloods.

**Animosity** - Saxon Orrik cannot be included in an army that includes Viktor Pendrake.

### Orrik
**Blind Spot** - When a melee attack made by an enemy warbeast misses Orrik he may immediately make one normal melee attack targeting the attacking warbeast.

**Dismember** - When Orrik hits a warbeast with a melee attack, roll an additional damage die.

**Expert Hunter (★Action)** - Target friendly model/unit within 3" of Orrik gains Blind Spot for one round.

**Fearless** - Orrik never flees.

**Pathfinder** - During his activation, Orrik ignores movement penalties from, and may charge across, rough terrain and obstacles.

**Stare Down** - When an enemy warbeast ends its normal movement in Orrik's melee range the warbeast must immediately make a command check. If the warbeast fails, it immediately ends it activation.

**Tough** - When Orrik suffers sufficient damage to be destroyed, his controller rolls a d6. On a 5 or 6, Orrik is knocked down instead of being destroyed. If Orrik is not destroyed, he is reduced to one wound.

**Trail Blazer** - While within 3" of Orrik, friendly models ignore movement penalties from rough terrain but cannot charge, slam, or trample across rough terrain.

### Skinning Knife
**Inflict Pain** - When Orrik hits a warbeast with a Skinning Knife attack, he may place one fury point on or remove one fury point from the warbeast.

| ORRIK | | | | | CMD 9 |
|---|---|---|---|---|---|
| SPD | STR | MAT | RAT | DEF | ARM |
| 6 | 6 | 7 | 7 | 15 | 14 |

| MILITARY RIFLE | | | |
|---|---|---|---|
| RNG | ROF | AOE | POW |
| 10 | 1 | — | 11 |

| SWORD | | |
|---|---|---|
| SPECIAL | POW | P+S |
| — | 4 | 10 |

| SKINNING KNIFE | | |
|---|---|---|
| SPECIAL | POW | P+S |
| Inflict Pain | 2 | 8 |

| | |
|---|---|
| DAMAGE | 8 |
| FIELD ALLOWANCE | C |
| VICTORY POINTS | 1 |
| POINT COST | 26 |
| BASE SIZE | SMALL |

west and thereby afford Vinter IV the chance to reclaim his birthright.

Saxon Orrik has since forgotten any life but the sun, wind, and sands. The Bloodstone Desert is his home, and he has mastered its vastness. He trained the skorne to cross the desert and conduct their war. He has led the way countless times and seems to draw strength from this hellish clime. Saxon has established contacts among diverse groups willing to hire him for his lore of Immorese terrain. His reputation now stands quite separate from that of his master. Indeed many of those who use his services neither know nor care about his true loyalties. His dark eyes reveal even less than his few words. His step remains sure, and those who follow his trail always arrive at their destination.

MINIONS

# Viktor Pendrake

## MINION CYGNAR ALLY CHARACTER SOLO

*This land is blessed with an innumerable variety of species and variations of life. Morrow willing, I will document them all.*

—Viktor Pendrake

A legend in his own time, Professor Viktor Pendrake has gained recognition across the Iron Kingdoms for adventurous daring and scholarly acumen. He has passed down wisdom gained from years spent in the wild by chairing the Department of Extraordinary Zoology at Corvis University. His series of tomes detailing the ecology and behavior of dangerous species across Immoren is required reading from Caspia to Korsk. Such research demands that he continually place himself in peril in order to observe and interact with his subjects firsthand.

Pendrake's background as a Cygnaran army scout makes him uniquely suited to his current endeavors. Trained by the notorious Saxon Orrik, a young Pendrake witnessed atrocities committed by his mentor and felt compelled to report them. Rewarded for both his adherence to Cygnar's laws and his obvious skill as a ranger Pendrake rose through the ranks, but the incident began to sour him on military life. While he enjoyed exploring the trackless wilds,

MINIONS

patrolling the borders for enemy insurgents was not to his liking. Despite these reservations, Pendrake proved to be an exceptional officer; his first taste of real command came when his superiors entrusted him with the leadership of an entire company of rangers just before his twentieth summer.

What might have been the auspicious beginning of a lengthy military career turned ugly in a hurry. After a risky reconnaissance run well past the Khadoran border, Pendrake's company was ambushed and slaughtered nearly to the last. Pendrake emerged as the sole survivor and nearly undertook desperate measures to retain the vital intelligence his company had gathered. In a now-famous incident Pendrake sought refuge amid a tribe of pygmy trolls, going so far as to strip down and disguise himself in mud and leaves in order to pass as one of them. This crazy ruse not only worked but also taught Pendrake a deeper love of studying wilderness creatures. He remained in his disguise for months to better learn pyg culture.

When he returned to civilization, Pendrake gave up military life and accepted a post at Corvis University, starting his career as an adventuring scholar and researcher of extraordinary zoology. It was here that he made his true name. He spent decades venturing into the wilds to study every monstrous creature he could track down. He can boast particular expertise on the subjects of troll and gobber breeds, and he has also become one of the few recognized experts on grymkin, dragonspawn, and even infernals. He has had countless close brushes with death during his travels, many of which he recorded in his *Monsternomicon*.

Pendrake's studies took a different turn after 603 AR when he witnessed firsthand the skorne invasion and occupation of Corvis. With his unique skills Pendrake was one of the few scholars to study these previously unknown species from across the Bloodstone Desert seriously. Even after the first occupation force was defeated, Pendrake could see the future threat they might represent to Cygnar. He felt compelled to contact Scout General Rebald to offer his services to the Cygnaran Army as an expert in both the skorne and the Bloodstone Marches in general.

While investigating skorne attacks on friendly trollkin kriels, Pendrake had an unexpected and unfortunate reunion with his old mentor Saxon Orrik. He was in the process of backtracking the skorne from a slaughtered trollkin village when he walked into an ambush. Pendrake's friend Quimut nearly died in this battle, and Pendrake himself was on the receiving end of a titan attack that would have resulted in his death had his captors not decided to take him alive. The titans hauled him back to the Abyssal Fortress in a cage. There he first gained an inkling of what was in store for Cygnar at the hands of Vinter Raelthorne, Saxon Orrik, and a massive and well-equipped skorne army. Pendrake's ordeal was not over: Vinter decided to send him east to document the greatness of the Skorne Empire and thereby write propaganda to undermine Cygnar's will to oppose him.

After a lengthy ordeal as a slave, Pendrake managed to escape and return west with new insight into the peril represented by the skorne. His unique knowledge and sense of duty drove him to temporarily put aside his scholarly pursuits in order to work for Cygnar full time. His unmatched scope of lore and the numerous friendships he

## SPECIAL RULES

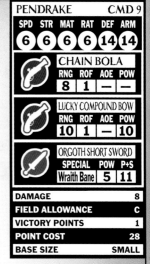

| PENDRAKE | | | | | CMD 9 |
| --- | --- | --- | --- | --- | --- |
| SPD | STR | MAT | RAT | DEF | ARM |
| 6 | 6 | 6 | 6 | 14 | 14 |

| CHAIN BOLA | | | |
| --- | --- | --- | --- |
| RNG | ROF | AOE | POW |
| 8 | 1 | — | — |

| LUCKY COMPOUND BOW | | | |
| --- | --- | --- | --- |
| RNG | ROF | AOE | POW |
| 10 | 1 | — | 10 |

| ORGOTH SHORT SWORD | | |
| --- | --- | --- |
| SPECIAL | POW | P+S |
| Wraith Bane | 5 | 11 |

| | |
| --- | --- |
| DAMAGE | 8 |
| FIELD ALLOWANCE | C |
| VICTORY POINTS | 1 |
| POINT COST | 28 |
| BASE SIZE | SMALL |

### Ally
Viktor Pendrake is a Cygnar model that will work for mercenary contracts that include mercenaries that will work for Cygnar.

### Minion
Viktor Pendrake will work for the Circle and the Trollbloods.

**Animosity** - Pendrake cannot be included in an army that includes Saxon Orrik.

### Pendrake
**Beast Lore (★Action)** - Target friendly model/unit within 3" of Pendrake gains Dismember for one turn.

**Dismember** - When Pendrake hits a warbeast with a melee attack, roll an additional damage die.

**Duck** - Pendrake gains +4 DEF against melee and ranged attacks made by enemy warbeasts and cannot be targeted by free strikes made by enemy warbeasts.

**Fearless** - Pendrake never flees.

**Pathfinder** - During his activation, Pendrake ignores movement penalties from, and may charge across, rough terrain and obstacles.

### Chain Bola
**Cumbersome** - Pendrake cannot make ranged attacks with the Chain Bola and Lucky Compound Bow during the same activation.

**Tangled** - Instead of suffering a damage roll, a model hit by the Chain Bola has its base DEF reduced to 7 and must forfeit its movement or action during its next activation. Tangled lasts for one round.

### Lucky Compound Bow
**Luck** - Pendrake may re-roll missed Lucky Compound Bow ranged attack rolls. Each attack roll may be re-rolled once as a result of Luck.

### Orgoth Short Sword
**Wraith Bane** - Orgoth Short Sword attacks may damage models only affected by magic attacks. Pendrake may charge incorporeal models.

has made abroad in the wild places makes him an invaluable asset to the Cygnaran Army. He can go where the military cannot. He provides singular insight on the struggles occurring on the fringes as well as serving as an intermediary between those forces and Cygnar. His lore of wild beasts extends not only to skorne warbeasts but also to spawn of Everblight, trolls, and even the wold constructs of the blackclads. With Khador knocking on Corvis' northern gate and skorne on the eastern one, Pendrake is glad to loan his sword to the fight—but those who know him understand that his most dangerous weapon is his mind.

MINIONS

# Lanyssa Ryssyl, Nyss Sorceress
## MINION MERCENARY NYSS CHARACTER SOLO

*Guilt hounds me for not being with my people in their hour of need. I will drown that guilt in the blood of our enemies.*

—Lanyssa Ryssyl

Lanyssa Ryssyl has seen the once-beautiful homes of her people burned to ashes. She has seen despair in the faces of those few who survived—the knowledge that their culture has been shattered and destroyed. Even worse than the slaughter is witnessing the blighted abominations claiming still to be Nyss. Lanyssa has faced the full horror that is the Legion of Everblight, and she has vowed to spend all her power as a sorceress to bring about their destruction.

MINIONS

She was not always like this. She earned her fame as one of the few Nyss to freely venture into warmer climes in search of adventure. In the towns and cities she visited she was not only the first Nyss the inhabitants had seen, but in many cases she was the first elf. Her cool beauty and sharp eyes intimidated many who would have liked to know more about this exotic stranger, as did the claymore slung across her feathered cloak. Lanyssa eventually found friendship among a chosen few outside her species.

By the standards of her long-lived race Lanyssa Ryssyl is just entering the prime of life, but her experiences abroad have given her rare insight into the world beyond the Shard Spires. Although she did not stay to complete the formalities of her training, Lanyssa is a sorceress of considerable skill. Among the Nyss the avocation carries a sacred weight; the shards hold such individuals as blessed by Nyssor, the God of Winter. Lanyssa was a prodigy who proved just as adept working with Aeric runes as she did fighting with a claymore. She did not have the patience, however, to stay cloistered within the isolated shrines of her fane.

She might have spent a contented lifetime away from her homeland had she not received word of northern terrors and the cataclysm that would destroy her people. Now she looks back on those years and wonders how things might have been if she had lingered in the north. Anger fills her over the devastation Everblight wrought, and she cannot ignore the guilt of her absence. In her calmer moments, however, she realizes she would not be the weapon she is now had she not tested her mettle in the far corners of Cygnar, Ord, Llael, and Khador.

Her last friends and fighting companions volunteered to accompany her on her trek back to her homeland after hearing rumors of strange events in the far north. She arrived too late to participate in the last stand of the untainted Nyss, finding only burned outposts and slaughter. This was the spark igniting her rage, and she could not be kept from hunting down the nearest tendril of Legion forces. What followed was a hopeless battle near the Nyschatha Mountains where she threw herself against Legion forces in a frenzy of hurled spells and blurred claymore. Her friends fought beside her and fell one by one.

She came to herself once the enemy was dead and realized she had sacrificed those closest to her. Her heart hardened and she denied her grief. She knew many more would die before she fulfilled her oath of vengeance. She must not regret any of their sacrifices.

Journeying south to find other allies, Lanyssa became acquainted with the refugees of her people in Khador and eventually made contact with both Cylena Raefyll and the Iosan mage hunter Eiryss, called the Angel of Retribution. Lanyssa was among the first to learn of the fate of Nyssor and the unholy forces conspiring against the ailing god.

## SPECIAL RULES

| RYSSYL | | | | | CMD 9 |
|---|---|---|---|---|---|
| SPD | STR | MAT | RAT | DEF | ARM |
| 6 | 5 | 6 | 4 | 15 | 11 |

| SORROW | | |
|---|---|---|
| | SPECIAL | POW P+S |
| Brittle as Ice | 6 | 11 |

| DAMAGE | 5 |
|---|---|
| FIELD ALLOWANCE | C |
| VICTORY POINTS | 1 |
| POINT COST | 26 |
| BASE SIZE | SMALL |

### Mercenary
Lanyssa Ryssyl will work for Cygnar and the Retribution.

### Minion
Lanyssa Ryssyl will work for the Circle and the Trollbloods.

**Animosity** - Lanyssa Ryssyl cannot be included in an army that includes Blighted models.

### Ryssyl
**Pathfinder** - During her activation, Ryssyl ignores movement penalties from, and may charge across, rough terrain and obstacles.

**Prowl** - While within a terrain feature that provides concealment, the AOE of a spell providing concealment, or the AOE of a cloud effect, Ryssyl gains Stealth. Attacks against a model with Stealth from greater than 5" away automatically miss. If a model with Stealth is greater than 5" away from an attacker, it does not count as an intervening model.

**Vendetta** - Ryssyl gains boosted attack and damage rolls against Legion and Blighted models.

### Magic Ability
As a special attack or action, Ryssyl may cast one of the following spells during her activation. Determine the success of a magic attack by rolling 2d6 and adding her Magic Ability score of 7. If the roll equals or exceeds the target's DEF, the attack succeeds.

- **Hunter's Mark (★Attack)** - Hunter's Mark is a RNG 10 magic attack. Friendly models may charge or slam a model hit by Hunter's Mark at SPD +5" without being forced or spending a focus point and regardless of LOS. Hunter's Mark lasts for one turn.

- **Ice Bolt (★Attack)** - Ice Bolt is a RNG 10, POW 12 magic attack. On a critical hit, target model must forfeit its movement during its next activation.

- **Winter Storm (★Action)** - Enemy models that begin their activation within 8" of this model lose All Terrain, Eyeless Sight, Pathfinder, and Wings for one round. Winter Storm lasts for one round.

### Sorrow
**Brittle as Ice** - Damage that exceeds the target's ARM is doubled.

Lanyssa knows that Khadoran wizards stole the sacred vault of Nyssor, a fact that has soured her heart to that nation, its government, and particularly the Greylords Covenant. She has offered to assist Eiryss and her allies in their efforts to fight those who have brought destruction on both of their races. Lanyssa has made contacts in the wild among groups unknown to Cylena or other less widely traveled Nyss, and she intends to make use of them to do what she can against both the Legion of Everblight and the Khadoran Greylords.

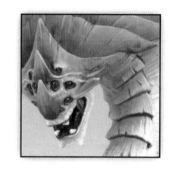

## DAHLIA HALLYR & SKARATH
### SOLO & UNIQUE HEAVY WARBEAST

## VIKTOR PENDRAKE
### SOLO

## LANYSSA RYSSYL, NYSS SORCERESS
### SOLO

## BRINE & RORSH
### UNIQUE HEAVY WARBEAST & SOLO

## WRONG EYE & SNAPJAW
### SOLO & UNIQUE HEAVY WARBEAST

## SAXON ORRIK
### SOLO

## BRUN CRAGBACK & LUG
### SOLO & UNIQUE HEAVY WARBEAST

# Painting Minions

## TATZYLWURM BODY

The length of the Tatzylwurm comes in three sections, each with its own colors: inner skin, underbelly plates, and back plates. On the front and rear armor plates you will shade before highlighting, but on the middle skin you will highlight first and shade second.

- Gnarls Green
- Wurm Green
- Coal Black
- Meredius Blue
- Arcane Blue
- Underbelly Blue
- Frostbite
- Menoth White Highlight
- Thamar Black
- Morrow White
- Green Ink
- Blue Ink
- Turquoise Ink

**1** Start by basecoating the inner skin of the wurm with a mix of equal parts Arcane Blue and Frostbite plus a touch of Wurm Green. Basecoat the underbelly plates with a mix of Frostbite and Meredius Blue. To complete the basecoating, paint the back plates with a mix of Meredius Blue and Gnarls Green.

## FARROW FLESH

Most living creatures have different colors of flesh. Trolls, for instance, have a lighter color on the belly than on the rest of their bodies. To make your organic models more realistic, look for ways to give their flesh different tones. The Farrow have one color for their basic flesh and another color for their snouts.

- Ember Orange
- Beaten Purple
- Sanguine Highlight
- Beast Hide
- Khardic Flesh
- Midlund Flesh
- Ryn Flesh
- Battlefield Brown
- Bloodstone
- Moldy Ochre
- Menoth White Base
- Menoth White Highlight
- Thamar Black

**1** Begin by basecoating the skin with Battlefeild Brown.

**2** Add Beaten Purple and a touch of Thamar Black to the basecoat color, and apply the mix to the shadows and recesses.

**3** Add Beast Hide and Moldy Ochre to the basecoat and blend it onto the raised areas to create highlights.

**4** Basecoat the snout and lips with Khardic Flesh. Add Sanguine Highlight to the Khardic Flesh and use it to basecoat the tongue.

**2**

Take the color you used for the basecoat of the inner skin, mix in some Menoth White Highlight, and use that mixture to highlight the inner skin. Next, mix Meredius Blue, Blue Ink, and Turquoise Ink to use as a shade for the underbelly plates. Lastly, shade the back plates with Coal Black mixed with a touch of Thamar Black.

**3**

Add Turquosie Ink, Blue Ink, and Green Ink to the color you used to highlight the inner skin and use that mixture to shade the inner skin. Next, add Morrow White to the underbelly plate base color and use that to highlight the underbelly plates. Lastly, add Underbelly Blue to the back plate base color and use that to highlight the back plates.

**5**

Highlight the lips, snout, and tongue with a mix of Midlund Flesh and Ryn Flesh. Basecoat the teeth and nails with Menoth White Base.

**6**

Shade the teeth with Ember Orange.

**7**

Apply Bloodstone to the deep shadows and recesses of the teeth.

**8**

Finally, highlight the teeth with Menoth White Highlight.

## Mixing Inks with Paints

One way to achieve vibrant colors is to add a bit of ink to your paints. That's the trick with the Tatzylwurm. The ink mixed into the shades and highlights is what gives it such a rich color. Ink goes a long way, so be mindful and add only a little at a time until you have what you want. Want a stronger red? Simply thin your red with a spot of Red Ink. Want your yellow to pop? Mix in some Yellow Ink. Experiment with inks, and you will be surprised at the colors you can produce.

We painted the armor plates on Brine below with a mix of Brown Ink and Thamar Black. Including the ink gives the armor's rust an intense appearance.

## ORBOROS BLEEDS

Mohsar the Desertwalker had been standing in the open facing the newly erected fortress atop the nearest section of the Castle of the Keys for too long. Even a single nondescript figure in a cowled robe would not evade notice from the sentries forever. The soldiers stationed atop those walls were scanning their surroundings for larger threats, but they would not ignore him if they spotted him. Proof came as a small squad of Venators marched down the staggered steps carved into the rock. He paid them no immediate mind.

If he had perceived the world with the mundane but common expediency of sight, Mohsar would have had less to occupy his attention. The nearly complete form of a sturdy skorne fortress squatted on the heights. Its architecture was unfamiliar to western eyes, but otherwise it did not seem to warrant extended scrutiny. The odd mix of workers toiling under skorne whips to complete the structure was unusual, so that might have drawn some notice: skorne, humans, trollkin, and even a hulking form that might have been an ogrun.

Mohsar was physically blind, but the senses he used to observe the world were more pervasive than vision. He stood upon the hot sands of the Bloodstone Marches, with his essence linked to Orboros, in an awareness trance that gave him a far better comprehension of his surroundings. To his senses something altogether unnatural lurked inside the stone fortification on that peak. It was an irregularity that went well beyond the blighted aftermath of a dragon's death throes and the indelible stain left by its spilled blood.

What Mohsar stared at was a yawning wound in the world itself, a rupture in the thick and imperishable skin separating Caen from Urcaen along the very body of Orboros. It seeped a cold poison like pus from a wound. He had first become aware of the strange manifestation some weeks ago when from hundreds of miles away he had felt a vague sensation of a polluted disruption within his desert. He had half expected the manifestation to vanish before he arrived to investigate it. A breach like this should have sealed quickly under the force of natural law, but at this proximity he could see the hole was instead gradually expanding.

The Venators reached the cliff's base and continued in his direction, and they pointed their weapons and shouted to get his attention as they approached. They gestured forcefully and waved for him to come to them. Mohsar continued to ignore them. One fired into the sand near his feet and their shouts became more insistent. Mohsar sighed and waved a hand to unleash a surge of violent power. A yawning chasm opened in the sands beneath the feet of the nearest one and quickly widened into a jagged rift that swallowed the rest. Their screams abruptly ended as the crevice closed.

Aware that those above had likely witnessed the deaths, Mohsar stared only a few moments more before turning to walk away. Two nondescript red sandstone boulders nearby suddenly shuddered and stood erect, proving to be woldwatchers. They followed after him as he muttered, "What a lich lord and an Orgoth artifact failed to accomplish, the skorne have stumbled upon by accident. Remarkable." Perhaps it was time for him to borrow the army Krueger was mustering. They did not appear to be occupied with anything important.

## GATHERING TORMENT

Morghoul's return to Halaak did not go unnoticed. He watched several less-than-skilled lookouts at the great gates scurry off to report to various handlers immediately on his arrival at the capital city. His appearance would prompt speculation, to be sure, but that was not necessarily undesirable. An atmosphere of fear and uncertainty would be useful in the days ahead.

Despite the speed of his return Morghoul had no doubt that rumor of Makeda's seizure of the Abyssal Fortress would reach the city soon if it had not already. He had to work quickly. Accordingly he hired a number of runners in the central market to take messages to every prominent master tormentor in the city, requesting an immediate meeting. He made no efforts to keep this secret, since speed was vital. He had to rely on the uncertainties of the situation and his reputation to draw the members of his caste. Those who did not know of Vinter's overthrow would obey out of fear. Those who had heard rumor of the events in the Stormlands would attend motivated by curiosity. Morghoul did not doubt lingering agents of the Conqueror might hear of this meeting. He was confident they would be unable to interfere.

He had chosen the location for the meeting in haste. It was a half-empty warehouse within the commercial district adjacent to one of the major enslaved beast providers for the city. The room was large and offered numerous routes of entry and egress, which would reassure the more paranoid. It was not a secured location, although his guests would suspect he had taken measures to make it such. Most importantly, from here Morghoul could sense the nearby presence of no fewer than a dozen enslaved cyclopes, a half-dozen basilisks, and two young titan bulls. Most were not fully battle conditioned, but he did not intend to use them to fight. He intended to leave them in their cages and draw on their strength if the need arose. Several of the invited masters could also divert injury to beasts through mortitheurgy, so while not a guarantee this provided a small degree of mutual assurance from assassination.

Morghoul said nothing in greeting as the master tormentors arrived but acknowledged each with a simple nod. They all belonged to the same caste, but unlike certain unified castes the paingivers did not have a structured hierarchy or appointed leader. That was about to change. The masked figures standing before him were the most skilled and respected paingivers outside the Army of the Western Reaches—excepting one who was notably absent.

Morghoul did not wait for the last; he had expected this rebuff. He spoke to the expectant masked faces, "This is not a time for careful language. I can confirm that the human we have called the Conqueror is deposed. The Skorne Empire now answers to Supreme Archdomina Makeda of House Balaash, who sits on the throne at the Abyssal Fortress."

Paingivers were versed in maintaining their composure and revealing little through body mannerisms. Morghoul still found enough hints in minuscule facial ticks, slight hand movements, and subtle muscle shifts to discern for whom the news was a surprise. One of these was Master Morzan, who spoke now. "Impossible! Is this a test of loyalty?"

"No test, only the truth. Makeda has driven Vinter Raelthorne from our lands fleeing in fear of his life. Some of you already know this, as the tale has arrived by those few who escaped the fortress before the siege ended." He looked at several of the masters, who reluctantly confirmed the news. Morghoul continued, "The supreme archdomina has granted me the right to create my own house and granted me absolute dominion over our caste. Our discipline and skill will no longer be employed at the whim of the petty disputes of lesser lords. This new house will serve as a vital instrument at the core of the empire."

The eldest of those gathered was Master Tormentor Kexaar, also known as the Whispering Blade, for he was said to be skilled enough to flay a skorne out of his skin before the victim realized he had been touched. Age had taken a toll, prompting his hands to tremble occasionally, so he rarely practiced his art. He was nonetheless influential, having instructed many of the caste in the finer points of anatomy. All went silent when he spoke. "I understand. Ambition is universal. A thirst for power." He stated his words simply, as if making no judgment of the facts.

"Tell me, Master Kexaar, who would you have described as the most loyal supporters of the Conqueror during the Second Unification? Makeda's suffering while her estates were besieged, her standing resolutely in support of her sworn liege while all Halaak betrayed him, would seem to contradict your analysis."

"Clearly things have changed. Perhaps time spent fighting in the west has given the archdomina a new perspective. New thirsts to slake."

"*Supreme* archdomina. I will not remind you again." The threat was softly spoken, and yet the masters watching him closely froze at it. "I will unite the paingivers as a single house. I did not ask you here for debate. There is an opportunity for each of you to play a vital role in the transformation of our society. Should you choose to stand in my way, I will annihilate you. We have no time for ambivalence. I chose to speak to you because it is important

those of your stature understand. Makeda of House Balaash did not depose the Conqueror for personal power."

Master Kexaar asked, "Can you say the same? Your record is rather . . . unclear on this point."

Morghoul inclined his head slightly. "While it may appear I have changed allegiances conveniently, my loyalties have always remained the same. Not to a single name, but to the skorne as a people. Makeda would have obeyed the Conqueror in anything, granted him dominion over everything, had he not violated that one essential principle. He chose to place his personal goals above those of our people as a whole. This was the one thing we could not support."

"So instead you ask us to give up our traditions and become a house ruled by a single master to support the Balaash claim. How is this different? Why should we break against all Morkaash set forward to support this one house?" There was nodding and murmuring among the others, but Morghoul focused solely on Master Kexaar. His argument was with the elder tormentor speaking for their ancient traditions. Others would follow.

---

## "What a lich lord and an Orgoth artifact failed to accomplish, the skorne have stumbled upon by accident. Remarkable."

---

"Morkaash prohibited his followers from joining houses because he saw that paingivers must exist for a higher purpose, a stronger principle. He did not seek to have us caught up in petty squabbles, and so he tasked us to stand apart. Separation from the houses was necessary because the skorne were divided. I have seen in the west those they call 'sell-swords,' mercenaries who trade fighting services for coin. They have no honor. We have become like them: fat and indulgent, seeking after profit instead of principle."

Morghoul could see he had touched some chord in the old master tormentor. He continued, "I seek to return us to the roots of Morkaash's instruction. We will serve the Skorne Empire itself, not Supreme Archdomina Makeda. She is only the empire's current leader. We will obey her in all things while watching for any violation of the principle by which the Conqueror was undone. I will serve at your sufferance similarly. Should you find me guilty of petty ambition, united you can destroy me. I will demand absolute obedience in all other respects. It will be my judgment alone that decides if our supreme leader must fall. Your eyes will be upon me even as mine are upon her. I offer us a place in the hierarchy to come. We will be the ultimate arbiters of the Skorne Empire, those who guard against corruption and pride. Our commitment to a higher

philosophy will give us the clarity of vision to stand as the empire's guardians and executioners."

Morghoul could see his words had reached the others, but they awaited Kexaar's opinion. After a pause the elder tormentor spoke. "There is wisdom in what you say, Morghoul. I would not stand against such changes given that our traditions and art remain intact. Without Master Tormentor Jyvaash Komorn, however, I am not certain what you hope to gain."

Morghoul crossed his arms. "I did not believe the Bloodrunners commanded so much esteem."

"It is less a matter of esteem than numbers. The Bloodrunners have become increasingly important in the capital in the time you have been gone. They are the primary method for house lords to resolve their differences without invoking the displeasure of the Conqueror's agents. Their numbers have grown substantially in the years you have served first at the Conqueror's and then at Makeda's side."

A voice spoke from the shadows near the back of the warehouse, amid the crates. "That is correct, Morghoul." Walking forward into the light with a confident swagger was Jyvaash Komorn and a dozen of his order, recognizable from their distinct raiment and masks. They wielded their jagged curved blades openly, and Komorn himself held the legendary Fan of Shadows closed in his left hand. Not only was this bladed instrument a symbol of Bloodrunner leadership, it was also a potent ancestral artifact. Komorn sneered as he continued, "The capital belongs to me. It is

the height of arrogance for you to intrude here making these demands. You are a disgrace to our caste, and your ambition stops here."

Komorn's followers spread out within the room as he spoke, some moving to cover obvious points of exit while others remained at the ready near the masters in case any made a move to interfere. Those Morghoul had gathered showed no evidence of fear—and perhaps even a certain degree of disdain—but they stood still nonetheless. They were not eager to provoke bloodshed. Bloodrunners focused less on the elicitation of pain and truth than on the more pragmatic arts of assassination, a warrior's interpretation of Morkaash's tradition. Without question they knew how to fight and destroy.

Jyvaash Komorn stared at Morghoul with unwavering eyes. The set to his jaw and the gathering momentum of his step suggested he did not intend to persuade. He stepped across the tiled floor with a single purpose. He was here to kill.

Morghoul wore a bladed claw on one hand, and his other rested on the sheathed hilt of Mercy. It was a long and exquisitely curved blade Makeda had gifted to him to represent sponsorship of his new house. He began to draw the weapon, and the Bloodrunner master leapt.

Komorn flicked the fan in his hand open as he jumped and shadows swallowed his body, boiling in the air like ink poured into a pool of water. The darkness dispersed almost immediately, and Komorn had vanished. Morghoul blinked and spun, but not quite fast enough to evade the Bloodrunner master, who was already slicing at his throat from directly behind him.

Morghoul managed to intercept that killing strike with Mercy's edge, but barely. The awkward parry left him open to Komorn's knife as the blade darted from one vital target to the next, forcing Morghoul to use all his skill to defend. The combatants' strikes and parries happened almost too fast to observe. Komorn was a peerless knife fighter, and Morghoul survived his first strikes only because he had once taken instruction from the master and thus knew his speed and favored style precisely. Even with that advantage, Morghoul was unable to retaliate, and he fell back after taking a piercing thrust in his side. He tried to divert the injury to a cyclops in the slave pens outside, but when he did his head spun with dizziness and he felt a sick sensation in his gut. His eye caught the shimmering edge of the Fan of Shadows, and he realized its darkness interfered with his ability to let others suffer in his stead.

A smile touched Jyvaash Komorn's lips as he anticipated the recognition. "Now this ends." At his words Komorn's subordinates advanced toward Morghoul with blades ready, clearly no longer concerned with the other paingivers in the room.

Against so many coming from all sides Morghoul knew he stood little chance, particularly with the Fan of Shadows interfering with his concentration. His eyes locked on it, and he considered the certainty that Komorn would not allow his men to get the killing blow. Pride required him to destroy Morghoul in front of his peers. The others were there to interfere, and if necessary to distract Morghoul long enough for their master to strike. They would be reluctant to attack him directly.

He leapt to his right in a sudden move, impaling one of the subordinate Bloodrunners on Mercy and slashing the face off another as he stepped by in a single swift motion. That one tried to scream as he clutched at the tattered ruins of his face, but he was already dying; Morghoul's lowest finger blade had slid neatly along his throat, opening a fatal wound. He spun to face Komorn and saw the master smile as he again invoked the Fan of Shadows. Predictably, he performed the same maneuver as before.

Morghoul did not even turn this time to see Komorn behind him. He felt a moment of perfect clarity and understanding of his foe. The master Bloodrunner was not accustomed to anyone surviving this attack. In his arrogance he had tried it again, exactly identical. It was his signature kill.

Morghoul twisted hard, almost dislocating his shoulder to bring his clawed hand up behind him to catch his enemy's blade just before it impaled his neck. Its edge bit through the leather of his palm and drew blood, but Morghoul continued the motion, twisting and turning. With his other hand he let Mercy's blade slice Komorn's chest, cutting through his armor as if it were mere cloth. Morghoul had struck with expert precision, laying open the muscles covering his adversary's stomach and crossing through two significant nerve clusters. It was not a lethal injury, but it prompted an explosion of agony that even one trained in the arts could not ignore. Such pain would persist even had Komorn the presence of mind to shunt his wound onto one of the nearby beasts.

Morghoul came in low as he stepped forward in a crouch. Komorn's left hand, responding to the pain, had weakened its grip. Morghoul caught Komorn off guard by cracking the flat of his blade against his opponent's wrist. The impact jarred the Fan of Shadows loose from Komorn's numbed fingers.

Morghoul had already released his adversary's blade, and with a sharp twist of his wrist and a compression of his fingers he let his clawed gauntlet fall to the floor. He scooped up the fan and turned to face his foe. Like a voice whispering in his mind, awareness of the operation of the Fan of Shadows came to him even as his fingers pushed its tines open. Morghoul stood on one leg, blade extending downward as he opened the fan behind his back. Komorn gave a ragged cry and lunged, hoping reckless speed would prevail where subtler skill had not.

Morghoul let the enemy thrust slide by as he stepped aside. Komorn staggered and fell to one knee. Moving forward as if to embrace the master Bloodrunner, Morghoul invoked the same entropy as had gripped him moments ago. As the two closed he let Mercy sink almost effortlessly into Komorn's flesh.

It happened so fast the others were still approaching. Seeing their master stricken they ran forward with weapons in hand, hoping to overwhelm the lord assassin by sheer numbers and bear him to the floor. Such a crude tactic could be surprisingly effective in confined quarters. Morghoul smiled and exploited one of his strongest mortitheurgical techniques, sending a wave of nerve-shattering pain to disrupt the optic nerves of his adversaries. A curtain of absolute darkness crashed down upon them, as if he had plucked their eyes from their skulls. They staggered toward him, slashing blindly at the air. Morghoul stepped among them economically and ended their lives with almost merciful swiftness. Such men might have been useful to his cause, but they were a necessary sacrifice. They would serve as an example to those he must visit next, Komorn's next tier of subordinates. It was they who would rally the Bloodrunners and spread word of their new master.

At last Morghoul stopped at the center of the room. The gathered masters had not moved a muscle during the clash. As they looked on the carnage, it did not escape their notice that not a single drop of blood Morghoul had spilled had landed on them. This was the *korum kofur*, or the "duelist's respect." Practicing the courtesy at such a time was a singular gesture and proof of mastery to even the most tradition-bound of his peers. He watched them now with his slick blade in hand but said nothing. After the shortest pause they bowed to him, bending almost completely to the ground.

Master Kexaar spoke first, his voice genuinely respectful and even awed. "Lord Morghoul, what is your command?"

# LEGACY OF GRIMMR

As they came into the clearing where Hoarluk Doomshaper camped with his dire trolls, Madrak Ironhide felt distinctly uneasy. Earlier in the day the trail had brought them through a small village of Cygnaran woodsmen left utterly annihilated by the passage of Doomshaper and his beasts. In this clearing Madrak saw ample evidence of fresh feasting, which at least meant the dire trolls might not be quite as hungry. Despite this, Ironhide could feel that the minds of the dire trolls ahead were closed to him, which was a bad sign. Their posture was wary and almost hostile. "Steady," he said as he held a hand up to the others. "Stay back." They gratefully followed his order although Borka seemed reluctant and made a point of standing in front of the rest. Madrak's trolls were close behind him, but at his instruction they lowered their weapons. The young bouncer Kald stood nearest, refusing to drop further back.

---

> **Looking up at this formidable creature Madrak felt something from his trolls he had never experienced before: the sensation of fear.**

---

Suddenly the most massive of the dire trolls leapt forward with an ear-shattering roar straight in Madrak's face. Madrak had never seen a creature so ancient. Its fierce face was lined by age and its back was so clustered with stony growths that it looked like a piece of a mountain despite the runes glowing on them. The ancient troll smashed an enormous club down that sunk two feet into the earth next to Kald, who had flinched and raised his shield against the expected blow. The impact was so great it almost knocked Madrak off his feet. Looking up at this formidable creature Madrak felt something from his trolls he had never experienced before: the sensation of fear. Behind Madrak the axer Bron murmured in an awed tone, "Mulg . . ."

"Back, Mulg. Let me through." It was Doomshaper's voice, and Mulg reluctantly stepped aside, still glaring at Madrak. The shaman had clearly recovered his belongings, for he bore his scroll cases once again. His garments were ripped and muddy, though, and despite the scrolls he still looked wild, almost feral. There was a different staff in his hand—a strange rod set with cylindrical rings of carved stone. Hoarluk tapped it thoughtfully into the palm of his other hand. "If you came to finish what those traitors started, think again. You are not strong enough to take me down. Should I force your own trolls to kill you?"

Madrak scowled. "What kind of greeting is this? Have you gone mad? We came here to rescue you, not to fight."

"A bit late for that." He laughed but it was an ugly sound. He squinted suspiciously at Ironhide. "You had no hand in my capture? Had to be someone in your camp. Someone

loyal to you. I have been thinking hard on this. I believe you decided that having me around was getting in your way."

"Blast it, I *should* kill you for that!" Madrak exclaimed, prompting Mulg to make a dangerous sound deep in his throat. "On Dhunia's womb, I had nothing to do with it. Nor would I. You are one of our blood. You saved my life. What kind of faithless kin do you take me for to repay you in that way? We may not always see eye to eye, but if I wanted to do you harm I would come at you myself. For damned sure I would not look to humans for a solution."

The shaman stepped to Ironhide and held out his hand as if offering a challenge. Madrak did not hesitate but clasped that hand with his own, and the two trollkin leaned forward to butt heads, staring with almost angry intensity into one another's eyes. The *Tohmaak Mahkeiri*, or "glimpse of the mind," was a serious ritual, one they had not engaged in since their first meeting after fighting the druid Ergonus. It was almost impossible to hide treachery or secrets in this trance-like state, particularly with someone of Doomshaper's age and power. The gathered trolls watched as the two remained locked, frozen, for what seemed a long time. At last Hoarluk broke away, apparently satisfied. His anger visibly faded, and it was mirrored by a calm in the shifting postures of the surrounding dire trolls.

Ironhide swayed a moment, feeling peculiar and unsteady after looking so deep into Doomshaper's mind. It was a dark and wild place with deep chasms and storms of ideas. Something else lurked there—something old and primal. It did not feel the same as when they had last shared the ceremony. It was as if in touching Hoarluk's mind Madrak had plunged into the minds of the dire trolls around him. On the heels of this strange sensation came another unwanted vision. For a moment Madrak saw humans marching through this clearing wearing archaic armor and holding long, wickedly barbed spears. Their banners were unfamiliar, but he sensed they marched to war and death. It faded quickly.

Hoarluk was lost in thought and had not noticed his distraction. He growled, "So it was the elders, was it? Those fat, mealy-mouthed maggots. They will pay."

Madrak blinked. He was startled that Doomshaper had seen so deeply into his thoughts; he had not intended to direct the blame to anyone else. "We can deal with them later. I still don't know which were to blame. I promise we will deliver justice."

Sensing the danger was past, several senior warriors had stepped forward to join them. Borka pushed ahead of them. "Hoarluk Doomshaper. Shouldn't you be dead already?" He loomed over the elder shaman.

Hoarluk squinted up at him and shook his head. "Borka Kegslayer? Gah! We have no need of this lout down here to trouble us." He looked back to Madrak, "Did you go off north to find this? I thought you had more sense than that."

Madrak chuckled to hide his lingering unease. "No, that was not my aim. He followed me back. We tried to lose him a few times, but we could not shake him." This prompted a deep laugh from Borka, who clasped forearms with Doomshaper. He then called his pygs forward with their barrels of heady drink. They filled and distributed stout mugs even as Madrak tried to discourage Borka. "This isn't the time," he protested half-heartedly, but the larger trollkin pretended not to hear him. Madrak had become used to this routine during their travels and knew his efforts were futile.

Although he was not in a festive mood, Madrak reluctantly accepted a mug and knocked it back. He then said to Doomshaper, "There is work to be done. I followed your path and saw the fruits of your labor—"

"They deserved it. They have only begun to taste my wrath." Hoarluk's eyes revealed a simmering anger ready to ignite again at any provocation.

"Let us direct that wrath somewhere better. The ones who took you captive are part of a larger plot. When word of your escape reaches those who arranged for your ambush, they will feel obliged to retaliate against Crael Valley as they promised. This is Cygnar's 4th Army, so it will be a bloody fight. Maybe one we cannot win."

"You want to go back there? Will take us some time," Hoarluk noted.

"Too long. No. That army also threatens the Gnarls kriels, who have been a great help to us. It is time to repay that favor. The army is moving east from their garrisons near Ceryl by way of the Gnarlwood Trail. If we can block the road it will stop their reinforcements. I talked to several kin in nearby kriels after we found your prison. They say caravans of soldiers have been marching that road every few days. I want to stop the next one. Teach them the price of threatening kith and kriel."

Doomshaper smiled, showing his teeth. "That does not sound like you, Madrak."

"Things have changed. They lifted the first axe. I would not have provoked them, but I will not sit by and let them turn us against our own. I hold them to blame for poisoning the minds of our elders."

"More drinks!" Borka's voice boomed as he handed each of them a mug. "To battle!" The three of them lifted and swallowed in a toast to the imminent bloodshed. On Madrak's back, Rathrok's runes gleamed.

"They're moving! Stand ready!" Grissel's voice rang out along their wall line as only a fell caller's could. She was standing atop the wall facing north, where she had the best perspective on the spread of the Cygnaran force coming toward them. She had to admit the enemy had taken a slightly unconventional approach; she had expected them to come by the easier western route. Most of the trollkin defenses were in the eastern and western ends of the valley, and their northern fortifications were incomplete.

Coming at them from the north required hiking up a difficult incline, and her people had done their best to make it even less appealing with large overturned logs, lines

of sharpened spikes, and several choke points between deeply dug holes. It looked to be slowing the warjacks from forming a proper line, but the soldiers were working their way through. Against a smaller approaching force they could have sent attackers forward to harass and fire on the advance, but here that would bring unacceptable losses.

Grissel was keenly aware of the range disparity. She had spread out her pygs along the walls ready to fire, but she had warned them against wasting ammunition in premature volleys. The enemy trenchers were doing what trenchers do best: moving into forward positions and hunkering down to evade incoming fire while taking periodic shots at her walls. Sheltered as they were, her pygs had little chance to hit them. They had not yet started throwing their smoke grenades, but she knew that would begin before the long lines of long gunners behind them advanced to fire in earnest. That was not an appealing prospect, but there seemed little she could do to prevent it.

She had thumper crews atop several elevated platforms, which should help, but their range was also limited. Grim was at the highest point alongside a cluster of pygs, impalers, and a few others with rifles. Taking shelter behind the partially completed wall segments were her warriors, champions, scattergunners, and Fennblades, all ready to sally forth at her orders but keeping under cover for now.

She had two blitzers down at the largest gap in the walls, ready to send slugger fire into any approaching force. A handful of pyre and slag trolls flanked them, each with its own formidable natural weaponry. Helping defend another gap were a number of farrow she had hired on, including Rorsh with his oversized pig Brine and a motley assortment of others wielding pig irons. Behind the eastern gate several groups of burly Long Riders stood ready to charge out to engage any force that set out along the wider sweep of flat ground. Grissel caught the eye of Horthol sitting atop his bison at their fore and nodded to him. He raised his hammer in salute. It was an impressive defensive position she could hold against any reasonably sized force.

As she looked out at the enemy arrayed against her, a more pragmatic instinct told her something else. "This is bad." She said it softly, but the words still escaped her lips.

There were thousands of Cygnaran soldiers out there and more seemed to be arriving by the hour. She had never seen them arrayed quite like this, in full military formation. There were reasons the kriels preferred to fight Cygnar in the forest rather than out in the open like this. She saw mostly long gunners and trenchers, but a bit farther off was the glint of knights in armor, including some few on horse. An array of older warjacks made their slow but steady way into position. On the right flank was a block of soldiers standing in square formation with halberds and helmets. They did not wear Cygnaran uniforms; Cygnar had clearly hired the Steelhead Mercenaries in good number, as Alten had warned her. The Steelheads had their own heavy cavalry closer to the eastern approach, ready to ride in and flank after their halberdiers engaged.

This was nothing like the smaller groups they had battled at the eastern defenses a few months earlier. The storm knights and household guard of Duke Ebonhart were exceptional warriors equipped with formidable weaponry, but they had been few in number. Grissel was proud of those victories, but what she faced now was something quite different. The worst part was that she knew this was only a portion of the 4th Army and by his estimation perhaps only the soldiers previously stationed at Stonebridge.

Calandra climbed up next to her with a large smile. "I think we will be fine. They can't break through. I doubt they even have the guts to attack. You ask me, this is all a bluff. They want us to break and run, but they know nothing about our resolve."

Grissel glowered at the shaman and snapped, "Are you out of your mind? Look out there!" She realized some of her nearest senior warriors were looking at her, and she lowered her voice. Calandra's optimism grated on her nerves, but she didn't want to shake morale. "We are hopelessly outnumbered," she hissed, "and this from someone who has made a career of fighting against the odds. I've held good ground against superior numbers, but that's not going to happen today."

Calandra shook her head, "This is Cygnar. Do you seriously expect them to throw soldiers at us until we get tired of killing them? Trust me, this is for show. They do not want to lose their people any more than we want to lose ours."

Despite herself Grissel wanted to believe those words. Calandra had a way of putting a good light on anything. In truth it made sense that Cygnar would try to minimize their losses, but something told Grissel today was different. Those soldiers did not look like they were putting on a parade. They were executing a deliberate plan. They might not commit all at once, but she did not believe this was a bluff. "What do your fortunes say?" She asked with a sneer.

Calandra ignored her sarcastic tone. "Shall we take a look?" She made a flourish of pulling forth a stack of waxed illustrated cards from one of the pouches at her waist. Despite her thick fingers she shuffled them with an expert's ease.

"I was joking," Grissel protested.

"No, no, let's see." Calandra came up and closed her eyes, murmuring prayers under her breath. With due ceremony she dealt a card onto the wall between her and Grissel. The fell caller saw a nearby kithkar leaning forward to steal a glimpse, but she snapped her fingers at him and he jerked back to return his attention to the enemy beyond the walls. Calandra mumbled, "Hmm. That is not good."

Grissel looked down and saw the painted image of an Orgoth warrior standing atop a pile of corpses, holding a decapitated head by the hair. Grissel was not usually superstitious, but the image gave her a sudden chill. "I don't know how those cards work, but—"

Calandra's skin had paled. "Just a second now. Let's try again." She reclaimed the card and shuffled almost frantically. She voiced her prayers with additional fervor before flipping over another card. This one showed a stylized black scaled serpent with bloodied claws, its mouth breathing fire that extended to fill the border. Calandra grunted, "That's even worse."

"I was worried enough before, Calandra," Grissel said through gritted teeth. "Now you have me even more concerned."

Calandra scooped up the cards and quickly put them away, looking acutely embarrassed. She cleared her throat. "The point is we make our *own* fate, our own fortune, regardless of signs or portents. I have faith we can hold this wall." She turned and stormed back toward one of the clusters of warriors down below, ready to lend her power to the fight. Watching her go, Grissel sighed. The Truthsayer was a tremendous asset in battle and her power was undeniable, but she could be a handful. Rumor insisted she had the genuine gift of foresight, which certainly put an ominous color on the cards they had just seen.

Grissel turned back to her warriors. The enemy was making solid progress setting up lines well out of their range. She considered trying to rush their advance but knew rifle fire would tear apart whatever she sent. Even the Long Riders wouldn't make it to the lines in time, and throwing them in too early would just get them killed to no effect. She spent some time marching along the lines, moving her people where they needed to be. She shifted her Fennblades to get them ready in the path of the likely cavalry approaches and commanded her scattergunners to stand ready to fire on the halberdiers when they made their advance.

A shot rang out with startling clarity, and Grissel looked up the wall to her left to see smoke from Grim's barrel. His hands were already busy reloading. In the distance across the field she saw a trencher lieutenant bleeding in the mud, having apparently come a bit too close. "So it begins." She drew her hand cannon from its holster at her waist and checked its chamber. Then she let loose a bellow loud enough to echo along the valley and stir all the gathered trollkin to sudden and complete alertness. In the field beyond their walls a curtain of smoke began to rise in front of the enemy, obscuring their view of anything beyond. The long gunners were coming.

They poured out from the dense trees of the Gnarls and smashed into the Cygnaran Army column like an irresistible tide. With a terrifying roar Mulg jumped forward to shatter a supply wagon and then picked up the next one in line and hurled it to smash horses and soldiers alike. Rangers riding ahead of the main column turned to raise their rifles with trembling hands toward the monster but quickly fell to pygs firing on them from unseen positions. Those horses that survived the first clash screamed in terror and broke their restraints to flee. A pair of young dire troll brothers attacked the middle of the column, spreading chaos and disorder as they cut the line in half by picking up long gunners and shoving them into their mouths.

The attack came without any warning. The column had only a few light 'jacks fired up and running; the heavies and the rest were still powered down and on wagons. The enemy soldiers clustered together. Although they were armed and ready for combat, even this wide road through the forest was not enough space to set up good lanes of fire. The sounds of rifle fire erupted sporadically and without proper coordination. As the trolls and trollkin rushed forward to engage them the nearest trenchers gave up firing to stab feebly with their rifle bayonets.

Flanked by Bron and Kald, Madrak screamed his war cry and crashed straight into the main cluster of armored knights with the eager edge of Rathrok. Bron clove through three knights in one swing with the heavy blade of his own axe. A Charger 'jack swinging its hammer moved to intercept him, but Kald crashed into it with his shield and then spun his chained ball to crush its metal head.

The knights reacted professionally, turning to strike with their Caspian blades, but Rathrok carved through their heavy steel and plated armor to the flesh beneath. From the edge of the roadside the impaler Jord threw a spear to hammer into a knight at the fore and send him flying through his peers behind him. As the rest of the knights backed up to regroup, Borka emerged behind them from the opposite side of the road with Trauma in hand, shattering skulls, ribcages, and arms wherever his mace swept.

Borka took a sword blow to his left side and roared in renewed rage, smashing his head into the attacking knight's helmet to knock him down before pulverizing him with a blow of the mace. The pair of winter trolls accompanying the trollkin were becoming increasingly ornery the farther they traveled out of their natural element and seemed eager to vent their frustrations. One after another, they exhaled great plumes of freezing wind to cut through the nearest knights and soldiers. Several were killed outright and others froze in their armor as it became encrusted with ice along the metal surfaces and joints.

Mulg quickly pushed his way through the army, his tree-sized runed club making quick work of anything in his path. The trolls soon eliminated all the nearest enemies and turned to find they had cleared a sizable section of the byway. The soldiers behind them had pulled back to line up in rows readying their rifles. The ones in front knelt below those behind them, presenting an impressive array of rifle barrels. Their sudden volleys of fire tore through the trollkin, sending a number of warriors to the ground. Several shots sank into Mulg's exposed belly, but he quickly regenerated.

Doomshaper stepped from the trees with an ancient scroll, reading aloud the guttural words of some archaic and nearly forgotten Molgur dialect. As Madrak heard the first words escape the shaman's lips the haft of his axe began to vibrate and the metal became so hot he could feel it searing his palms. Almost against his will his hands gripped the haft and would not let go despite the pain. He gritted his teeth and the world around him faded.

He hung by chains on a wrack, surrounded by humans assaulting his flesh with a variety of torturous implements. He knew they had been at work for quite some time, but he endured it defiantly. He could feel his life nearing its end.

They wanted him to bow to the human Creator. He laughed at them even as he felt his existence fading away. Gathering what strength he had he at last opened his lips and spoke a curse upon them, a seething invective of hate and disdain. Other bound trollkin looked up at his words and saw the spark of rage kindled in their eyes. He laughed and cursed his enemies even as the last of his life fled. His soul fell into a howling darkness, and horror consumed him. Even as this vision faded Madrak had the sense that he was not alone and that some other entity watched this ancient vision alongside him.

As Madrak came back to himself he realized the words Doomshaper had spoken were the same he himself had spoken in his vision. Rational thought fled as the trolls around him gave war cries filled with the condensed rage of the curse. Mulg's shout seemed to shake the trees as he vaulted forward with unnatural speed. The other trolls rushed the soldiers as well, eating the ground between them in loping strides to smash through the human line of riflemen and crush them underfoot.

> **Borka emerged behind them from the opposite side of the road with Trauma in hand, shattering skulls, ribcages, and arms wherever his mace swept.**

In Madrak's hand the white-hot Rathrok blistered his flesh, and yet he found he was grinning and felt no pain. Blood madness was upon him. "For Horfar Grimmr!" He screamed and charged, as eager as Doomshaper to kill every human he saw. They would slaughter them to the last, they would fell them in groves, and they would chase down those who fled screaming into the trees and laugh as dire trolls devoured them alive.

In the aftermath of the battle Madrak's blood cooled and he shook off the thoughts he knew had not arisen from within his own mind. He felt almost sick with the sensations he had experienced hacking through the Cygnaran soldiers. It was not squeamishness—the carnage of war was by now familiar to him. Rather, he knew the joy he had just taken in slaughter was not a natural part of him. He regarded the bloodied axe in his hands and wondered anew what he should do.

Looking around at their victory he tried not to dwell on these dark thoughts. He felt pride in his warriors, for they had fought admirably. They could now block off this road against future reinforcements. Perhaps by their work Crael Valley could outlast this latest threat. His own discomfort did not matter in the face of that.

"I guess you were right. We are definitely not going to win," Calandra finally admitted as they fell back in a fighting retreat from the main wall. Fresh blood coated her curved dagger, and her armor was soaked with the evidence of recent kills. Grissel had her hammer in hand, having just delivered the finishing blow to a half-wrecked Ironclad that had managed to break through the line. The air was hazy with smoke and reeked of burnt powder mixed with the even less savory smell of fresh death.

"We did better than I had hoped," Grissel allowed, having gained even more respect for the Truthsayer during the fight. She had never seen another woman so fierce in battle, so protective of her soldiers. Calandra's magic was subtle but pervasive, and Grissel could almost feel fate twisting to their advantage by the force of her will. During the worst of the massive onslaught a thousand small miracles had kept their warriors alive despite a hail of gunfire the likes of which neither of them could ever have imagined. In one case she had seen a pyg ducked down behind a small sliver of unbroken wall while the rest were chiseled away by rifle fire. Grissel had bellowed her own great calls into the battle alongside others of Bragg's blood, inspiring the champions and Fennblades to fight on.

The bodies of the slain were thick on the hillside; the toll they had reaped among the enemy army was awesome and terrible. Quickly it became clear, though, that the kin had expended their all while the 4th Army had lost only its first and second waves. The tactics of the enemy general had been an odd mix of brilliant adaptation and foolish risks, and she had seen many strangely terrified and young faces among those sent to attack them. She did not understand how he could be so careless with the lives of his own. Nothing in previous battles against Cygnaran soldiers would have led her to anticipate this. In the end she had to ascribe it to the lack of field experience by the 4th Army. Ignorance had made them stupidly bold.

Grissel spotted Runeshaper Elder Sorgot rushing toward her, and she called out to him. "What news? Did they make it?" She had to scream over the din of metal clashing on metal and the explosive sounds of firearms and cannons.

"Yes, they are all safely away!" the albino sorcerer called, panting to catch his breath. They had reached a narrow section between buildings, several already crumbling to ruin under the punishing hail of incidental fire. They both ducked as a Defender shell slammed into the wall above and behind them to send bricks flying. Instinctively the runeshaper invoked his power to raise a band of stones to whirl around his person, sorcery intended to intercept incoming fire.

Grissel yelled to him, "Go find Grim and tell him to begin the retreat! Spread the word that we are to fall back in turns. Be sure we take anyone still alive, no matter how badly hurt. Do not leave any injured behind!" He nodded and rushed off within the eye of his stone storm.

She felt some relief to know the noncombatants among their kith were safe. Early in the fighting she had received a strange note delivered by a brave gobber who had snuck past their lines to bring it to her. It had stated, *I've done what I can to persuade them not to attack the western gate. I feel reasonably certain they will not follow if you retreat by this route. Wish I could be of more assistance.* The note was signed only "VP," which Grissel thought must be Viktor Pendrake—though she had no idea how or why he had been involved. She would have some pointed questions for him the next time they met.

His assessment had proven accurate. Early along they had been able to encourage the elders, the young, and others not able to take up weapons to hasten out the western gate with instructions to head toward the Gnarls if given the signal. It had only been a precaution, but as the fight wore on it became clear such measures would be necessary. The enemy had proven too numerous for them to hold.

A collection of her most resolute champions had vowed to fight as long as necessary, and Grissel smarted at leaving a field of battle, but they had done their job. Madrak's orders had been specific. She called for retreat and the trollkin backed away to the western gate, fighting any who ventured too near. The enemy pressure relented almost immediately when it became clear they were withdrawing. This increased Grissel's humiliation as they made the western gate, leaving Crael Valley burning behind them.

"At least we made an accounting they will not soon forget," Grissel said to Calandra darkly. The shaman nodded, but even her enthusiasm was dampened. They began the hike west, their minds filled with the shame of defeat and the guilty relief of having survived.

# THE ONE WHO WATCHES

The wind had its own edge this far up the peaks, sharpened by the toothy wall of mountains surrounding them. Krueger had brought only a minimal escort, having left the bulk of his army divided into three distinct camps. The nearest awaited in a sheltered valley several days' hike to the northeast at a site chosen to evade the notice of Highgate patrols.

Kromac had doggedly stuck with him despite the difficult path. At times the Tharn king relied on his ability to leap unnatural distances; at others he pulled himself up by raw strength and agility. Meanwhile Krueger took to the air to fly from one impossibly sheer cliff to another. Roundabout routes to these locations existed, but he was impatient. Periodically they rested to allow a small group of satyrs to catch up; these belonged to a local mountain clan with long ties to the Circle Orboros. Two woldwardens also followed at a distance. They had less difficulty with climbing than might have been expected, but their sheer size and weight required them to follow a different path.

Krueger sensed his objective ahead, but he had no delusions that his approach had not gone unnoticed. After working their way along the precarious ledges of a rock face they reached a crevice descending into a shallow alcove. A familiar figure waited there. The rear of the alcove opened to a larger cave, and Krueger sensed Lortus had not come alone. Stone constructs waited just inside that cave, including one of unfamiliar size and configuration. This time Lortus' expression was less than amiable. Krueger considered that the omnipotent would have chosen to intercept him at a place not easily bypassed on the way to the dragon. This meant Blighterghast should be close.

Krueger held up a hand to forestall any immediate challenge. "Omnipotent Lortus, we are not here to fight."

"And yet you also seem disinclined to obey. This puts us at an impasse."

---

## She did not understand how he could be so careless with the lives of his own.

---

"When did our order, which endorses natural chaos, become so focused on obedience?" He saw Lortus scowl. Krueger's voice was unyielding. "I must speak to Blighterghast. I know we are close. You must not stand in my way."

It was dark in the alcove, but their eyes had adjusted to the shadows. Between blinks a cowled figure appeared behind and to the right of Lortus, standing like a statue that had been there all along. Krueger felt a strange jolt of pain toward the back of his head as he looked at the figure, and he blinked against a sudden dryness in his eyes that prompted them to water. A stench like that of rotting flesh assaulted his nose. The figure leaned on a long slender staff of white wood. The robes it wore were thick and many layered, revealing nothing about what was beneath except the single forearm and hand that emerged to grasp the staff. The pale arm and hand were covered in leprous scaled growths. A male voice emerged from the cowl, precisely enunciating its words. "Blighterghast will hear you. There will be a price."

Lortus tensed only slightly, but Krueger could see he had not planned for this. His glare communicated volumes but he did not speak. Krueger turned his attention to the new figure. "What price?"

There was a pause. "There are Cryxians near here. Lortus is aware of them. Eliminate them. That is half of the price. The other half shall be held for another time."

In any other situation Krueger might have hesitated at such a vague request, but he was in no position to barter. "Agreed," he responded.

The existence of this intermediary intrigued Krueger. Nothing he had heard of Blighterghast suggested the dragon valued anything approximating subordinates. There was no evidence of even the smallest cabal serving it. The dragon seemed to prefer remaining in the shadows, though along the Broken Coast there were sailors claiming to have seen it flying far above the cliffs.

Despite the proximity of the Cygnaran city of Highgate, most people there did not believe the dragon actually existed. Most were ignorant that the blighted horrors that periodically descended from the mountains were proof of a draconic presence. Blighterghast had been, so far as dragons went, an almost perfect neighbor: elusive, unseen, a myth.

The Circle Orboros had its own theories regarding the dragon's isolation. Until Krueger had closely examined the Wyrmstone he had only dimly understood the details of those hypotheses.

The figure was silent so long that Krueger started to believe the initial contact was over. He had just concluded that he needed to perform the requested attack immediately when the voice came again. "Follow me. Alone."

Krueger nodded and turned to say a few quick words to Kromac. "Find out the details of this base from Lortus. Return to our nearest camp and begin to prepare. I will join you . . ." his voice faltered slightly, "when I can." Kromac scowled at Lortus dubiously but said nothing. Krueger turned to follow the figure, who was stepping toward the cave entrance.

Lortus moved to intercept him and spoke in a low but urgent tone. "Krueger! Turn back while you can. You are making a grave mistake."

The cowled figure stopped to interpose his white staff in front of the omnipotent. "Do not interfere."

Krueger looked between them and spoke to the druid who was allegedly his superior. "The time for caution is ended. We must break with the past." Lortus made no other move to stop him as Krueger followed the robed guide into the darkness of the cave.

The cave ascended through the mountain for some distance. Krueger followed in silence behind his guide, who said not another word. In several places they emerged to walk along narrow ledges along the outer surface of a sheer rock face. Heights held no fear for Krueger, but the experience left him increasingly unsettled nonetheless.

His unease was compounded by more than the stench of rotting flesh that wafted at varied intensity from the figure ahead. There was a strange ache in his muscles not associated with any physical exertion. His lungs felt raw, as if he had been breathing the smoke from a fire, and he found it difficult to draw an entire breath. Pain settled into his joints, particularly in his fingers. It was almost as if he could feel his body rapidly aging as they walked, as if a toll of years descended upon him with every step. More alarming was the sensation that his own power, as much a part of him as his blood, was thinning. He thought he could muster a storm if he focused, but the power seemed to come slowly, resisting his pull.

They emerged from another long subterranean ascent to a wider summit, a flat section of ground that looked unnaturally smooth. They had ascended high enough that the mountains of the Wyrmwall extended to the left and right in an endless profusion of jagged spires. Looking ahead through the occasional mist of lower clouds Krueger saw the ocean and the jagged line making up the nearest segment of the Broken Coast. They were not quite at the mountain's peak. Krueger turned to look up to its height and his breath caught. The silhouette of the dragon towered above him, coiled atop the mountain's highest point with its scaled head peering resolutely west across the open expanse of ocean.

From where Krueger stood it was almost impossible to get a proper sense of scale, but still the sight of that looming shape hit him like a hammer and sent a surge of atavistic dread through his nerves. It required a strong effort of will to stand still and not flee back to the caves. He forced himself to be calm and to ignore the impulses of his weak flesh. He reminded himself that he was no mere human, no simple mortal, but a druid of the Circle Orboros. He forced his eyes to see and clenched his teeth against the urge to look away.

It was late twilight and the sky was overcast, but the dragon impressed itself upon the world with an undeniable presence that defied external illumination. An umber glow from within seeped light through countless gaps of its dark mirrored scales. It was difficult to make sense of what his eyes told him. In one moment he saw something utterly black leeching all radiance from the world. In the next the dragon's form pulsed with orange light and he could feel tremendous heat radiating from it, even this far away.

A wash of stagnant air struck his lungs like exhaust from a blast furnace. He tasted ash and for a moment was bent over with a violent fit of coughing. A deep wracking pain filled his chest. He looked down at his hand and saw spots of blood on his palm. He drew his power to heal the tissues, but what should have been reflexive instead took great concentration and effort. The damage was slow but continuous; in every moment he could feel different parts of his body withering.

Even when he was not looking directly at the dragon, Krueger's supernatural senses interfered with his eyes. Waves of blackness seemed to pass over his vision like clouds before the sun. He knew this to be raw blight, not actually visible to the naked eye but perceived by the instinct he used to sense and shape the raw natural energies of Orboros. The most frightening aspect of this entire experience was the certainty that Blighterghast was restraining himself, deliberately controlling his deadly blight. There was no other sign the dragon even knew he was present.

"Speak." It was the robed figure who had led him here, now standing in front of him with the dragon far above like some menacing incarnation of death. Krueger found it easier to focus on this form despite its shapeless anonymity. It took an effort of will to remember why he was there.

Krueger cleared his throat, almost driven to coughing again. "First, tell the great Blighterghast that I apologize for interrupting his vigil." He waited for some acknowledgment but received none. The cowled figure stood once more like a statue. Krueger continued after struggling to recall the words he had planned to say. "For some time we have been operating under a foolish misapprehension. We have assumed that those of his kind must be aware of the events transpiring in the world. It is only recently that my eyes have opened to our conceited stupidity. Why should one such as he care what passes between us? The rise and fall of mortal nations is meaningless. What is a war among insects? It must be merely noise, or worse, a potential distraction."

"Nothing you do could distract me." The cowled figure spoke. Startled by his use of a personal pronoun, Krueger wondered if the dragon spoke directly to him through this creature. He decided to adjust his own tone accordingly.

"Of course," Krueger hastened to agree. "However, with the importance of your vigil, certain matters relevant to your immortal kind may not have come to your attention." After another brief fit coughing more blood into his hands, Krueger tried again, hearing his voice starting to lose its strength. "The matter that brings me here involves your sibling Ethrunbal, maybe known to you by other names. The one who did not join your alliance."

"I know him." The figure spoke, sounding impatient. "He is bodiless. Defeated. Irrelevant." There was a note of finality in the words.

"It appears he is no longer bodiless. He has gathered an army and created many spawn bearing the mark of his blood. More importantly, he recently defeated Pyromalfic. I know not what name you use to refer to that being." He attempted to speak a different name he had found inscribed on the Wyrmstone, but he was uncertain of its pronunciation. "I believe he *was* a member of your alliance. I thought you should know that Ethrunbal has destroyed and consumed him."

The temperature seemed to increase in a sudden rush, making Krueger gasp and retch. The heat across his skin was so intense that he wondered for a moment if his robes had ignited. He looked up to see the baleful eyes of the dragon like burning fires on the peak. Blighterghast was looking directly at him for the first time, and Krueger felt pinned by those eyes. The robed figure spoke again. "Impossible. You speak nonsense."

"It is the truth!" he gasped, again forcing vitality into his failing flesh. Never had Orboros felt so insubstantial, like grains of sand through his grasp. He struggled to finish what he had come to do. "Seek confirmation after I am gone by whatever means you choose. Check on Pyromalfic if you can. I do not claim to understand your alliance, but I assume you can warn the others should your vigil reach its final hour. This is only the first taste; Ethrunbal will thirst for more. He does not move cautiously like the rest of you. He is impatient, impulsive, and rash. Ask Lortus, if you trust his testimony." He felt certain he was about to die and that these would be his last words.

In his mind Krueger saw the many ways it could happen: He might choke on ash and cinders. His flesh might be seared from his bones in a single explosive wave of imperishable fire. Perhaps the dragon would stretch forth a claw to tear him in half—though he did not believe he merited even that much personal attention. Blighterghast could merely take wing and by a maelstrom of wind sweep him off the mountain to smash into the earth.

*No. I will not die here. I am the Stormlord!* He focused on the one thought, trying to escape crushing dread.

He realized he had closed his eyes and had fallen to his knees, but now he opened them to look up. He saw the dragon's mouth open and for a moment Krueger's sanity left him entirely, but instead of fire a great booming voice emerged. A charnel wind laced with sulfur carried the only word not voiced through the robed figure: "Begone."

---

**Perhaps the dragon would stretch forth a claw to tear him in half—though he did not believe he merited even that much personal attention.**

---

Krueger was fleeing into the cave from which he had emerged before he even realized his legs were moving. The voice from the hooded figure chased him. "Remember your debt."

It was some long minutes of unthinking descent before the Stormlord could remember what debt that was. Having such a vague obligation was unsettling, but the fact that he had succeeded in gaining access to the dragon and had not been slain in the process distracted him for a time. As he combed through his clouded memories of the meeting much later, though, he realized he could find little evidence his words had had any impact. Uncertainty gnawed at him.

## A SUMMONS

Rhyas looked to Lylyth and raised an eyebrow in silent query, the rest of her face obscured by her helmet and cowl. Lylyth gave a single nod, standing a dozen yards away with her bow at the ready. Rhyas vaulted forward with the sword Antiphon in hand, taking the Tharn ravagers completely by surprise.

She had swept the head off the shoulders of the first savage and moved on before they were even aware anything was amiss. Shadowy afterimages seemed to follow behind her as she struck and killed and then moved and struck again across the rear edge of their ragged line. Their burly leader gave a bellow that was cut off as a pair of arrows sank into his chest in quick succession. The next shots from Lylyth's bow took out the shaman next to him, and the entire group was down. Rhyas gave Lylyth a small smile, and the pair of them faded into the trees.

Their war party had been leading the Circle Orboros on a merry chase, thoroughly confounding them while pushing ever closer to reunion with Thagrosh. The main Legion army continued on, pushed beyond exhaustion despite all the blessings of their blighted flesh. They had managed to divide and confuse the Circle pursuit several times, although the main force regrouped each time and kept driving forward with surprising obstinacy. Clearly they thought they would back the Legion against a wall after they passed through Llael. Allowing the army to press on, Lylyth and Rhyas had dropped back behind them with a few warbeasts to ambush any smaller reinforcements. The tactic had kept the Circle scattered and unable to muster their full strength at any one point.

---

## If they could catch the main body of the blighted army they could rip it to pieces and deliver an unrecoverable blow to the Legion.

---

"I think we've done enough. She should arrive any moment now," Rhyas remarked, wiping the blood from her blade. Their restored full connection to Everblight made it clear she referred to Absylonia. "Let's rejoin them."

Lylyth hesitated. "I'm going to gather my archers and stay here. Go ahead without me. I want to maintain the pressure elsewhere and keep the enemy off balance."

"Very well." Rhyas offered a respectful nod. "I enjoyed this even more than I expected. Saeryn and I will look forward to joining you later." The words carried across their athanc shards an undertone of pleasing images, including thoughts of Lylyth fighting alongside the twins against their enemies. With that she was gone.

Lylyth stood for a while, wondering at her reluctance to join the reunion. For reasons she could not put in words, she did not want to look on Thagrosh or Absylonia yet. She sensed no objection from Everblight. She could tell the dragon was pleased with her work, and Everblight's approval filled her with something that approximated happiness.

Morvahna became increasingly agitated as the chase wore on, no longer maintaining even the slightest veneer of civility or temperance toward her subordinates. It was plain to all of them they were gambling their lives. Morale throughout the ranks had plummeted as random strikes nipped at their edges. They had yet to suffer major losses, but their reinforcements had failed to arrive and those at the fringes died one by one.

At the same time they were convinced the enemy's endurance was at its last. Several times they had overtaken small groups of exhausted Nyss swordsmen or archers and cut them down with almost pathetic ease. If they could catch the main body of the blighted army they could rip it to pieces and deliver an unrecoverable blow to the Legion. All of them believed this, and it gave them the strength to press on despite their growing fears. The enemy, cornered in the mountains with the entirety of Rhul behind them, had nowhere left to run.

Descending out of the southern Rhulic peaks to catch them entirely by surprise, an unfamiliar force closed on their advance from the north. Seraphim flew ahead with a number of harriers behind them. Other flying creatures appeared to be bearing riders, while carniveans, shredders, teraphim, and nephilim approached on the ground. A number of hulking armored ogrun marched among them shouting war cries. Those to the fore bore thick heavy spears and looked eager to use them.

These blighted reinforcements had chosen their timing well, and the forward ranks of the Circle's force had no choice but to endure a deadly rain of spears and blight-fire followed by the clash of a wall of draconic flesh and claws. At the center of the newly arrived mass was a bizarre blighted creature that appeared vaguely female. Morvahna watched in horror as it swept forward on arm-like wings that transmuted into extended claws the being used to tear apart one of the satyrs at the fore.

From the northeast, the direction in which the exhausted Nyss had been fleeing, came two entities even more terrifying. One was a thick-bodied spawn with three heads, each hissing hungrily. Alongside it was something equally foreign and yet somehow familiar. She might have mistaken the hulking winged creature for a gigantic nephilim—except its horned skull and double-bladed weapon sparked fearsome recognition. Morvahna knew after only a moment's hesitation that this must be Thagrosh, the Abomination, now become something even more terrible. Other spawn accompanied him along with several Nyss who were recognizable from the battle at the Castle of the Keys, each of them a powerful general in the dragon's army.

"Withdraw!" Morvahna yelled, even as she saw warpwolves, satyrs, and woldwardens torn apart at the front line. Scores of Wolves of Orboros disintegrated into smoking flesh and ash as the three-headed creature arrived breathing blight fire from each of its fanged maws. Her forces reacted instantly to her orders, but she could see that might not be enough.

Most terrifying of all was the sight of the carniveans tearing through the Tharn so easily. These creatures were heading straight toward her. She sent a woldwatcher ahead to hunker down as solid stone, hoping to buy some time, but she could feel her death in the ravening fanged mouths of those beasts. She unleashed the gorax she had kept in reserve and stumbled back, focusing her magic to heal her forces. Tharn ravagers just recently torn apart stood again as their flesh instantly mended, rising up from the soil to seize their axes and rush to retaliate against the blighted beasts. Another burst of draconic breath and half died again, their return having been short-lived.

Suddenly a shadowhorn satyr arced forward to intercept the nearest carnivean, leaping with sublime grace to hammer at the scaled monstrosity before knocking it aside with its powerful horned head. There was a blurred streak as a white-furred and hugely muscular wolf in bronzed armor dove into the path of the carnivean nearest Morvahna. It bit savagely into one of the enormous spawn's forward legs and almost tore it loose with a single great jerk. Kaya appeared next to the wolf with a double-bladed spear and perforated the carnivean's chest with a rapid sequence of stabs. Morvahna's gorax arrived in time to finish off the great beast by hammering down with its powerful fists as its mouth frothed with rage.

Morvahna had no time to consider the multitude of questions the appearance of Kaya and the unfamiliar wolf provoked in her mind. The reprieve was temporary at best, and she knew she must make the most of it. "Retreat! Fall back to the last hill!" she called as she headed that direction. Her senior druids relayed her orders and began to respond in kind, although the retreat quickly devolved into a full rout despite their best efforts. The tremendous wolf was soon running at Morvahna's side, its eyes gleaming with strange intelligence. It bore superficial resemblance to the war wolves bred by the Wolves of Orboros, but she could see immediately that it was something far more. She tried to touch its mind, but a slick wall surrounded its psyche. The animal's eyes gave her the unnerving impression of amusement.

There was a dark shimmer to the air, and suddenly Kaya was again at Morvahna's side, breathing hard but looking unharmed and wearing a triumphant expression. The two women shared a look but said no more as they retreated to a better position, pursued by flying spawn.

As the weary Legion army cheered at their salvation, so did the warlocks rejoice at their reunion. They welcomed first Absylonia and later Rhyas with an outpouring of grateful affection felt across all their connected athancs. The minds of Thagrosh and Everblight radiated the raw intoxication of a dragon victorious and churned with ambitious plans and ideas. For the moment they took time to delight in their victory and let the beasts feast on the dead, exchanging thoughts and emotions so rapidly across their athancs it was impossible to separate them

into individual conversations. Even Lylyth was there with them through her own not-so-distant athanc.

They all felt the need to move to their new base—now almost unrecognizable as having once been a dwarven village—to fortify and allow their army rest and recuperation. They knew they must prepare for retaliations; they had won a reprieve, but it would be brief. Their present location practically guaranteed imminent strife, sandwiched as it was between the nations of Rhul and Ios. Each of those people knew quite well the threat of dragons.

It was into the midst of this almost celebratory atmosphere that a shiver of something powerful and foreign swept through them. Vayl gave a gasp and staggered as she clasped a hand to her breast. Saeryn shook her head as she sat down, frowning deeply. All the others felt it as well: something had sent a jolt through them, unquestionably originating from their athanc shards. They turned to Thagrosh whose expression was grim. He walked slightly away from them to peer south with his wings half-spread behind him. Everblight had not felt the sensation before but immediately recognized its source. For a moment the dragon pulled away from them to ponder private thoughts.

It was Saeryn who asked aloud, walking up behind Thagrosh, "What was that?"

Thagrosh did not turn or answer, but they all heard Everblight's voice in their minds. "Blighterghast's summons. We felt just an echo, as he sought to exclude me. He calls to the others." Everblight's mental tone seemed bemused and even proud. "I think he calls them not because Toruk stirs, but because I do."

# HOBBY SHOWCASE

Over the following pages, scenes from the *HORDES: Metamorphosis* storyline come to life with strikingly painted models and detailed terrain. Let these images inspire you to enhance your tabletop gaming experience with diverse scenery and uniquely converted models.

*Kaya the Moonhunter was a part of the formidable army Morvahna the Autumnblade assembled to pursue the Legion of Everblight horde in the aftermath of the Castle of the Keys. Over many harrowing weeks they chased the Legion north in an ill-fated effort to extinguish the bulk of the force before it could recover its former strength.*

*A number of hulking armored ogrun marched among them shouting war cries. Those to the fore bore thick heavy spears and looked eager to use them. At the center of the newly arrived mass was a bizarre blighted creature that appeared vaguely female. Morvahna watched in horror as it swept forward on arm-like wings that transmuted into extended claws.*

Lylyth waited amid the branches of the trees. A single raek was with her, lying almost flat to hide in the undergrowth at the tree's base. Also accompanying her were several hand-selected striders. They were as still as death itself.

Baldur's eyes blazed in hate and defiance as arrow after arrow sank into his stone-hardened flesh. He coughed in a single spray of red mist and sank to the ground as his blood seeped into the hungry earth. The stone sword tumbled from his fingers.

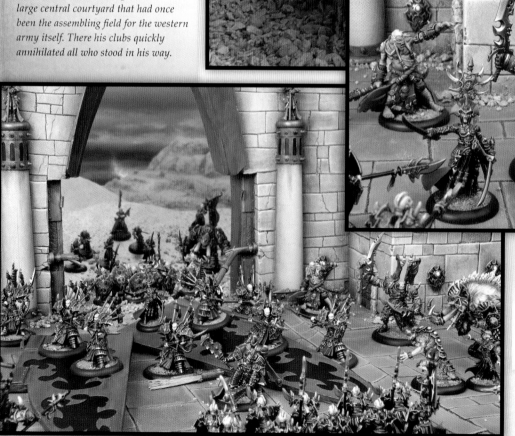

With her army stretched out behind her in perfect columns, Archdomina Makeda of House Balaash stared ahead to the darkening clouds of the Stormlands. Ahead was the hall where the Conqueror awaited, as if daring her to commit the ultimate act of defiance.

Xerxis led the cataphracts in a bold strike past the shattered gates into the large central courtyard that had once been the assembling field for the western army itself. There his clubs quickly annihilated all who stood in his way.

Makeda bloodied her own sword in this last assault. Alongside her the cyclops giant Molik Karn wielded a great scimitar in either hand, reaping death.

Praetorians bearing ladders made their courageous assault and quickly scoured the battlements. Following them, Morghoul made his way into the fortress and deep into the heart of the defenders to sow terror among the officers and weaken the enemy's resolve.

Borka pushed his way forward amid the champion line and let loose a bellow as he joined the fight directly. "Ah! This is glorious, Madrak!" he shouted. "Better than expected! Wherever we go, you find an enemy worth killing! A stroll in the woods turns into a clash with the entire Khadoran Army!"

"They're moving! Stand ready!" Grissel's voice rang out along their wall line as only a fell caller's could. She was standing atop the wall facing north, where she had the best perspective on the spread of the Cygnaran force coming toward them.

The ceiling of Hoarluk's underground cell suddenly shuddered with a single great blow, sending stone tumbling down. He stood up to see Mulg peering down. In moments the ancient pulled him up to stand among those who had answered his call.

A number of farrow Grissel had hired on helped defend the gaps in the wall, including Rorsh with his oversized pig Brine and a motley assortment of others wielding pig irons.

They poured out from the dense trees of the Gnarls and smashed into the Cygnaran Army column like an irresistible tide. With a terrifying roar Mulg jumped forward to shatter a supply wagon and then picked up the next one in line and hurled it to smash horses and soldiers alike.

The gatormen of the Marchfells occasionally endure ambushes by aggressive packs of bog trogs seeking to seize their native territory. These battles are difficult and bloody even without the intervention of an infamous bokor like Wrong Eye and his companion alligator Snapjaw. Wrong Eye enjoys aiding his brethren not out of any goodwill but to make them beholden to him and therefore eager to repay his favors by fighting at his whim elsewhere.

Everblight was back among them in full presence with an overpowering sense of manic triumph. Tightly bound into the dragon's mind, Thagrosh reveled in the power of his transformed flesh.